THIS IS IT

A Manager's Guide to
Information Technology

THIS IS IT

A Manager's Guide to Information Technology

John Eaton, Jeremy Smithers & Susan Curran

SECOND EDITION

Philip Allan

OXFORD AND NEW JERSEY

First published 1982 by
PHILIP ALLAN PUBLISHERS LIMITED
Market Place   and   171 First Avenue
Deddington   Atlantic Highlands
Oxford OX5 4SE   New Jersey 07716
(UK)   (USA)

Reprinted 1984, 1986

Second edition published 1988 by
PHILIP ALLAN PUBLISHERS LIMITED

© John Eaton, Jeremy Smithers and Susan Curran, 1988

British Library Cataloguing in Publication Data
Eaton, John, *1942–*
    This is IT: a manager's guide to
    information technology. — 2nd ed.
    1. Information systems – For management
    I. Title II. Smithers, Jeremy
    III. Curran, Susan
    001.5
    ISBN 0–86003–560–3
    ISBN 0–86003–660–X (Pbk)

Library of Congress Cataloging in Publication Data
Curran, Susan, 1952–
    This is it: a manager's guide to information technology/Susan
    Curran, John Eaton, and Jeremy Smithers. — 2nd ed.
    p.   cm.
    ISBN 0–86003–560–3. ISBN 0–86003–660-X (pbk.)
    1. Business-Data processing. 2. Management-Data processing.
    3. Information technology. I. Eaton, John Richard. II. Smithers,
    Jeremy. III. Title.
    HF5548.2.C86   1988
    651.8—dc 19   88–19294
                     CIP

Typeset by Columns of Reading
Printed and bound in Great Britain by
Bookcraft (Bath) Ltd, Midsomer Norton, Avon

To Anna, Henry, Joe and Neil:

it's their future

Contents

Preface   ix

Part I   Information Systems

1   The Process of Information Exchange   2
2   The Development of Data Processing   10

Part II   Computer Fundamentals

3   Hardware — the Physical Equipment   26
4   Software — Instructing the Computer   42
5   File Organisation and Processing   75

Part III   The Advent of the Microchip

6   The Technological Base   93
7   The Semiconductor Industry: its Economics and Characteristics   112
8   Applications of Microelectronics   125

Part IV   The Convergent Technologies

9   Distributed Data Processing   148
10   Telecommunications   159
11   Office Products   188

Part V   Office Automation

12   What is an Office?   200
13   The Electronic Office   216
14   The Challenge of System Development   226

Part VI   The Impact on Society

15   Privacy, Data Protection and Security   246
16   Work, Skills, Education and Training   257
17   Employment, Economic Activity and Government Policy   267

Keeping Up to Date   301

Glossary   305

Index   327

Preface

To the UK Department of Industry, Information Technology (IT) is 'the acquisition, processing, storage and dissemination of vocal, pictorial, textual and numeric information by a microelectronics-based combination of computing and telecommunications'. This is a somewhat unwieldy definition, but it is difficult to condense it without losing part of the essential meaning of the phrase. The French use the word '*télématique*' which captures something of the flavour of the subject, while in the USA Harvard's Antony Oettiger constructed the ghastly term 'compunications'.

In essence, IT is a relatively new name for a collection of old ingredients: it embraces technological fields such as computing, telecommunications and electronics which until recently enjoyed different natures and histories. The separate development of these technologies was rooted in their intrinsic differences, but was subsequently confirmed by the action of regulatory legislation and other external pressures.

More recently, shifts occurred in both of these separating influences. The result has been a significant change in the nature and structure of these technologies, and in the industries which have been based around them, and the slow emergence of a more coherent information technology industry.

Most influential of all was the development of microelectronics. The 'microchip' rapidly became the basic component of a massive and previously disparate group of industries which had earlier employed quite different technologies.

The other major shift was in governmental attitudes to regulation, in the UK and elsewhere. Slowly, regulatory bodies came to realise the artificiality of the distinctions they had been perpetuating, and adapted monopoly legislation so that telecommunications firms could engage in computing, computing firms in telecommunications, and so on.

This book was written with the aim of providing managers, managerial students and other interested people with an understanding of what Information Technology is, how it can be applied, and the wider issues it raises. We believe that it is important for managers to have a sound conceptual knowledge of these issues. For too long they have been at the mercy of technical experts, particularly in the data processing world. This is no longer an acceptable situation, in a world where the impact of IT on all aspects of business and social life is inescapable, and where it is necessary to understand something of the technology in order to take decisions with major social, economic and political implications for individuals, organisations, and countries as a whole. These issues are too large to be left to technologists alone; every manager, every intelligent individual, should be equipped to participate in the debate and in the decision-taking required.

The book is organised in six parts, each of which deals with a different aspect of IT.

Part I examines the historical context of information processing, and attempts to categorise its different aspects.

Part II introduces the fundamental concepts of computing, from the basic operation of the hardware to the nature and problems of software. This section ends with a discussion of different approaches to file processing.

Microelectronics is the theme of Part III, which considers how the microchip has developed, looks at the economics of the microelectronic industry, and considers current and future applications of this seminal technology.

Part IV looks at telecommunications, with particular stress on digital techniques and on types of network. It also examines the converging paths of telecommunications, computing and office products.

Office automation is the topic of Part V. It considers what makes up an office, reviews technical solutions to office automation, and examines how suited these are to users' real needs.

In contrast to the first five parts, which all consider specific technical and management aspects of IT, Part VI deals with the wider social and economic implications. Specifically it discusses the debate on privacy and data protection, and the changing nature of work, with its implications for the balance of skills, education and training. It concludes with an examination of the role of government in stimulating economic activity and its responsibility for aggregate employment, and the place of IT as an agent of technical change in the national economy.

At the back of the book is a comprehensive Glossary of the particular terms and jargon which abound in this industry, as in every other.

John Eaton and Jeremy Smithers wrote the first edition of this book in 1982, and it grew initially out of their need to provide teaching material for courses at the London Business School. This second edition has been edited and revised by Susan Curran, to incorporate full details on subsequent technical developments and on new legislation affecting issues such as data protection, and to reflect the maturing of the debate on the social and economic implications of Information Technology.

John Eaton
Jeremy Smithers
Susan Curran
May 1988

Part I

INFORMATION SYSTEMS

Information Technology (IT) has developed in response to a demand for information processing. In many ways this requirement is a relatively recent phenomenon, brought about by the industrialisation of society. A far older, much more basic, requirement is the process of exchanging information. In the following pages we look at the exchange process and examine the effects of automation. We see how this gives us a natural progression into an information processing requirement.

1

The Process of Information Exchange

Information Exchange

In looking at information exchange, it is possible to identify three quite different forms of this process.

First, there is *individual communication*, in which information is exchanged on a one-to-one (or one-to-few) basis. This is the earliest and most basic form of communication and unlike the other forms it can be most effectively carried out without the use of any technology at all. Technology becomes necessary only when the communicators are apart. In this sense it widens the scope of individual communication, but it in no sense enhances the quality. Personal communication is best done face-to-face, and all the current technologies seem poor substitutes for this direct contact.

Second, there is *broadcasting* of information, which can be represented as a one-to-many process. The vast spectrum of information that may be broadcast includes facts, opinions, propaganda etc. These exchanges may be initiated either by the transmitter or by the receiver. In the 'transmitter-driven' mode, an individual (or homogeneous group) wishes to transfer information to a number of individuals (a heterogeneous group). The receivers may be self-selecting, or the audience may be specifically targeted. The type of information communicated may range from religious or political doctrine to commercial advertising. In the 'receiver-driven' mode, the receiving group itself selects, or demands, the information from a particular source. Examples of this are status reporting and forecasting (e.g. weather forecasts and road traffic reports).

Education falls into both these modes. At one end of the spectrum, authorities decide on the benefits of education and prescribe its dissemination; at the other, individuals wish to learn a particular subject, and they set about acquiring the necessary information. This 'one-to-many' process is possible without the use of technology – for example, at a public meeting – but the process has been vastly amplified by the use of technology.

The third form of information exchange is *accounting* (with a small 'a'). This word has gathered a quite specific connotation in connection with one commercial aspect of this process, but we use it here in the wider sense of the exchange of information in order to keep a record of some activity.

Consider for a moment how individuals learn about a particular event. It might be experienced directly, or perhaps watched on television, or a commentator or observer might describe it. These methods can all provide good qualitative information, though this will tend to be subjective. They are all inclined to give very little quantitative information. For example, someone attending a big football match will know whether the stadium is crowded or not, but will find it difficult to estimate accurately the number of people attending. An experienced reporter or commentator, who knows the capacity of the ground and is used to judging crowd sizes, will make a better guess – but even this is unlikely to be any more accurate than, say, to the nearest 10 per cent. However, the management do need to know exactly the number of customers present, and will have a means of measuring this accurately.

As Lord Kelvin once remarked, without measurement our knowledge of a particular subject is meagre. Measurement provides objective information about events, and this allows us to make comparisons and classifications. The initial gathering of information involves observation, measurement and recording. Once measurements are recorded, then the information must be classified and structured in some way: in other words, records need to be kept. However, these may not always be accurate or unbiased: the organising process inevitably introduces some subjective elements.

To organise information, it is necessary to have some model or view of how it is to be used, and of the real-world phenomena to which it relates. In the execution of this process, the original data are liable to be irreversibly transformed.

The process of accounting (in the general sense) has been greatly affected by technology. Measuring, recording, classifying and structuring information are all processes that have been transformed by the application of information technology.

To summarise, we consider that there are three quite different forms of information exchange:

1. Personal communication (one-to-one)

2. Broadcast communication (one-to-many)

3. Accounting (event/activity to records)

Each of these forms of information exchange uses different types of media and of technology. We shall identify the automation trends in each one of these forms, and demonstrate that the three streams are being brought together into one interrelated whole.

Information Exchange – the Automation Trend

Personal Communication

The first real communications technology was the written word. Using simple materials, it is possible for an individual to communicate messages over long distances, albeit very slowly. This was perfectly satisfactory for many purposes and reflected (indeed, to some extent dictated) the general pace of life.

For the major part of the time that written messages have existed, they were delivered individually or personally. Then the distribution system started to be automated by the introduction of collection, sorting and delivery systems, a development that partly responded to, partly reflected, a general increase in the volume of messages sent.

The postal network is very simple to use. In technical jargon, it has a simple 'user-interface'. It is sufficient to know the address, fix the correct stamp and put the letter into an appropriate collection box. Behind this simple exterior, though, a complex infrastructure has developed. Until recently this was based on relatively low technology and many people, but slowly this has changed, and parts of the sorting system are now highly mechanised and require little if any human intervention.

From the user viewpoint, perhaps the greatest change in the entire process of sending written messages was brought about by the invention of the typewriter. Though any improvements in the speed at which messages were set down were small (and sometimes negative), this greatly enhanced the clarity of the text.

A more recent innovation has been the ability to send textual information over the telecommunications network: initially as telex or telegrams, and more recently via facsimile transmission systems (fax) and computerised message systems. It is interesting to note that during this process the user-interface became considerably more complicated. Telex sending required the use of specially trained operators. This was an economic drawback in the long term, and it is now possible to trace a movement towards simpler to use and more accessible transmission methods.

The telecommunications system was developed primarily not for this purpose, of course, but to provide a long-distance method of spoken communication. Face-to-face conversations are always more effective than their long-distance alternative, but they are often not practicable. With the telephone it is possible to speak to another person almost anywhere in the world. The quality of sound is not always high, but it is usually quite adequate to enable the users to recognise each other's voices.

Behind the simple interface provided by the telephone receiver lies probably the most complex system yet built by mankind. We describe it in some detail later in this book. It is now possible automatically to connect oneself to any one of over 700 million people (98 per cent of them automatically from the UK), and the telecommunications system itself is diversifying into an increasingly wide range of uses. Another major development is the current trend towards portable telephones.

People communicate on an individual basis, not only for personal and social reasons, but also for business purposes. Major changes are taking place in this area, particularly when the purpose of the exchange is almost entirely practical rather than social. People seem prepared to adopt new forms of communication if they prove more efficient for tasks such as ordering stock, or checking the availability of an item, even if a side-effect is to reduce the level of human contact involved in the procedure. In other contexts, there can be a high degree of resistance to dehumanising developments.

The general effect of technology, then, is to improve the 'quantity' of personal communication. It is now possible to send messages or to converse over longer distances, more quickly and cheaply than ever before. The earliest technologies were of vastly inferior quality to person-to-person communications, but gradually the quality is improving and the choice increasing. The development of videophones and teleconferencing should further this trend, but we do not believe that remote communication can ever be a full substitute for face-to-face communication.

Broadcast Communication

The earliest way of broadcasting information was by voice, with a speaker or performer addressing an audience without benefit of technological intervention. This still occurs in many contexts today: obvious examples include church sermons, theatrical plays, and political meetings with live speakers.

The great limitation of this process lies in the number of people whom the message can reach at any one time. If the information has only a small audience, relatively easily assembled in one location, this need be no problem. But many items of information are designed for, or required by, far larger or more geographically widespread audiences.

Handwritten documents provided another non-technical method of circulating information. But again, this could only be used to access a small audience, and copying texts was a slow and laborious process. A great breakthrough came when Gutenberg invented the printing press. For the first time, automation played a significant part in the process. With the benefit of historical perspective, we can see how rapidly new ideas and beliefs swept through Europe in just a few years after its inception.

Today the printing process has reached, and perhaps even passed, its maturity. Undoubtedly it will start to decline in the twenty-first century. Perhaps its major drawback (apart from depleting the world of timber) is its basic inability to tailor the information to the individual recipient. As a general rule, every copy of a book contains the same words, even though every reader may be trying to fulfil different requirements for information.

The economies of printing are tied very much to volume production. While the mass-market paperback or newspaper may be with us for many years to come, there is already a trend towards the use of different (and often higher) technologies for the dissemination of more tightly focused textual information. Among these has been the growth of different methods of reprographics: from various cumbersome forms of stencil-based duplicating, to modern photocopying technologies, to today's increasing dominant technology, the laser printer/copier.

Using a photocopier, or a printer linked to a computer on which necessary data is held, small numbers of copies of any short-to-medium length document can be made without skilled help, rapidly and at a modest cost. This development has had marked effects on the privacy of information, and on the general spread of organisational democracy. It is now almost impossible to restrict information within an organisation, indeed at all, and a further trend away from paper originals and towards electronically stored information can only exacerbate this process.

In the broadsheet era, the printed word had a relative advantage over the spoken word; but with the arrival of radio, this balance tipped once more. Here was an even more efficient way of disseminating information. The capital cost of building and equipping radio stations was high, but the cost of receivers was small (and borne by the listeners, not by the broadcasting organisation), and the potential audience seemed virtually infinite in size. The very word 'broadcast' was seized upon by the organisations operating these facilities, and it rapidly became synonymous with the output of radio and subsequently television. Movie films serve some of the functions of a broadcast medium, but they are very much 'receiver-driven', in the sense that people have to go to special places to see them. This is not so with radio's more powerful child, television, and it is little wonder that after an incubation period when consumers were acquiring their first sets, television soon came to dominate the broadcast media.

Watching television requires so little effort, and the information rewards can be so great. This medium effectively works in a 'transmitter-driven' mode: it is the broadcasting organisation that selects the information to be disseminated, and, particularly in the era when the choice of programmes has been severely limited, there has been cause to question the extent to which viewers discriminate in their choice of programmes. Often viewers receive information passively: not by choosing to switch on to a particular programme, but by choosing not to switch off! However, with a steady increase in the number of television channels, and the growth of video-recording, this trend looks set to be reversed. Though there are plenty of 'lowest common denominator' programmes on offer, there is an increasing availability of specialist programmes, tailored to small (and geographically widely spread) audiences which could not previously have been catered for. In fifty years' time it will surely seem a strange aberration that there could have been an era when millions of people regularly sat down to watch the same television programme at the same time. Now, with a wide diversity of programmes on offer, the onus is once more on the consumer to choose, so that broadcasting in some ways becomes 'narrow-casting'.

In the late seventies and early eighties, much was made of the potential that new technology provided for two-way communication: for example, for television serials in which viewers voted on which way they wanted the story to develop, and for electronic voting on issues serious (local political questions) and not so serious (talent shows). Though not all the early experiments have withered away, this now looks increasingly like a notion whose time has not yet come. There has been no rapid development on these lines, and though the potential remains, it is currently difficult to see when and how it will be exploited.

Accounting

All the information exchange media we have discussed up to now have one thing in common: they act only as passive carriers of information. They are oblivious to the information content, and incapable of taking any action based upon it. The accounting process in particular can gain a great deal from a technology that can record the information in an intelligent manner: that is, in a manner that can subsequently be interpreted automatically and acted upon.

The earliest forms of record keeping had no such facility; they consisted almost entirely of the quill pen and the ledger book. Only around the start of the twentieth century did there begin to appear mechanical methods of storing and processing quantitative information. The earliest systems were very crude, usually recording information by the presence or absence of a series of holes on a piece of paper or card. These holes could automatically be detected by a machine that counted, sorted or tabulated the cards.

The first major use of 'tabulators' was in the US census of 1890, when they were used to handle the overwhelming volume of information needing to be processed. It was soon recognised that mechanical devices such as these were relatively slow and unreliable, and that the future lay with electronics. The major breakthrough was the realisation that information in a 'binary' form could be represented electronically as a simple series of switches.

Years before this, it had been realised by Charles Babbage and Lady Lovelace that it was feasible to build a machine capable of manipulating information, not in a manner fully predetermined, but according to instructions which were themselves a part of the information. This paved the way for the development of the electronic computer. In the next chapter we review the historical development of the computer and its role in organisations. As we shall see, the computer is not a direct descendant of the early accounting machines, but is more like an adopted child. However, early uses of computers were strongly accounting-oriented, and only in the very recent past has our conception of what computers can be used for matured sufficiently to take them out of this confined cloister.

With this maturing came a new era, that of information technology (IT). No longer is it possible to classify a piece of information as being solely applicable to one of the three types of information exchange. Instead the technology developed for accounting purposes is being applied to personal and broadcast communication (e.g. electronic mail, digital TV, editing machines). Similarly, technologies developed for personal or broadcast communication are being used in the accounting process (e.g. the telephone network and videodisc).

This process is known as 'convergence'. It is most visible in the increasing overlap between the telecommunications, computing and office products industries. In Part IV we discuss this phenomenon in greater detail.

The characteristics of each medium of exchange, the different technologies applied, and the effects of increased automation are summarised in Figures 1.1a and 1.1b.

	Personal	*Broadcast*	*Accounting*
3000 BC	Speech Handwriting	Speech	
		Handwriting	Handwriting
1500 AD		Printing	
1750		Newspapers	
1850	Postal system Telegraph Telephone		
1900		Radio Films	
	Telex		Tabulators Accounting machines
1940		Television Reprographics	Computers (electronic filing)

Figure 1.1a *Development of Key Technologies in Information Exchange*

	Personal	*Broadcast*	*Accounting*
Effect of Technology	More quantity, less quality	Amplify	Enable
Complexity for User	Simple to transmit and receive	Complex to transmit, simple to receive	Complex
Type of Exchange	'Dumb' carrier	'Dumb' carrier	Intelligent

Figure 1.1b *Characteristics of Technology*

2

The Development of Data Processing

The previous chapter provided an historical overview of society's development of communications and its growing need for a more sophisticated information processing capability. In this chapter we review the major milestones in the application of computer systems in data processing (dp); in particular, we attempt to relate developments in the basic technology to parallel developments in software applications.

The present foundations of the information technology industry are heavily dependent upon the history of the dp and communications industries, both in the structure of the industry and in its customers' perception of its nature. The present computing industry, though dominated worldwide by one manufacturer, IBM, with over 45 per cent of the world market, is nevertheless an extremely competitive industry. In contrast, until recently most of the telecommunications industry was in the hands of either state-owned authorities (as in most of Europe) or very closely regulated monopoly suppliers (as in the USA). This situation has changed significantly over the last few years, and there is continuing debate on how far this deregulation process should, or can, be allowed to go.

Although the focus of this book is on information processing, the historical origins of the computer lie in the development of the calculator, particularly in the work of Pascal, and more especially Babbage and his collaborator, Ada, Lady Lovelace. Babbage provided in the design of his 'Analytic Engine' the basic conceptual design (though he was never able to realise it fully in practice) for the components of an information processor — input and output units, store and processor — and indicated that the instructions to the processor could be changed, i.e. it was programmable. Lady Lovelace, perhaps even more importantly, enunciated the basic concepts of programming: that the machine, however sophisticated, could only follow blindly the program of instructions provided to it.

Electro-mechanical Equipment

However, the first practical dp application that would be generally recognised as such today is, in its way, a classic dp application — involving simple, but repetitive, calculations on a vast body of data. It involved the census returns for the USA, where traditionally, tabulation had been undertaken manually by an army of clerks. The problem was that the clerks had only just finished their work for the 1880 census when the 1890 census was sent out. Herman Hollerith, a statistician employed on the census, devised a machine for automating this process. Like Babbage he used the punched card (an adaptation of the cards used to control Jacquard looms) as his data input medium, but his big step forward was to use an electro-mechanical device, a *tabulator*, to sense electrically the position of the holes punched in each card and then to count and tabulate the data. Hollerith's machines enabled the census to be completed in a third of the time that would have elapsed if the purely manual methods had been used.

From the 1920s through to the 1950s, equipment based on Hollerith's original ideas formed the basis of commercial dp. Data was recorded, stored and processed on punched cards. The processing in the tabulator was fixed by the way it was wired up. It could only be reprogrammed by rewiring, and relatively sophisticated schemes were devised to enable such rewiring to be accomplished speedily. The tabulator was joined by a *sorter* (to sort cards into a specific sequence) and a *collator* (to merge two different sets of sorted cards), enabling basic commercial operations requiring the maintenance of data files to be accomplished. Such equipment was generally known as 'unit-record equipment', in that each unit to be processed (typically a punched card) usually contained one data record.

The Electronic Computer

The Second World War saw a fundamental change in the motivation for computer development. The US government realised the strategic military importance of computers and funded a massive R & D programme. Without this considerable, continuous funding from the US government and associated agencies (e.g. NASA) over several decades, the computing industry today would not exist in its present form. The event which sparked off the original funding was the development of the electronic computer, with its ability for unheard-of speed in calculation, vastly widening the scope of feasible computational problems. In America, the motivation was the need rapidly to complete the vast number of complex calculations necessary in the development of the atomic bomb and to complete them accurately. In Britain, the motivation was provided by the need of the code-breakers at Bletchley Park to tackle the job of decoding German messages. The needs of nuclear physics, rocket design and space missions meant that this funding was both to continue and grow. From the beginnings in the late 1940s the role of computers has broadened dramatically. This is illustrated in Figure 2.1.

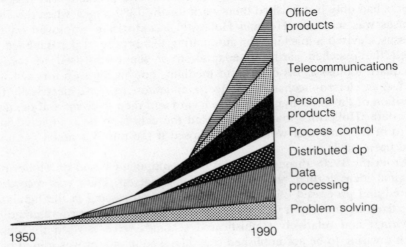

Figure 2.1 *Developments in the Application of Computers*

Thus, the initial role was in what we have termed 'problem-solving' — the traditional calculation that the computer was originally designed for. This area has continued to be a major field for the application of computers and is likely always to be so. One of the more interesting developments of the 1970s and early 1980s has been the recognition that not only is there a market for microcomputers, but also one for giant machines at the opposite end of the spectrum involved in enormous number-crunching exercises. Soon it was realised that computers could play a major role in processing the volumes of data involved in running a business, and the commercial dp industry was born. Together with the more recent developments in 'distributed' data processing, this role has turned out to be perhaps the most significant for the computer. But computers have also found roles in many other areas: instrumentation and process control; in personal products, such as calculators and watches; in telecommunications; and most recently in a range of office products, especially typewriters and copiers. Traditionally, the computing industry has been seen to be largely concerned with commercial data processing. But now the roles that computers play in processing and storing other types of information are becoming of equal importance, and provide the major focus for this book. However, the historically dominant and significant role of the computer in data processing cannot be overlooked, and provides a natural starting point.

The first electronic computer, ENIAC (which stands for Electronic Numerical Integrator and Calculator, thus beginning the computer industry's obsession with acronyms), ran successfully in 1946, employing more than 18,000 valves, each of which had to function perfectly in order for the machine itself to work. ENIAC was still programmed by direct wiring. Later in 1946 John von Neumann wrote a famous paper detailing the design concepts of a 'stored-program computer' and how it would work, which has been the basis for almost all subsequent computer designs. The first operational stored-program computer was the Mark 1 from Manchester University (in 1948), closely followed by several in America. In America the designers and builders of ENIAC, Presper Eckert and John Mauchly, had left Pennsylvania University and formed the first company to manufacture electronic computers commercially, UNIVAC. The first UNIVAC machine was sold in 1951, but the first UNIVAC sale for commercial dp purposes was not made until 1954, when a machine was sold to the (American) General Electric Company.

The First Commercial DP Application

In fact, the first computer to be used in business for commercial purposes had been developed in the UK by the J. Lyons company. Those readers beyond a certain age and with a good memory will remember that the Lyons company operated a large chain of tea houses. The nature of this business involved a very large number of low value transactions with relatively small margins, so the company had long been interested in more efficiency administration and office management. The senior management of the company became aware of electronic computers whilst on a visit to America, and on their return contacted the group working at Cambridge University under Maurice Wilkes, with a view to using his machine (known as EDSAC, Electronic Delay Storage Automatic Calculator) for business purposes.

One of the major problems they encountered was that the input/output devices used on these early computers were incapable of handling large volumes of data. As we have seen, they had been developed and perceived as very powerful calculators in which, although the calculations might be extremely complex, the volumes of data were very small. (Business data processing at this time was still using electro-mechanical machines derived from Hollerith's tabulator.) However, the problems were overcome and in January 1954 the first Lyons payroll was processed on their computer — the first business dp application on an electronic computer.

Significantly, the Lyons computer was known as LEO — Lyons Electronic Office — and it was certainly perceived by the management of the company at that time as an aid to automation of the office. It is important to appreciate that most of the traditional dp applications (e.g. payroll, accounting, order processing) were originally major office functions — they were composed of structured, formalised, well-understood procedures relatively easy to automate. Present discussion of office automation is directed at functions which are relatively unstructured and not well understood — and thus more difficult to automate. Ever since this first application in 1954, dp has slowly been automating more and more office operations. As we shall discuss later, present office automation plans are significant because they address those unstructured functions which are presently the prerogative of management, rather than the clerical operations automated historically by dp.

The second half of the 1950s saw a rush of companies following UNIVAC in America and LEO in the UK into the business dp market. Companies manufacturing tabulators, sorters etc., entered the market — IBM in America and ICT in the UK. Other companies came from a background in electro-mechanical and electrical equipment, such as NCR from cash registers, Honeywell and Ferranti from switchgear and control equipment, and RCA, General Electric and English Electric. At this time the main markets for computers were still with the government (and the military in particular), and universities and research establishments. However, the more farsighted could see the vast potential in business data processing.

Stages in the Development of DP

Historically, the development of commercial data processing can be divided into five distinct phases: four current, and one which is envisaged for the relatively near future. Although the precise title given to each phase (first, second etc. generation) is usually thought of as reflecting purely technological developments, in practice many other changes occur in parallel with these, particularly in relation to the role of computers in an organisation.

These phases and their major characteristics are set out in Figure 2.2. The specific dates chosen to represent the boundary of each phase are

	1950–60	1960–70	1970–80	1980–90	1990–?
1. Component Technology	Valves	Transistors	ICs	VSLI	ULSI
2. System Characteristic	One-off	Mainframe	Mini	Micro	Network
3. Approx. Entry Cost (1988 prices)	£8m	£4m	£0.4m	£1,000	£500
4. Environment	Specialised building	Specialised rooms	Power/air conditioning	Normal office	Normal office
5. Operating System	None	Batch	Time-sharing	Virtual	Intelligent
6. Application Software	Machine code	High-level language	Packages	Application languages	AI languages
7. Computer People	Genius	Technical	Application	End-user	End-user
8. Application Objective	Problem-solving	Efficiency	Effectiveness	Flexibility	Self-generating
9. Characteristic Applications	Computational problems	Accounts/administration	Mainstream operations	All operations	Operation direction
10. Processing Cycle	Month	Week	Day	On demand	Self-selected
11. End-user Contact	Once removed	Twice removed	Once removed	Direct	Direct
12. DP Organisation	Local	Centralised	Distributed	Best-fit	Maintenance oriented
13. DP Budget	Small	Growing	Exploding	Controlled	Controlled

Figure 2.2 *Historical Development of DP*

obviously no more than approximate: in practice the phases overlap, and there has always been considerable difference between the practices in advanced and less-advanced organisations. Many of the terms used in Figure 2.2 are specialist computer jargon. Part II gives an understanding of their meaning, and there is a glossary at the end of this book.

Stage 1: The Early Days

In the first of these stages, computers were largely the preserve of the universities and research laboratories, computing 'engines' to drive research. Although the equipment had many undesirable characteristics, the relationship between the machine and the people using it was often good. Specialists within these organisations built and cosseted the machines, and knew how to get what they wanted from them. Typically there was a direct contact between the user (in this case, the researcher) and the machine, with the user having a good technical knowledge of the machine and its capabilities. However, as computers moved into commercial data processing (into the adventurous organisations during the first of our stages, but into almost every large organisation in the industrial world in the second) this close relationship broke down, for several reasons.

Stage 2: The Mainframe Era

The characteristic equipment of this period was known as a *mainframe* computer — it was built on a large central frame — a delicate piece of electronic and electro-mechanical equipment, which had to be housed in a very carefully controlled environment. The equipment (hardware) was physically large and heavy, and it required as much electricity as a large village in order to function. Almost all of this electricity was turned into heat, which then had to be dissipated. The cost of the equipment alone was colossal. In 1988 prices the cheapest would be about £4 million (by 1970 this entry-level cost would have dropped to about £0.5 million). Given this high investment cost, organisations acquiring this new technology had to try and maximise its utilisation; in practice this meant looking for *high-volume* activities, and *centralised* processing (few organisations could afford more than one of the beasts).

These early applications all tended to be in the accounting and administrative areas, for two main reasons. First, these procedures were well understood (or thought to be) and formalised (accountancy practice imposes a fairly formal set of procedures). Second, in most organisations there were a lot of financial transactions which were often already processed manually in batches in weekly or monthly cycles. The computer equipment of this era was far from reliable, and the earliest machines seldom worked for more than a few hours before breaking down; once (broken) down, they could stay that way for several days. Consequently, the technology was unsuited to applications requiring processing in 'real time' (i.e. as events occurred). Further, the computers of the day were typically organised to process only one task at a time. Thus the only efficient way to organise this was to collect a large volume of similar transactions (such as time sheets) and process them as one large batch. Not surprisingly, this form of computer organisation was termed *batch processing*.

As they could only afford one computer, and in order to use it efficiently, most organisations began to centralise functions which previously had been dispersed. However, this also gave birth to the rift between the users of the computer's services and the people who ran and looked after it. This situation was made worse by the personnel requirements of the new technology. It was very complex and needed to be supported by highly-trained specialists of a type not previously employed by most organisations. Working times and practices were also different as the computer was often operational 24 hours a day, so that patterns of behaviour in the dp department often became very different from those in the rest of the organisation. Typical amongst these were working strange hours, erratic time-keeping, casual (if not weird) appearance, informality, long hair and large salaries! On top of this, computer experts delighted in talking a language of their own, often using normal English words in a different context. All of this reinforced the sense of alienation between the users and providers of computing services. The dp department often became a business within a business, with loyalties to the computing industry, and motivations apart from those of the rest of the organisation.

During this second stage, users could be, and often were, given an appallingly bad service — viewed as a nuisance to be tolerated, occasionally humoured, but more often ignored. A major misconception by the dp department (which unfortunately is still true in many organisations) was that the world stood still whilst an application was being developed. Many misunderstandings arose. Users would attempt to specify a new application, which the dp department, perhaps after a considerable lapse of time, would suddenly announce had been implemented. The hard-pressed experts naturally became disaffected when told at this stage that circumstances had changed, the world had moved on. Such sequences of events tended to confirm the dp department in its belief that the user could never make up his mind what he wanted.

In most organisations during this second phase, the dp departments were firmly in control of data processing policy and development. The whole process appeared so complex that senior management typically abdicated all responsibility and the individual user did not have the knowledge or resources to do anything about it. However, the nature of the technology was slowly changing, and during the third of our stages the balance moved back towards the user.

Stage 3: Enter the Mini

This began at the end of the 1960s with the arrival of what are termed *minicomputers* (this was at a time when minis of all sorts were in fashion). These machines took advantage of developments in technology; they were smaller, much more tolerant of their operating environment, and above all were cheaper. On their initial introduction they did not directly compete with the mainframe computer manufacturers and their commercial dp market, as they were designed for laboratory and engineering applications. Originally they had been designed as 'real-time' machines — processing data rapidly, on demand, and usually communicating directly with several 'users' (originally other pieces of laboratory equipment). In a commercial context, this was translated into computer systems which were 'interactive' (they communicated directly with a user at a terminal) and which could service several such users apparently simultaneously.

The traditional mainframe manufacturers tended to dismiss such systems as an irrelevance in the commercial dp world — but they were proved to be wrong and the minicomputer manufacturers, notably DEC (Digital Equipment Corp), HP (Hewlett-Packard) and DG (Data General) experienced a decade of exceptional growth. Sophisticated organisations spotted that this was a way round their major problem of an overcentralised dp facility. Minicomputers could be installed as satellite stations, or dedicated to a single application — beginning the trend towards 'distributed' data processing which we discuss more fully later in the book. Interactive computing was also attractive to users, giving them the opportunity to develop applications which required such interaction and for which the processing cycle had to be in hours or less, rather than days. The nature of dp applications began to change from an orientation towards efficiency to one of effectiveness. Computer time-sharing bureaux appeared, giving the user an alternative source of computing resources.

This was the time when the users began to get organised. As the processing cycle of applications became shorter and shorter, so the importance of that processing to the functioning of the business tended to increase (the classic example being the development of airline seat-reservation systems). As a consequence, senior management began to become aware of the problem and set up organisational procedures to attempt to bridge the gap between the users and the dp department. This often took the form of a steering committee, on which the users were a majority, to set dp policy, agree on priorities, and allocate resources; and a project team for each application in which the user had a dominant role. By the end of the 1970s structures such as these were beginning to show success in overcoming alienation.

Stage 4: The Micro Comes of Age

The next stage in the development of dp in organisations was the arrival of the *microcomputer*. A discussion of the technology that made this possible, and of its impact, constitutes a significant part of this book.

The microcomputer is so significant because its cheapness turned the traditional rationale for dp development on its head. The equipment became so inexpensive that, for some applications, it was possible virtually to ignore its cost. Instead of requiring intensive use, day in and day out, acquisition of a computer could be justified on the cost-basis of even five minutes' use per day. The desktop computer became a background tool: to be used when the user chose, and as the user chose.

On the other hand, creating software (the instructions telling the computer what to do) became increasingly expensive, and at times prohibitively so, as the number and complexity of potential applications began to mushroom. Old application programs also needed to be maintained, or at times transferred to newer computers which were not always fully compatible with the original systems, and this too produced a high cost burden.

The change in cost basis had major implications for software development. Much early software development had focused on improving the utilisation rates of the hardware. This ceased to be a high priority. Today, the focus is on performance: on making life easier, not for the computer, but for the end-users. How efficiently the computer performs its tasks is much less important than *what* it can be induced to do, and how much human time and effort it can save in the process. This is true not only for end-users, but for programmers too. The new emphasis is on tools that ease the programmer's task, often by increasing the computer's processing burden.

There are two major schools of thought — not mutually exclusive — about the most appropriate method to develop and maintain software in a cost-effective manner. One suggests that the answer lies in the widespread use of packages. Since it is rarely economic to produce tailor-made software from scratch, the answer lies in adapting what is available 'off the shelf'. Only in this way can the enormous development costs be spread over enough users to give an affordable unit cost.

The other school believes that packages are too rigid an answer for all but very specific applications (such as word processing and spreadsheet data analysis). For other applications, they argue that the answer lies in providing more high-level tools, such as application languages (e.g. those already available to financial planners or design engineers) or more general aids such as English-like query languages for 'accessing' (reaching into) databases. We discuss some of these issues in greater detail, both in Part II which covers software in general, and in Part V in the particular context of office automation.

The great advantage of the microcomputer is its potential to be *personal*. It can be used successfully for a single application or by a single individual. This makes it a very flexible sort of technology from the organisational viewpoint. It also dramatically changed the role of the dp department. Instead of acting as guardians of the computer, inter-mediaries through which access to the rare and expensive resource was controlled, data professionals have increasingly turned into servicing personnel, going out to user departments and advising them on how to manage their own equipment.

It is little wonder that the advent of microcomputers was initially treated with much scepticism, even with derision at times, by dp professionals. Much the same reaction greeted the advent of minicom-puters and time-sharing systems at the end of the 1960s. It was largely a defensive response to a threatening situation. DP professionals welcome radical change no more than do other members of an organisation, and they had particular reason to fear this development, which would not merely drastically change, but at times even destroy their own role.

Getting into the computing profession used to have all the subtlety of 'Catch 22': if you had experience, then everyone would hire you; if you didn't, no one would. The result was the development of a rather narrowly based profession of technical specialists. But now the avail-ability of microcomputers in schools has demonstrated that basic computing skills can be acquired at a very early age, and that programming skill has no necessary correlation with more traditional measures of academic ability. The mystique went: a new generation of end-users started to filter through into the workplace, knowledgeable end-users who knew what they expected their computer to do for them, and who were not prepared to be dictated to or condescended to by the data processing department. Computer professionals are still highly skilled experts — perhaps even more so than before — but there are now many more people who would not describe themselves as computer professionals, but who nevertheless work intensively, on a one-to-one basis, with personal computers.

The advent of the microcomputer has not, however, spelled the death knell for mini and mainframe computers — though their technology, too, has inevitably advanced. There are still applications for which a centralised approach is desirable, and in which the dp department provides overall control, though most end-users now access the mainframe computer by using terminals (or treating their personal computers as terminals) rather than by sending off batches of input forms.

The emphasis here is not on *computer* productivity gains, but on *human* productivity gains. Cutting out middlemen wherever possible frequently leads to gains in productivity, and the reduction of response times. It is as a side-effect of this that there has been a tendency for control of the technology to be taken back by user management.

Stage 5: The Fifth Generation Computer

Though it is possible to identify four generations of computer development to date, this concept of generations has never been widely adopted to describe each broad advance in computer technology. We talk today of micros: we do not talk, to any significant extent, of 'fourth generation computers'.

But the fifth generation is different: not least because major national initiatives are under way in many advanced technological nations (and overwhelmingly so in Japan) to chart the characteristics required of a next-generation computer, and to set about producing such a machine by the early 1990s. 'Fifth generation' is a catchword for where computers will be going next. And it is not easy to summarise the expected shape of developments in any other simple way.

There will undoubtedly be further technical developments in the next few years. Different types of integrated circuits may be developed, and their density of circuit integration will almost certainly be increased. At any level from the smallest home computer to the largest 'super-computer', the amount of processing power per pound spent is likely to increase. Microcomputers are likely to be developed upon networked lines, linking together to provide meshes of interconnected applications. But what makes fifth generation computers different from their predecessors is less likely than ever before to be the underlying hardware technology, and far *more* likely to be their software. The rush is on now to make computers 'intelligent'.

This represents a focus partly on *what* computers will do, and partly on *how* they will do it. Already we have seen the computer make great strides towards 'user-friendliness'. From the days when it took an expert to operate a computer, we have advanced to an era when almost everyone, in their daily lives, deals directly with the all-pervasive machines. But still we have to interact with computers in a very artificial, regimented way, pushing buttons or formulating our instructions within very narrow limits. Tomorrow's computers should be more flexible. We should be able to specify our requirements far less precisely, and still have them understand us. Computers may not hold natural conversations with us in colloquial English for many years to come: but they are steadily coming to communicate in something that is much more like it than any previous method of user-interaction. From the era when the programmer tells the computer what to do, we are entering the era when the computer works out for itself what to do. The programmer does not specify every step required to handle every task: he or she sets out objectives, and the computer figures out how to meet them. This is what we mean by 'intelligent' machines.

'Artificial intelligence' as a concept has been around as long as have computers themselves. But now, at least in a small way, it is becoming a reality. 'Expert systems' simulate the activity of human experts, applying their knowledge to solve problems set to them. Computers programmed in the new ways can make inferences from the data provided to them. They can 'learn' from past experience. They come to seem less like our tools in dealing with our daily tasks, and more like our partners.

From the era when we thought of computer functions in terms of specific, and clearly separated, 'applications', we may be moving into an era when we see the computer as a general-purpose tool, drawing on *all* its stored knowledge and capabilities in order to address every new task in the best possible way.

Computers and Organisations

During the second two stages of their development, three characteristics of computers and the data processing industry arose, which subsequently have caused it and its customers immense harm, and which only now are beginning to be dispelled. First, there is the image fostered by both the industry and the media of the computer as a miraculous, superhuman machine, capable of almost anything, but very intimidating and mysterious, to be understood only by those with a PhD in mathematics. Whilst the computer is indeed a very sophisticated and complex machine, an understanding of the basic concepts of a computer system is nevertheless not beyond the understanding of that famous character 'the average intelligent layman'. For example, many people have a good conceptual, if not detailed, knowledge of how, say, a car or aeroplane functions and of the role they play in transportation systems; yet in their own way they are no more complex than a computer. Yet this lack of a basic understanding, in truth perhaps more a major misunderstanding of the components and capabilities of a computer system, is now a significant social, educational and management problem. Too many organisations have relied upon dp 'experts' to make technological judgments and decisions which have major *business* impacts. The user managers concerned provided little or no inputs, and little attention was given to the business as opposed to technical dp aspects of the decision.

Second, stemming in part from this misunderstanding of its true capabilities, and in part from the commercial necessities involved in developing a vast new market, the computing industry grossly oversold itself, its products and its capabilities. Particularly during the 1960s, tales of the excesses of computer salesmen were legion — the miraculous computer would be a panacea to solve all the problems of the business, and the customers all too often believed it! The result is that the computer industry as a whole probably has a worse public image than almost any other. There still persists a considerable degree of scepticism about the claims of the computer industry in general and their own dp departments in particular, amongst the senior managers of many organisations. Unfortunately, there is some evidence that the painful and expensive lessons learned by the large companies during the 1960s and 1970s are not being passed on to the smaller organisations presently becoming first-time computer users. One still hears far too much emphasis on the physical hardware aspects of an application, rather than the software and, perhaps most important, the impact on the organisation and the people in it.

Third, the introduction of a miraculous, mysterious, apparently very complex and expensive machine, requiring a considerable amount of cosseting in its operational environment and what might be termed as tender loving care from those looking after it, naturally led almost all of the organisations acquiring computers for general data processing to set up a centralised dp department. Given management's perception of the machine (and usual lack of any real understanding of its capabilities), and its cost, such a response was understandable. Thus, whatever the general organisational structure adopted, dp was almost invariably a centralised facility — often physically remote from the user departments, certainly keeping its distance from individual users, staffed by specialists who perceived their loyalties and career paths to be within the dp industry as a whole, rather than the organisation currently employing them. This attitude was inadvertently fostered by organisations which kept dp management separate from the rest of the organisation and provided few, if any, routes for dp managers to move into the general management mainstream.

Whilst this degree of sophistication might have been an organisational cost that could have been borne at the time, as we have progressed through the 1970s and 1980s it is perceived as being increasingly inappropriate and in some instances a major constraint on organisational development. Throughout the past two decades the tendency has been towards a greater and greater degree of decentralisation of decision making in organisations, making managers as far as possible responsible and accountable for the attainments of their goals and objectives. A centrally organised and controlled dp operation has become an increasing source of frustration in such circumstances. This has been compounded by the developments of cheaper mini and microcomputer systems; and the movement towards on-line, interactive computing, which brings the end-user into much closer contact with the computer system, and removes many of the buffers and barriers built up around the dp operation. In most organisations these phenomena appear as a movement towards some type of distributed data processing (usually referred to as 'ddp') — typically an attempt to make the organisation of dp more closely mirror the decision-making structure of the organisation as a whole. However, there are many problems and pitfalls in moving from the concept of ddp to the reality — both technical and organisational — which we will review in more detail in Chapter 9.

First, though, in the next part of this book we will attempt to provide you with an appreciation of the basic components of a computer system and their function, as well as an understanding of the meaning of the jargon and 'buzz-words' shrouding computers.

Part II

COMPUTER FUNDAMENTALS

We aim here to provide you with a basic understanding of how a computer works. Although a significant theme throughout this book is to identify and emphasise the software component of systems and, above all, the role of the people who have to use them, this doesn't mean that the technology is irrelevant or that its significant characteristics can be overlooked. In our view, it is of critical importance for user management to have a basic understanding and appreciation of the capabilities and characteristics of the relevant technologies. Only on this basis can informed, intelligent decisions about the potential business impact of such technologies be made. It is perhaps appropriate to reiterate that the primary focus of this book is to provide an insight and understanding of the developments in information technologies, their impact on organisations, their business and their employees at all levels, and on the socio-economic environment in which they live and operate. A proper understanding of the technological base is critical to this.

3

Hardware — the Physical Equipment

What is a Computer?

At the heart of every computer system lies a machine which is able to obey our instructions (telling it how to manipulate some data) at a truly phenomenal speed — relatively commonplace minicomputers may well be capable of obeying more than 1 million instructions per second, whilst the industry giants can process at rates of about 100 million instructions per second. For example, it takes about one-tenth of a second for you to blink your eye — in this time a minicomputer might have executed 100,000 instructions! Assuming we can feed it with instructions and the necessary data at a fast enough rate, and similarly accept the results of its processing, then this machine will happily carry on processing say, 1 million instructions each second, 24 hours a day, 7 days a week, without getting tired or bored, making mistakes, or suffering from any other of the ailments that eventually affect humans engaged in continuous work. We will discuss the form and nature of the instructions that the machine needs in the next chapter — in this chapter we describe the basic physical equipment, the *hardware*, in a computer system. The machine that we have just described, the *processor*, is only a part of our computer system — we need to have a lot more equipment linked to the processor in order to try and satisfy its voracious appetite for ever more instructions and data.

For example, we need equipment with which to enter our instructions and data and to display the results of the computation — known as *input and output devices*. The processor itself requires an associated storage area in which the instructions being executed and data being processed are stored; this is known as the *primary memory* and, together with the

26

processor and some logic circuits enabling the processor to communicate with other pieces of equipment, is referred to as the *central processing unit (or cpu)*.

There may be many other pieces of equipment connected to the cpu, apart from the input and output devices already mentioned. For example, almost all computer systems require a large file storage area in which may be stored instructions and data not presently being worked on. Computer systems often communicate directly with other systems; this too requires a further item of equipment. These additional components of the system are known as *peripherals*. A general diagram of a computer system is shown in Figure 3.1.

In everyday use the two terms 'computer' and 'computer system' are often used synonymously, but conceptually there is an extremely important distinction between them. Strictly speaking, a computer is a calculator, a machine which can perform many calculations automatically. It is what lies at the heart of a computer system: the central processing

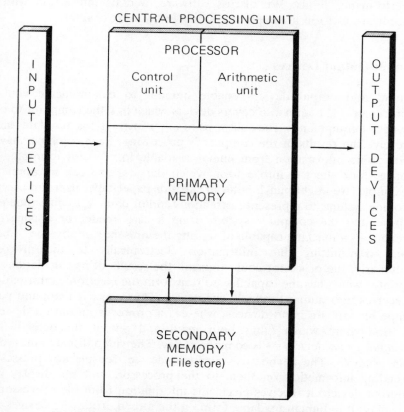

Figure 3.1 *A Schematic Diagram of a Computer System*

unit, a physical piece of equipment. A computer system, in contrast, includes both all the necessary physical equipment (the hardware) and all the instructions (the software) needed to enable the machine to perform useful, user-oriented tasks. The processor, or computer, is roughly analogous to a car engine; the computer system is the entire car. A computer as a physical piece of equipment is in general of little direct use to the end-user, just as the car engine is useless until it is set into a chassis and surrounded by the other necessary components. From the user's point of view, a computer system is defined as whatever is necessary to be able to handle his or her problem.

In this chapter we discuss the physical equipment that goes to make up a computer system. However, it is the instructions which the hardware obeys that tend to define the usefulness of the system to an end-user. The end-users are interested primarily in what way the system can support them in performing their jobs, and this is typically directly related to its software capabilities, with the hardware setting absolute capacity and performance limits. We discuss software, and its interaction with the hardware to form a computer system, in the next chapter.

Input/Output Devices

Input and output devices enable humans to communicate with the processor. (The term also covers devices which link the computer to other types of equipment.) They allow us to enter instructions and data, and to receive the results of the computer's processing. Such machines have to transcribe information from human-readable form — for example, data on a stock sheet — into a form which the machine can interpret. For example, we might punch holes in cards or paper-tape, using an accepted coding system, to represent instructions and/or data. We could then enter these into the computer system using a card reader or a paper-tape reader — a machine capable of sensing the presence or absence or holes, and transmitting that information electronically to the processor. Similarly, the processor could transmit the results of its calculations to a printer which has the capability to transform the electronic information it receives into human-readable characters. Thus, card readers and paper-tape readers are input devices, whereas a printer is an output device.

Equipment which fulfils both input and output functions — *input/ output, or i/o devices* — is common today. The video display unit (vdu) is an example. The keyboard is an input device, sensing key presses and sending information on them to the processor, and the display is an output device: it receives electronic information from the processor and displays it in human-readable form on the screen. Today i/o devices are a critical part of almost any computer system. They form a man–machine interface which affects a user's whole view of the computer; therefore great effort has gone into devising attractive and easy-to-use i/o media. For example, light pens, graphics tablets, touch screens and voice-input devices now provide rivals to the keyboard as input devices, while the monochrome video screen is rivalled by colour displays with graphics capabilities, and with synthesised voice output. Figure 3.2 lists the major input/output devices.

Input	Output
Keyboard	Printer
Bar-code reader	Display screen
Optical character reader (ocr)	Plotter
Magnetic tape and disc	Magnetic tape and disc
Laser-read disc	Laser-written disc
Microphone/voice analyser	Voice synthesiser
Punched card and paper-tape readers	

Figure 3.2 *Input/Output Devices*

The Functions of the Processor

The processor itself is not a monolithic unit, but has three components (as illustrated in Figure 3.1): an arithmetic unit, a control unit and a storage unit. It also includes the interfaces necessary to enable it to communicate with input/output and other devices.

The *arithmetic unit* is capable of performing arithmetical and logical operations electronically. It works very rapidly, carrying out thousands or even millions of instructions each second. It works in much the same way as a personal electronic calculator.

The storage area, known as *primary memory*, is the working memory of the computer system, in which the instructions to be followed, the data to be processed, and the results of the processing are stored. It is comparable to paper and pencil which might be used in conjunction with a personal electronic calculator to record the form of the calculations, the initial data, intermediate results, and the final answer.

The *control unit* fetches instructions in sequence from the primary memory, decodes them and acts on them. For example, a sequence of instructions may be to move a number held in a particular location in primary memory to the arithmetic unit, then to move a second number from another location to the unit, then to add the two numbers, then to move the resulting sum to a particular location in primary memory, and so on. In terms of our analogy, this is equivalent to your role in entering data into your calculator in the correct sequence, pressing the keys for the calculations that you require, and noting down intermediate results and the final answer.

It is perhaps not widely appreciated that the capabilities of the arithmetic unit in a computer are extremely limited. Basically all it can do is add (or subtract) two numbers, or compare them to find the larger or smaller. Other more complex arithmetic operations have to be built up from these basic capabilities. Let us briefly examine how the hardware actually stores and processes our instructions and data. This involves understanding a few straightforward characteristics of the binary number system. It's at this point that the faint hearts give up — but if the majority of children in their early teens can manage it, surely you can! And once you are over this hurdle, it's all downhill. As we emphasised earlier in the book, we are primarily concerned with the impact of information technology — but without a thorough understanding of the technology itself, we feel it to be impossible for you fully to appreciate its impact. And representing information *digitally* — by coded sequences of binary digits — is the key common factor underlying recent developments in information technology.

How the Hardware Works: the Binary System

One of the fundamental factors differentiating an electronic computer from the previous mechanical and electro-mechanical calculators and tabulators is that it can process instructions and data represented only by using the binary number system. In the binary number system there are only two digits, 0 and 1, compared with ten in the decimal system, 0, 1, 2, 3, 4, 5, 6, 7, 8, 9. In the decimal number system with which we are all familiar, each position in a number indicates a power of 10. For example, the number 321 could be represented as follows:

$$1 \text{ times } 10^0 = 1 \text{ (any power of zero = 1)}$$
$$\text{plus: } 2 \text{ times } 10^1 = 20$$
$$\text{plus: } 3 \text{ times } 10^2 = 300$$

$$\text{total: } \quad 321$$

Thus in the decimal system, each position has the following value:

power of 10:	etc . .	10^4	10^3	10^2	10^1	10^0
value	: etc . .	10000	1000	100	10	1

In an exactly analogous fashion, each position in the binary system represents a power of 2, thus:

power of 2:	etc ..	2^4	2^3	2^2	2^1	2^0
value	: etc ..	16	8	4	2	1

For example, the decimal number 9 would be represented in binary as 1001, thus:

$$1 \text{ times } 2^0 = 1$$
$$\text{plus: } 0 \text{ times } 2^1 = 0$$
$$\text{plus: } 0 \text{ times } 2^2 = 0$$
$$\text{plus: } 1 \text{ times } 2^3 = 8$$

$$\text{total:} \quad 9$$

You may like to verify for yourself that decimal 321 would be represented in binary as 101000001.

We can perform arithmetic in any number system, binary, decimal, or any other — all we have to remember is at what point a value has to be carried to or from the next highest position. For example, in the decimal system if we were to add together 5 and 7, then we now know automatically that one unit of ten has to be carried to the next higher position to give the answer 12. (Though it is automatic now, as schoolchildren we did have to learn this!)

As we have noted, in a binary number system there are only two states, 0 and 1, so that on any occasion in which two binary 1s are added, a carry to the next position will be generated. For example, suppose that we add 5 and 7 together in binary; decimal 5 is equal to binary 101 and decimal 7 to binary 111. The sum is:

$$\begin{array}{r} 101 \\ +111 \\ \hline 1100 \end{array}$$

i.e.
$$0 \text{ times } 2^0 = 0$$
$$\text{plus: } 0 \text{ times } 2^1 = 0$$
$$\text{plus: } 1 \text{ times } 2^2 = 4$$
$$\text{plus: } 1 \text{ times } 2^3 = 8$$

$$\text{total:} \quad 12$$

Thus we are able to perform simple arithmetic using the binary number system, and are able to specify the logical rules for the performance of that arithmetic.

The importance of the binary system from the point of view of the electronic computer lies in the fact that it has only two digits, or states, which can very easily be represented by a switch on or off; an electrical current flowing or not; the presence or absence of an electrical charge;

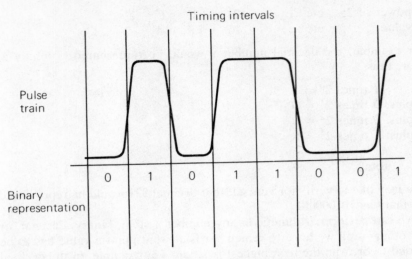

Figure 3.3 *Electrical Representation of Binary Digits*

the presence or absence of a magnetic field. The speed of the electronic computer is derived from the speed at which electrical pulses travel — the speed of light (186,000 miles per second!) — and from electrical switches operating enormously faster than their mechanical equivalents. The significant developments in the technology of processing and storing binary coded information electronically are discussed in Chapter 6.

The movement of electrical pulses at high speed between all of these components requires some very careful synchronisation. Thus a very important component of a cpu is some form of clock. As the electrical pulses pass to a device, the identification of whether a binary one or zero has been received requires the measurement of a time interval, and the determination of whether a significant voltage (compared with some reference value) was detected during this given time interval (thus representing a binary one). Schematically this is illustrated in Figure 3.3. For any processor you will see a reference to its *clock rate* — the frequency at which the basic reference pulses will be generated. The higher the clock rate, potentially the faster the processor will operate, though whether this potential power can be tapped for the user will be discussed later.

Thus electronic hardware can store binary data, or instructions coded as binary data, in either an electronic (i.e. the presence or absence of an electrical charge) or magnetic form (i.e. the presence or absence of a magnetic field). Further, it can transfer such binary coded information as a sequence of electrical pulses at a very high rate between different pieces of equipment. And, finally, it can electronically perform elementary arithmetic operations on such binary coded information, again at a very high speed.

File Storage Equipment

To return to a discussion of the hardware components of our computer system, there is one major component we have not yet looked at — the file storage area. As described above, the primary memory of the processor has to hold the instructions and data which the processor is following and operating on; yet further consideration of the analogy of you in your office should make it apparent that there is also a need for other storage media. For example, using the office analogy, the desk surface represents tasks which are currently being worked on (of which there may well be several different items) and other information, typically of a reference nature (telephone directories, diaries, etc.), which you know full well that you are almost certain to want to refer to at some point during the day. Other information and data is stored in files, each file having some known structure (for example, alphabetic sequence, or date order), which enables its contents to be searched in a logical manner, and for items to be retrieved. Similarly in our computer system, in addition to primary memory there is a requirement for some other type of storage media, capable of holding very large quantities of information; this is known as *secondary memory*.

Units of Computer Storage

The smallest unit of information stored or processed in a computer is a binary digit (i.e. zero or one), known as a *bit*. However, this is too small a unit of storage to be useful to the normal user. Typically, users wish to store and process characters (actually, groups of characters — names, addresses, part codes, etc.) and numbers (or quantities — invoice amounts, stock levels, etc.). Thus, from a user point of view, the smallest basic unit of information represented in this way is a character, i.e. the capital letters A–Z, small a–z, digits 0–9 and special symbols such as £ $ () + − / and so on. In computer terms, all possible characters can be represented by a group of eight bits, known in computer jargon as a *byte*. For your purposes, a byte and a character are synonymous.

A byte is essentially a unit of computer storage and transmission. The data storage capacity of a disc drive is normally represented as being so many K (thousands, or more precisely 1,024s), M (millions, or mega) or G (giga, or thousand millions) of bytes, either per drive or in total for the computer system, and the speed at which a terminal transmits input to, and receives output from, the processor is measured in terms of so many characters per second (cps). With eight bits it is possible to represent the numbers 0–255. This provides more than enough codes for all the numbers, letters (large and small) and special characters. But before this can be done, a recognised coding system must be specified.

There are two common ways of coding the bits in a byte to represent characters. ASCII (American Standard Code for Information Interchange), which is an internationally adopted standard code; and EBCDIC (Extended Binary Coded Decimal Interchange Code), which, because it is the code used by IBM in their computer systems, has become a *de facto* standard code. Generally speaking, you do not have to worry about how a particular instruction or piece of data that you input to the computer is translated into binary; but it is important to be aware that this system function is undertaken for you, and in addition it provides a commonly used standard for information interchange between computer systems.

Magnetic Disc Storage

Magnetic discs can take many forms but generally comprise one or more flat circular surfaces in a vertically spaced stack, very similar to a heap of gramophone records. Each active surface is coated with a material capable of being magnetised. A read/write head at the end of a movable arm can position itself over any portion of the surface. Logically, this surface is divided into many concentric storage areas, known as tracks, and the read/write head can directly position itself over any one of these tracks. The operations of a disc drive are illustrated in Figure 3.4.

Many discs operate inside units which have been hermetically sealed at the time of manufacture, so that the head can literally 'fly' closer to the disc surface, thus leaving a narrower magnetic footprint, enabling tracks to be set closer together and thus more information to be stored in a given area. The first developer of such units was IBM which gave them the internal code name of 'Winchester'. Such disc drives are still often referred to as 'Winchester drives' or 'Winchester discs', though 'hard discs' is now an equally common designation.

Technological advances allow increasing amounts of storage to be placed in smaller and smaller boxes. Even as late as the late 1970s, it was not uncommon for the cheapest business-oriented microcomputers to use not disc storage but cassette tape for data storage. Nowadays many home computers have disc drives with a capacity for holding more data than expensive commercially-oriented drives could handle twenty years ago, and in a fraction of the space. Work stations used by engineering and management professionals often have 20 or 40 MBytes of hard disc storage, which heightens concern about back-up and archiving, and the

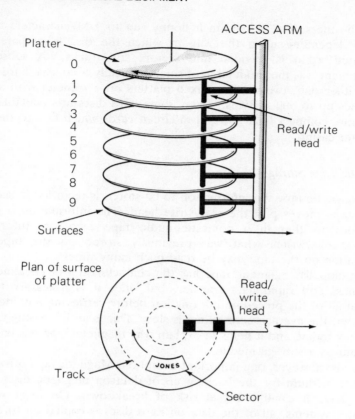

Figure 3.4 *Components of a (Multiple Platter) Magnetic Disk Unit*

capability to share data.

Traditional large discs in mainframe computer systems are made from rigid 14-inch platters of aluminium — in packs of between one and eight platters per spindle. With the development of more sophisticated terminals, word processors and personal computers, a new disc storage medium was developed: the flexible or floppy disc (sometimes also called a diskette). In the original versions (still extant today), a 5¼-inch or (increasingly rarely) an 8-inch diameter vinyl disc with a magnetised coating is spun inside a protective cardboard envelope. Newer discs, most commonly of 3½-inch diameter, have more rugged plastic protective containers. These discs are not sealed inside their drives; instead they can be inserted when required, and replaced as necessary, so that the user builds up a 'library' of discs (perhaps a hundred or more, for use in a single drive) containing his or her data bank. Apart from its removability, the concept and operation of a floppy disc unit are the same as for its larger brothers. On the 5¼-inch floppy, up to 1 M characters can be stored, depending upon the way in which the disc is prepared and 'formatted' (that is, divided into sectors and tracks). A subsequent development was the production of small (typically 5¼-inch) 'hard discs', using either one, two or three fixed platters on a spindle, with storage capacities up to 500 MBytes. Today some hard discs are available in an even more compact form, on slot-in circuit cards which fit into the main computer casing.

Magnetic Tape Storage

On a magnetic tape the information to be stored is recorded in sequence as the tape moves past the read/write head. The information is exactly analogous to that in a domestic audio tape recorder. Information recorded overwrites what was previously stored on the tape. The information on the tape may be read back many times.

Operationally, magnetic tape has the characteristics of cheapness and robustness and rapid data transfer, but since it is necessary to read through all of the preceding information before retrieving any individual data item, the average access time is slow. This is an increasingly severe drawback today, and it helps to explain why magnetic tape has fallen out of favour as a storage medium.

There is, however, one important exception. Magnetic tape provides an excellent medium for the backing up of data on magnetic discs, which always have a small but real risk of breakdown. On most well-run computer systems, all of the data on hard discs is copied on to another medium at regular intervals, and tape is proving an increasingly popular medium for this purpose. The units used for this purpose are either reel-to-reel tape, which is slowly becoming obsolete, or *tape streamers*, known sometimes by their typical tape width of a quarter inch. The market for ¼-inch cartridge tape drives was a scant 250,000 units in 1984, but by 1987 it had risen to an estimated 1 million, and it was expected to increase still further.

Small tape cassettes, identical in appearance to audio cassettes but generally of higher recording quality, were used for a period in the early 1980s as a popular storage medium for home computers. These were cumbersome to use, however, and frequently unreliable, and with the increasing cheapness of disc storage they have largely been superseded today. In the near future, the tape back-up medium for disc drives (at least to 100 MBytes) will be provided by a variant of the domestic DAT (Digital Audio Tape) cassette system. This will offer high capacity, compact size (smaller than a current cassette tape), low cost, and a form of direct access through indexing of the tape.

Compact Disc Storage

A still newer, and still fast-developing, technology for data storage is the use of compact discs (effectively identical to audio compact discs and videodiscs).

There are two types of compact disc data storage. The CDROM provides read-only memory in compact disc form. These discs are sold with information in place (for example, with directory or encyclopedia information on them) and are then read by the disc player. WORMS, the other type, provides write once, read many times, storage. These discs are sold blank, and the user system writes data on to them. Once written they are not erasable (though research is continuing into disc formats that will permit erasure and rewriting), and so they are most appropriate for archival information. WORMS is, predictably, much more expensive than CDROM: typically, a WORMS system today will cost ten times as much. ANSI (the American National Standards Institute) is currently finalising standards for CDROM, and when (and if) the standards are generally accepted this should greatly enhance the acceptability and growth of the medium.

Until a fully read–write CD is developed, this medium will never be a direct rival to the magnetic disc. However, it has some major advantages. The discs themselves are robust, relatively cheap (and likely to become significantly cheaper) and they have an extremely large storage capacity.

The compact disc stores data in 'pits' marked in an aluminium surface, protected by a clear vinyl coating. A typical single disc today has 2 billion pits (tiny markings) 0.12 micrometers deep and 0.6 micrometers wide, at a density of 16,000 tracks per inch. Discs are currently being manufactured in 12″ and 5.25″ sizes. A 12″ disc typically holds about 1 GByte: that is, 1,000 million characters of data, or more than 1,000 typical capacity floppy discs, or 300,000 printed pages. The capacity of 5.25″ discs is more in the region of 100–150 MBytes per side.

WORMS archival systems sometimes include input scanners for converting paper documents to digital data, and laser printers for hard-copy output. An increasingly common use of WORMS units is in the distribution of software documentation and manuals, for printing locally by the user, since they go through a long cycle of amendment and update. At present WORMS systems tend to cost many thousands of pounds. But CDROM systems are coming down rapidly in price, and Atari's latest system (1988) costs only £399, which makes it extremely competitive with other forms of secondary storage.

Though CD data storage and audio compact discs use the same technology, there is a difference in today's disc players. Data systems need to incorporate very sophisticated error-checking circuitry, since even a tiny error can cause much havoc in a computer system. Audio systems, in contrast, can tolerate small error levels. Though audio players cannot be used for computer data, it is however possible to do the reverse, and Atari's player is an example of one that fulfils both functions.

Price/Performance of Storage Media

In terms of both operation performance and cost, there are major differences between primary memory and the forms of secondary memory commonly found in computer systems. In the primary memory area of the computer, any storage location can be accessed directly in order to retrieve its present contents, or to place new information in it. In the jargon, each location has an unique *address*, which can be used to refer directly to it. The primary memory area can be thought of as comprising thousands (or millions) of pigeon holes, each of which is big enough to store just one character or byte. The identifying sequence number of the pigeon hole constitutes its unique address.

The processor circuitry at the heart of any computer has the capability to handle only a limited range of these unique addresses. The exact size of the range depends upon the make-up of the processor, and in particular on its 'word length', which determines the length of numbers which can be directly processed. For example, a processor with an 8-bit word length (that is, capable of handling individual binary numbers with eight digits) can handle 64K (just over 64,000) different addresses. By modern standards, this is a very restrictive number. A processor with a 16-bit word length has a far greater addressing capacity. Depending upon its software and hardware configuration, the computer may be able to use larger quantities of primary memory by dividing it into 'pages', each of (e.g.) 64K capacity, only one of which can be active at any time.

Originally, primary memory comprised thousands of minute ferric cores (hence the name 'core' memory originally used to describe this type of memory) each of which could be individually magnetised to represent a binary zero or one. Now such memory is made up using semiconductor components, either *random access memory* (RAM), which would more logically be named read/write memory, or *read-only memory* (ROM) which, as its name suggests, cannot have information written to it but only read from it. RAM is dynamic memory: its contents normally exist only while the computer is powered up, though in some systems they are maintained by secondary power circuits when the computer is not actually functioning. ROM contents are permanent, embodied in the pattern of the circuitry, and coded into it either at the time of manufacture or (with some special subtypes) in a subsequent one-off (or erasable only with difficulty) writing process. ROM is typically used to store the computer's operating instructions, and most computers have a relatively small proportion of this form of memory. Occasionally, particularly in microcomputers, it is used to store application programs. RAM and ROM together make up the addressable primary memory of the computer, and together share its available memory addresses. Semiconductor devices are discussed further in Chapter 6.

To a significant degree, the overall speed of a computer is determined by the time it takes the control unit to locate and fetch an instruction or data item from main memory. This is known as the *memory cycle time*, and in modern computers is typically measured in micro- or nano-seconds (i.e. millionths or thousand-millionths of a second). Largely because each memory location has to be directly addressable, it is much faster for the computer to obtain data from primary memory than it is for it to obtain it from secondary memory. However, the need for speedy access places restraints upon the way in which primary memory is produced, and this is one reason why it tends to be relatively more expensive than secondary memory, though the price per K of memory has been steadily falling ever since computers were invented.

Forms of RAM which can retain their contents when the main power to the computer is switched off tend to be considerably more expensive than the more common dynamic RAM. In the case of secondary memory (whether tape, disc, or CDROM, or various other less common forms) information can only be stored or retrieved in blocks. Each block contains not a single byte, but several items of information; the exact size depends upon the data format used. Individual items of information are accessed by copying a block from secondary memory into an area of primary memory, where each individual location can be addressed. To pursue the metaphor of a postal system, a block of secondary memory might be thought of as a large pigeon hole which contains a number of letters. The only way to find one individual letter is to empty the entire contents of the pigeon hole on to a table (or, in this case, into RAM) and then look at them individually. In other words, addressing in secondary memory depends upon the way in which that storage area is organised, and in any case can only be carried out for blocks of data.

The concept of a 'block' is used to mean two different things in computer jargon, and it is important not to confuse them. Storage devices physically 'block' out the available space on the storage medium (e.g., they divide a disc into tracks and sectors), in a way that is constant for all the data stored on that device. A particular application program may also employ a block structure to define the way in which its data is stored, and its definition of a block of data may encompass a number of physical blocks on the storage medium. We discuss this further with particular reference to file systems and database management in Chapter 5.

Further, as we have noted, primary memory is purely electronic, and it incorporates no moving parts. RAM and ROM circuits are 'solid state' devices. Secondary memory devices, in contrast, are normally electro-mechanical in their operation. Both tape and disc drives incorporate major mechanical components. In the case of tape, these control the physical movements of the tape past the read/write head, and in the case of the disc they control the rotation of the disc and the positioning of the arm over any specific track. These mechanical operations also contribute to secondary memory being less reliable and slower in operation than primary memory.

The storage capacity of secondary memory can be virtually unlimited, in that (except for fixed-disc devices) as many reels of tape, disc packs or discs can be stored as are desired. However, it is very important to distinguish between the drive units on which the tapes and discs are mounted, so that the information stored on them can be accessed by the computer, and the tapes and discs themselves. Although the system may have access to a large library of tapes or discs, in any particular computer system the actual number of drive units will be very limited. So at any one point, only a few actual tapes or discs will be directly available ('on-line') to the computer. Thus the secondary storage capacity of a particular computer system is usually specified as its on-line capacity.

To repeat: there is a discussion of the principles of file organisation on tape or disc and alternative processing methods in Chapter 5.

Representing and Processing Numbers

Finally, before moving on to a discussion of the software necessary in order to make all this equipment function usefully for us, there remains one major characteristic of the way computers operate that we must examine. In our previous discussion of the units of computer storage, we illustrated how a byte, representing a character, is the basic unit used. Clearly, for a lot of information-processing applications, a character is a relevant storage and processing unit (for example, for information that would naturally be represented in character form, such as names and addresses, or any textual material).

However, in many instances we wish to store and process numbers as numbers (i.e. not as series of numeric characters), and it is necessary to illustrate how a computer handles numbers. This involves a third unit of storage, namely, a *word*. Basically word and word length are different ways of looking at the same thing — the raw capabilities of a processor. Like a byte, a word is a group of contiguous bits (i.e. a group of adjacent bits, operated on as a whole); but whereas for all practical purposes a byte is always composed of 8 bits, a word differs in size (i.e. its length as measured by number of bits) from processor to processor. A word indicates how many contiguous bits a processor can interpret and act on at any one point in time. When a processor fetches the next instruction or item of data from main memory, the word length indicates the maximum number of bits that it might transfer.

The word length of a processor confers two important characteristics on its host system. First, any instruction (and, in some cases, the address of the memory locations whose contents are to be operated on) to be executed by the processor is linked to the word length. Thus in general, a longer word length indicates a more powerful processor. The instructions that the processor is able to obey directly are known as its *instruction set*. In many ways it is the fundamental parameter of a processor. A larger number of bits available for coding the instructions in general implies a larger, richer, more powerful instruction set, and thus a more powerful processor.

Second, it is important to realise that our discussion of storage and processing above only involved information represented as characters. Obviously, in data processing we are primarily concerned with storage and processing numbers as numbers, not as a group of characters. It is crucial to appreciate that the number 67.4 is fundamentally different from the individual characters '6', '7', '.' and '4', which happen to be stored in that sequence. It is feasible to store and process numbers represented internally in the machine as strings of characters such as this, but it is extremely wasteful of memory capacity. It also makes for a very, very slow computer, since each character is the subject of an individual fetch from memory; and makes arithmetic difficult. Thus, within most computers there are in fact several different storage formats, one of which is, of course, character form. The other forms are largely concerned with storing various numeric quantities — either *integer* (i.e. whole numbers) or *floating point* (i.e. with a decimal point) — to varying degrees of accuracy.

To store a floating point number takes at least 32 bits; thus personal computers (typically 8- or 16-bit) and minicomputers (typically 16-bit) take more than one instruction to manipulate these numbers. Most large business machines have 32-bit processors, which speeds up the processing of decimal arithmetic; but for really complex and accurate scientific calculation, 64-bit processors have been developed.

Software — Instructing the Computer

In the previous chapter we described the major pieces of equipment that go to make up a computer system, and illustrated the technical basis on which they operate. In this chapter we describe the various software components and illustrate their function. The first point to bear in mind is that software, as its name suggests, is somewhat less tangible than the pieces of equipment that we have just described. Software comprises the instructions to the equipment which enable it to function usefully from your point of view. They are only tangible when printed or displayed in some human-readable form. As we shall see, a set of instructions may exist in one of several forms within the machine, each of which requires different skills for their understanding. For the purposes of describing its function, software is usually divided into two distinctive categories: *operating system software*, which includes the instructions necessary to enable our equipment actually to function as a computer system; and *application software*, or programs, which instruct the system on how to perform a particular user-oriented task.

In the first part of this chapter we will concentrate on what is known as application software, or programs — instructions specifying the necessary steps to perform a user-oriented task such as preparing a payroll, updating a file of stock records, preparing an invoice, and so on. A complete set of instructions to perform some particular task is known as a *program*.

The Nature of Software

All programs have three basic components, namely *input, processing* and *output*. First, nearly all programs need some input data on which to work;

for example, this might be the weekly time sheets, a batch of invoices, a series of cash flows, or a discount rate. Accurate data input is a vital part of data processing and we discuss it more fully in Chapter 9. Second, the input data is processed — multiplying hours worked by rate per hour, cash flows by discount rate etc. Processing may also involve the retrieval of previously stored information: for example, to get pay to date, or tax to date. And, increasingly, it may also involve communication with another computer or remote terminal. Finally, after the relevant processing has been done, then the results must be displayed or reported in some form, such as a payslip, the sales ledger or simply a net present value. Thus a simple model of any program could be shown as in Figure 4.1.

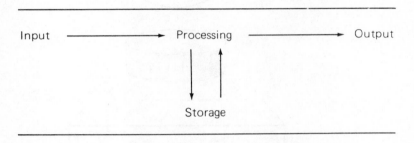

Figure 4.1 *A Simple Model of Data Processing*

To understand a little more about the nature of software, it may be useful to consider the analogy of making a cake. Consider the instructions in Figure 4.2. The inputs would be butter, eggs, flour and sugar; the processing instructions might be: 'Mix ingredients together, put in greased tin, put tin in the oven (350°F), remove tin from oven after 20 minutes'; and the output would hopefully be a sponge cake. In this example a number of separate inputs have been combined and manipulated to produce the desired result. The processing instructions contained a number of key words that were meaningful to the 'cooking processor'. However the analogy with a computer program breaks down, because with the computer there is no fundamental difference between the data (inputs and output) and the processing instructions themselves.

Consider next the simple data processing example shown in Figure 4.3, where the inputs are a series of names: Jones, Brown, Smith and Williams. The processing instructions are to sort these names into ascending alphabetical order. Note that in this context 'sort' is a keyword which has a special meaning to the computer. The output is then a list of names sorted in alphabetical sequence: Brown, Jones, Smith, Williams.

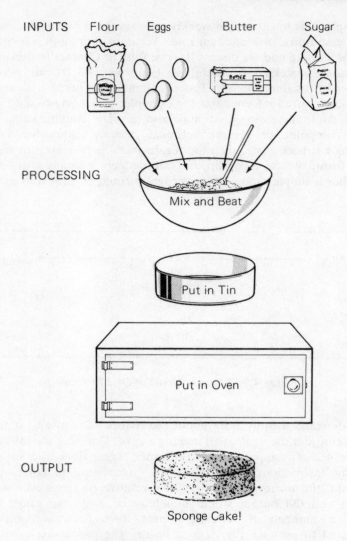

INPUTS   Flour   Eggs   Butter   Sugar

PROCESSING

Mix and Beat

Put in Tin

Put in Oven

OUTPUT

Sponge Cake!

Figure 4.2 *A Cooking Analogy*

This example illustrates the point that, in a data processing environment, the 'data' to be processed need not be numeric information; in this example it was characters (often referred to as *text*).

The input data will be represented as a series of bits (binary data), as will the processing instructions. Consequently, it is not uncommon for the data being processed by one program to be the instructions for another program. Later in this chapter we will describe the role of an operating system, which is the major component of system software. Whereas

INPUTS: Smith, Brown, Jones, Williams

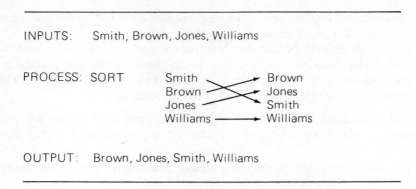

OUTPUT: Brown, Jones, Smith, Williams

Figure 4.3 *Sort Example*

application software is specific to one particular task (such as payroll, or stock recording), system software is generic to all application programs and is shared by all users.

All software specifies the logic — the set of rules — by which the 'data' are to be handled. Note that, in the context of this book, we are concerned with the processing of all information — be it in data, text, voice, video or facsimile form — and that the operations specified in this chapter, though nominally written as 'data processing', could be applied to all forms of information processing. We can summarise the basic building blocks of any system as instructions to the hardware to:

accept   store   retrieve   process   transmit   display

data (or information). All of the above steps will be present to a greater or lesser degree in any application program. These steps specify what the application program actually causes the computer to do with the data — it will accept, store, retrieve, process, transmit and display the data on receipt of the appropriate instructions. But what form do these instructions take? Why can't we simply instruct the computer in straightforward English?

Machine Code Programming

All instructions and data internal to the computer must be coded in some agreed fashion, using the binary number system. Furthermore, the processor at the heart of the computer system can function only on receipt of instructions drawn from those available in its own repertoire, known as its *instruction set*. Thus despite the way in which we as humans may arrive at the function and form of the instructions that we wish the computer to obey, the processor dictates a fundamental requirement —

the instructions that it obeys must be presented as binary codes according to the specification of its instruction set.

The programmers of the first computers back in the 1950s had no choice — they had to program directly in binary using the processor's instruction set — in what today is usually termed *machine code*. This procedure had several major disadvantages, such as:

it was relatively laborious, since machine code instructions are very simple, and many of them are required in order to perform even simple tasks;

it was very complex, as the programmer had to have a good knowledge of the workings of the computer;

as everything was in binary, it was easy to make mistakes, but difficult to find them (and almost impossible to find them in other people's programs).

Thus there began a process to try to reduce the impact of these deficiencies, and ultimately to increase the productivity of the programmer. The first stage was to replace the binary codes of the instruction set with an exactly comparable set of mnemonics, such that there was a unique one-to-one correspondence between each mnemonic and each instruction in the processor's set. These mnemonics were thus still at the detailed level of the processor's instruction set — for example, ADD to add together two numbers, MOVE to move a number from primary memory to a specified i/o device, and so on. The advantages from a programmer's point of view were that they were less likely to make mistakes with the mnemonics and the resulting program was easier to follow and comprehend.

Even so, programming in these mnemonics — usually known as *Assembler* — was still very tedious and prone to error. For example, an Assembler program to add three numbers together might be written as follows:

memory location (address):   19   20   21   22
   contents (data)   :   125.2 73.1 527.8

i.e. the three memory locations (pigeon holes) numbered 19 to 21 inclusive contain the numbers 125.2, 73.1 and 527.8 respectively.

We will assume that our processor in this example has two reserved memory locations (called *registers*) which its arithmetic unit accesses when adding; these will be referenced as registers A and B. Our program might then be:

1   ZERO,B   (set contents of register B to zero)

3   MOVE,A,19 (move the contents of memory
                location 19 to register A)

5	ADD,B,A	(add the contents of register A to those of register B; result is left in B)
7	MOVE,A,20	(move contents of location 20 to A)
9	ADD,B,A	(add contents of A to those in B)
11	MOVE,A,21	(move contents of location 21 to A)
13	ADD,B,A	(add contents of A to those in B)
15	MOVE,22,B	(move contents of register B — the answer — to memory location 22)
17	END	(no more instructions)

These instructions are executed in sequence until the 'END' statement. (There could have been an instruction to transfer control to a point in the sequence other than the next instruction.) The numbers to the left of the instructions represent the memory locations where they are stored (two locations for each instruction). So that, in primary memory, locations 1–18 represent the instructions and locations 19–22 represent the data. If the 'END' instruction was missing, then the computer would have attempted to interpret the data in location 19 as an instruction, which would probably have caused it serious indigestion.

Apart from being laborious to develop, machine code and assembler programs have one other great limitation. They can be used only on the specific make of computer for which they were developed, thus 'locking-in' the user to a particular manufacturer. The advantage of machine code is in its efficient execution — this, however, is becoming less critical with the increasing power of the hardware.

High-level Programming Languages

To overcome some of these problems, high-level languages were developed. These went some way towards improving the productivity of programmers, and enabled the programs to be moved between different manufacturers' computers (albeit with difficulty). But we still haven't answered the question, why cannot we instruct the computer in plain English? The problem is that in general usage English is ambiguous. It is often the case that a long and complex statement (such as might be necessary to instruct the computer to perform some realistic application) can be interpreted in more than one way. It may be clear to a human reader of these instructions how to interpret them in the light of the specific context in which they are set, but a computer is in general incapable of such sophistication and is unaware of the specific context of a given set of instructions. The instructions presented to the computer must be unambiguous in their interpretation. A high-level programming language is a very restricted subset of the English language (or any other appropriate language) in which each word or symbol has a unique and precisely defined meaning.

The first high-level languages were developed in the second half of the 1950s. The first in general use was *Fortran* (which stands for FORmulation TRANslation) in 1957, for which the first international standard was developed in 1959. As its name suggests, Fortran is a language designed with scientific applications in mind. Thus Fortran can easily handle complex mathematical formulae, but its data processing capabilities are relatively weak (since scientific applications traditionally did not involve substantial volumes of input and output).

However, typically commercial data processing applications do involve considerable amounts of i/o, whilst the computations to be performed are often trivial. Thus *Cobol* (COmmon Business Orientated Language) was developed by 1961, though it did not receive significant widespread support from the computer manufacturers until 1966, when the US Department of Defense specified the Cobol language as a requirement in a tender for computer systems. From then on Cobol achieved widespread acceptance.

Fortran and Cobol are now well over twenty years old, and their age shows, in spite of regular improvements and extensions. They were designed for the days of batch-processing computers, when input was typically by punched card and output appeared on a line printer, and they do not contain extensive capabilities for on-line dialogue between user and computer, or for the use of video display screens. Today there are more appropriate languages which make better use of the current state of computer capabilities and programming theory. However, the very large volume of applications written in Cobol and Fortran ensures that these languages will play a significant part for the foreseeable future.

Other languages of this generation which have been extensively used in large commercial data processing centres include RPG, PL1 and Algol.

The development of interactive, time-sharing computer systems in the 1960s, and the subsequent development of cheap personal computers in the 1970s, led to the popularity of the *Basic* language (Beginners' All-purpose Symbolic Instruction Code). Basic was specifically developed for use on terminals with a minimum of formal i/o conventions, and was intended for use by non-computer personnel. This latter point has meant that it is one of the easiest computer programming languages to learn, and it is typically the one taught to schoolchildren and many students. Unfortunately its popularity has led to a proliferation of alternative versions, so that today Basic is one of the few languages without a widely-accepted international standard.

Other languages used extensively in educational contexts include Pascal and the 'turtle' language LOGO, which has specific instructions to drive a small robot-like device.

Of the newer languages developed during the 1970s, perhaps the one with the widest take-up has been C, a simple but powerful general-purpose language with a wide range of potential applications. Ada, a real time language developed for the US Department of Defense, was fully specified by 1980, and has slowly gained a wider following.

Other developments with significant potential for the future (but with a limited effect on the present activity of commercial data processing) have been the appearance of 'fourth generation languages' (which we discuss shortly) and of 'artificial intelligence' oriented languages such as LISP and Prolog.

Standards and Dialects

High-level languages are not computer-specific. They can be used on any computer which corresponds broadly to their hardware demands, and which has an appropriate compiler or interpreter. However, this does not mean that it is always a simple or straightforward matter to transfer programs originally written for one computer system to another system which supports the same language.

International standards for almost all of the major high-level languages have been set down by specific committees, the majority of whose members are often computer manufacturers and software houses producing language compilers and interpreters. But in this situation agreement is a long drawn-out process, and, even when it is achieved, the specification of the standard tends to the lowest common denominator of the implementations of the language in question by the various software houses (since no software house wants to agree to a language specification that it cannot itself meet).

Additionally, computer systems have distinctive design characteristics as selling points — specific capabilities which users naturally wish to exploit. To enable them to do this, manufacturers provide appropriate extensions to the current language standards. If the computer has a touch-sensitive screen, for instance, or particularly good graphic capabilities, then the versions of the language offered for that computer may support these capabilities. Systems analysts and designers naturally make full use of these language extensions; thus the application programs are written in a non-standard version of the language, and it is a major task to rewrite them to run on other computers which may not offer the same capabilities, or which may implement equivalent capabilities in quite different ways.

Quite apart from this situation, the specifications of the language standards are themselves sometimes ambiguous, so that implementation often differs from manufacturer to manufacturer.

Characteristics of High-level Languages

In a high-level language, each program statement (i.e. each instruction in that language) is equivalent to many machine code instructions (hence the 'high-level' designation). Even 'ADD 1 TO 1' (and most languages provide some equivalent of this instruction) demands a lengthy series of machine code instructions specifying where the original numbers are to be stored in the computer, where the result is to be stored, and how the result is to be transmitted to the user. The difference in number of statements between a high-level language and machine code could easily be tenfold (i.e. there would be ten times fewer statements in the high-level version). In addition, the memory locations addressed by these statements are generally designated by user-selected names, rather than by their absolute binary addresses. So a high-level language programmer might talk of 'PAY' or 'TOTAL' where a machine code programmer talks of 'Register A', or 'Memory Location 10110110'. From the pro-grammer's point of view, this results in far fewer instructions to write, test and 'debug' (that is, ensure that they work correctly), and much more easily readable and maintainable code.

We will now briefly review the characteristics of some popular high-level languages.

Fortran

Fortran was the first of the high-level languages to be developed and, as its name suggests, it was primarily intended for use in applications involving mathematical procedures. Thus it continues to find its major use in scientific and engineering applications. However, because such applications characteristically involve complex computations, but rela-tively small volumes of input/output, Fortran's ability to represent complex mathematics or logic is high, whilst its input/output capabilities are limited and rather arbitrary. Various international standards for the language have been agreed upon. The most recent is Fortran 77, though its predecessor Fortran IV is more widely used.

As an example of a Fortran statement, consider the following:

$$NETPAY = (HOURS*RATE) - TAX$$

whose meaning is probably fairly clear to you. Two *variables*, *HOURS* and *RATE*, are multiplied together (when instructing a computer, the multiplication symbol is '*'), and then the variable *TAX* is subtracted from this product to give the value of the variable *NETPAY*. All high-level languages use *symbolic variable names* (e.g. *HOURS, RATE*, etc.), chosen by the programmer, to reference memory locations, and to express the operations required in their contents. That is, the computer will assign a symbolic name used by the programmer to a unique actual memory location which it will automatically access every time that particular name is used. Thus the programmer can program using symbolic names which have meaning in the context of a particular program. Consider a second Fortran example, this time analogous to our previous machine code example. Suppose that as before we wish to add three numbers together, then a Fortran program might be:

$$TOTAL = 0$$
$$DO\ 100\ J = 1,3$$
$$100\ TOTAL = TOTAL + RENT(J)$$

The *DO* statement tells the processor to execute the statements up to and including that labelled '100' for each value of the index variable *J* as it increments from its initial value (in this case '1'), to its final value (in this case '3'), in steps of 1 (which is implied in the form of the statement). Thus, in the example, the statement labelled '100' is executed three times, with *J* taking on the values 1, 2 and 3 successively, and thus accessing the three memory locations occupied by the variable *RENT*. This illustrates a further point of advantage when programming in a high-level language: namely, that a symbolic name can be given not only to a single memory location, but also to a consecutive block of such locations, considerably aiding the processing of large tables of data. In this example the variable *RENT* refers to such a block of memory — the specific individual location to be accessed within the block is indicated by the subscript J. This example is a very small illustration of the greatly increased power available to the programmer when using a high-level language. It is not that it enables him or her to do anything over and above what can be done using Assembler: the point is that it can be accomplished so much more speedily and accurately. High-level languages primarily improve the productivity of the programmer.

Cobol

In contrast to Fortran, Cobol was explicitly designed to be a language whose syntax would be especially suited to applications in commercial data processing. Relative to Fortran, statements in Cobol are in one sense at a higher level in that they are closer to pure English. Indeed, it was one of the design objectives of Cobol that the basic purpose of a program should be understandable from reading its statements. Because Cobol is closer to English, the process of translation into machine code is much greater relative to that of Fortran. As in the case of Fortran, well-established international standards for the implementation of Cobol have been established, the current one (and the one most generally implemented by computer manufacturers) being Cobol 74.

The capabilities of Cobol are much more oriented towards the handling of large volumes of input/output than are those of Fortran, especially in the handling of files of data and in the formatting and layout of output, but they are much less oriented towards handling complex mathematical procedures. For example, the first of our simple Fortran examples above would be written in Cobol as follows:

MULTIPLY HOURS BY RATE GIVING GROSS PAY
SUBTRACT TAX FROM GROSS PAY GIVING NET PAY

As can readily be seen, this is very close to English and its function can be easily understood, even if a little verbose! Another feature of Cobol is that the program is divided into four different sections, or divisions. Each division has a different function — for example, to describe the operating environment of the particular computer. The specification of the file and data layouts is separated from the processing instructions so that, for example, the less skilled programmers could simply code up the processing instructions and not have any control over the file and data specifications.

Basic

Basic is a more recent development in programming languages, but is not significantly 'higher' than Fortran or Cobol. Rather, it simply had a different objective in its design. Basic was originally designed as an easy-to-learn-and-use language, particularly oriented towards problem-solving programs developed on interactive, time-sharing computer systems. Consequently, the specification of the language was kept as simple as possible, and in particular the input/output conventions were kept to a minimum. For these reasons, Basic has proved to be a very popular language in which to get started on programming, as it enables relatively inexperienced programmers to produce programs handling complex problems in a fairly short period of time. However, in terms of encouraging good programming practice, Basic leaves a lot to be desired (largely because it sacrifices formal structure in the interests of ease of use), and it is generally considered to be unsuitable for use in large-scale data processing applications. Also, versions of Basic have proliferated over the years so that now there is little common standard amongst the various implementations of the language.

As an example of the use of Basic, the example presented previously when discussing Fortran could be written in Basic as follows:

$$P = (H^*R) - T$$

The similarity of the above with the Fortran equivalent can be seen; in general Basic only allows a single character (or character plus a number) as variable names, making large Basic programs difficult to read and understand. However it must be added that Basic retains great popularity amongst the amateur programmers and users. It has become the *lingua franca* of the microcomputer and there are probably more people in the world who can program in Basic than in any other language. It is rather scorned by the computer professionals and this may be in part because it threatens their existence by enabling the end-user to instruct the computer.

C

'C' is a very simple language, with only a small core number of instructions: there are a bare 28 'keywords'. However, the programmer him/herself can extend it, by combining these instructions to produce other, more complex instructions (known as *functions*) which then effectively also become part of the language; in this way, C's very simple basis builds up into considerable power. A very small C compiler may include only 50 or so inbuilt functions; a larger C compiler will have 200 or more, which greatly enhances its power.

C is a relatively portable language, available on a very wide range of computers from personal to large mainframe systems. It is used to develop operating systems, business applications, text processing systems, database applications, spreadsheets, communications facilities, compilers of other high-level languages, and for many other purposes.

C's merits include a powerful data definition method — that is, it tells the computer very precisely what type of data (alphanumeric, integer number, floating point number or whatever) it will be working with — and a powerful instruction set of data operators which tells the computer how to manipulate this data. Because of its loop-coding capabilities (i.e. the way in which the same section of code can be used many times over), C programs can be very concise. They are highly structured, which is an advantage when coding complex applications. And the free-form way in which C programs are written means that the programmer can space the instructions on the page as he or she chooses, and include as many comments as are desirable to make the program easily comprehensible to anyone who wishes to amend or update it.

Though C uses many symbols when compared with a discursive Cobol program, its programs are quite readily comprehensible. Here is a very short example:

```
/*      program name: simple prog*
# include 'stdio.h'
main ()
|
    printf( 'Hello there' ); /* display message */
| /* end of main */
```

Structured Programming

Programming a computer, even in high-level languages, has always been an art. It has a strong creative element: ten programmers, given a problem, will come up with ten different (often radically different) programs. Their programs may all achieve more or less the same output for a given input, but they will probably behave differently when operated outside their original design specifications, be more or less efficient, more or less user-friendly and more or less difficult to modify. The difference in performance between even trained professional programmers can be astonishing. Tests at Boeing, on a large sample of programmers given the same problem, showed productivity ratios of 5 to 1 between the best and worst programmers. It is not always obvious in a large computer department which programmers *are* the best and worst, due to the complex interactions that go into developing big systems.

Structured programming is an attempt to turn software production into a science. This reduces the acceptable ways of writing any program, so that it is more rigidly planned and executed, more easily comprehensible, and can be subjected to better quality control and maintenance.

One of the basic concepts of structured programming is that instead of long formless stretches of code, programs should be divided up into small modules which interact only in clearly defined ways. Unfortunately, languages such as Fortran and Cobol were not devised to be used in this manner. In order to meet the new requirements, enhanced versions have been developed: they are known as Structured Cobol, Structured Basic, and so on. Most of the newer programming languages take for granted the requirement for modularity, and include these features as standard.

Procedural and Declarative Approaches

The languages we have discussed up to now have been *procedural* languages. In other words, they are concerned with *how* the computer produces what is required, and provide detailed instructions in order to enable it to do so. Each program in a procedural language basically consists of a series of instructions; the computer performs these in a sequence which is specified within the program itself.

In a Basic program (and in some other languages too) the lines of code are usually numbered, making the bones of this approach very evident. This is a typical short Basic program:

```
10   LET a = 5: LET b = 10.
20   PRINT a + b
30   END
```

But this is not the only practicable approach; indeed, it is not a particularly desirable approach in an era which has seen the change from an original stress on making the computer carry out computations, to a new emphasis on using the computer as an information resource.

The information resource concept is at the core of a newer generation of languages which work not in a procedural but in a *declarative* way. In these languages, the stress changes from telling the computer *how* to do its work, to telling it *what* the user wants to know. The computer itself is then left to figure out how to provide the required information. Using a declarative approach, the programmer does not write self-contained programs which the computer executes once — after which it stops and waits for the next task to be given. He or she primes the computer with a *database* of information, and with various capabilities to manipulate that information. And then when information is needed, the user requests it, and the computer uses its already available resources to provide it.

This is a lot more difficult to achieve than it sounds. The move from procedural to declarative working methods has been going on for some time, but even today it is not yet complete. However, it is possible to see it at work in many languages oriented towards 'artificial intelligence' applications, and, in a slightly different way, in what are now commonly known as *fourth generation languages*, or 4GLs.

Artificial Intelligence and Expert System Software

In the 1970s, 'artificial intelligence' or 'ai' was a much-touted concept which sometimes seemed rather empty to those who looked closely into it. Many researchers spoke grandly of giving computers more 'intelligence', but their actual achievements fell considerably behind their aspirations, and to some extent the disappointments are evident today. We still do not have computers that can talk to us in totally free-form natural language, understanding everything we say — though some computers can briefly appear to do something not dissimilar, in restricted circumstances. We still do not have computers that can recognise complex new objects, however they are positioned. But researchers have made limited but real strides in the field of natural-language interchange and pattern recognition, and some of these strides are reflected in a new generation of ai-oriented products with real everyday uses.

Predominant among the contemporary applications of ai are *expert systems*. An expert system is a computer system into which has been fed the kind of knowledge that a human expert in a certain, usually fairly restricted, field would possess. For example, there are expert systems which deal with the diagnosis of types of disease, propose sites for geological prospecting, and deal with financial information (e.g. the effect of new tax or pension legislation).

There is nothing intelligent about an encyclopedia-type system which simply has information available to be looked up. But expert systems do more. By studying the ways in which human experts interrelate their knowledge, and the conclusions to which they come, the expert system evolves its own *knowledge structure*. Advanced systems are then able to recognise similar patterns in new data which are presented to them, to make inductions from their existing knowledge, and to suggest at least tentative conclusions. For example, from its bank of data on disease symptoms and diagnoses made by doctors, an expert system can ask questions about the symptoms of a new patient and then suggest a diagnosis; or, from data about geological patterns and the mineral discoveries made (and not made), an expert system can study a new patch of territory and suggest the most promising sites for test drillings.

Two types of product are now available which enable new expert systems to be developed. The first are *expert system builders*: programs that provide the shell of a knowledge structure and an induction system, which enable programmers or end-users to tailor an expert system to their own requirements and to feed data into it. (Examples of successful products are Intelligent Environments' Crystal and Expertech's 'Xi'.) The second are declarative languages in which both expert system builders and actual expert systems can be programmed from scratch.

Many languages of this type use a *list processing* paradigm. The information provided to the computer is structured in lists. Lists can be nested together, sometimes to considerable depth, thus providing the basis of a data structure. LISP (for LISt Processing language) was one of the earliest examples of this approach. First developed in the late 1960s, it is today very widely used. Another language using a similar method, but developed about ten years later and reflecting some more advanced thoughts on the same lines, is *Prolog* (Programming in Logic).

Prolog

The Prolog programmer begins an application by giving the computer information: providing it with a database of information which is structured in a fixed way. For example, here is a tiny database of information about the relationships within a mythical company:

> *boss(smith, jones).*
>
> *boss(smith, wilson).*
>
> *boss(evans, smith).*

The term '*boss*' here describes the kind of relationship between the two following terms. Though it is a relationship that is reasonably obvious to human beings, the computer need not in any way understand *what* the relationship here is: only that there is one. Once the computer has this information in its memory, the user can go on to ask whose *boss smith* is, or who *smith*'s subordinates are, or any other question which concerns the data included in the database and which is asked in a way the system can handle.

Other Prolog statements cover issues like 'if *x* is *y*'s *boss*, and *y* is *z*'s *boss*, then *x* is *senior* to *z*'. In this way the computer can 'learn' and report to the user a relationship between, say, Evans and Jones, even though it has not been given any statement that directly relates those two individuals.

Programmer and User Productivity

One of the great motivations behind the development of high-level languages was to increase the productivity of application programmers. To a certain extent this has been successful: programmers code applications today that simply could not have been contemplated in the days when Assembler reigned supreme. Yet even so, gains in programmer productivity have been slow. One reason for this has been the sheer volume of program maintenance that needs to be carried out: professional programmers in large organisations typically spend by far the majority of their time on this work. But another reason has been the relative slowness with which programming itself has been automated as an activity. Though the activities which are analysed are increasingly being automated, systems analysts tend to work in an almost entirely manual way — sometimes even down to setting down their findings using pencil and paper.

Today, however, tools are being developed which help to automate the programming task, and thus to enhance programmer productivity. Sometimes this is at the expense of program efficiency, but in an era in which processing power is cheap and people-power expensive, this is a desirable trade-off.

Similar tools are also making life easier for end-users, and we consider this aspect shortly. Although these new types of programming tools are commonly known as fourth generation languages, they are regarded as part of a wider discipline known as *software engineering*.

Fourth Generation Languages and Software Engineering

Fourth generation languages are actually not application languages in the sense that they replace Cobol, Fortran and the languages that might be described as 'third generation': rather they are tools for the programmer which supplement the earlier products. In a sense they are 'ultra high-level languages', providing a layer of software that is *above* the normal high-level language.

Though each fourth generation language differs from every other, there are some standard features which characterise all these tools. Now that graphics is a standard feature of many computer systems, it is essential that a programmer should be able to use the video screen fully and easily. With the increasing trend away from procedural programs and towards declarative programming, it is necessary for programmers to have tools, including good query facilities and report writers, that allow them to get the best out of stored databases. Usually there is an interface to one or more database management systems (DBMSs). And there will be interfaces, too, to conventional high-level languages, or the provision of some kind of proprietary 'language'.

Examples of this new type of language are Mantis, PRO-IV and Powerhouse. In general, fourth generation languages have been targeted at those programmers involved in developing commercial data processing software.

A more recent term for this type of approach is CASE, which stands for Computer Aided Systems/Software Engineering. CASE is currently focused at situations in which the productivity of programmers, in terms of time to develop the application and the accuracy of the resulting program, and the maintainability of the software are critical. This tends to be in areas in which the software is embedded in other products (e.g. guided missiles, radar, or cars) or very large software environments (e.g.

operating system software, or telecommunications switching software). A current manifestation of CASE is in IPSE (that is, Integrated Programmers/Project Support Environment): in effect, a software framework in which a variety of tools (e.g. compilers, database managers, user interfaces, or query languages) can be 'slotted' to be used by the programmer in a consistent, coherent and replicable way. Improvements in programmer productivity through a variety of software engineering tools is a vital concern for a whole range of companies using IT. Among the generation of increasingly multipurpose programming environments that combine a wide variety of programmers' tools is Software Generation's APS Development Centre.

Application Software Systems

Another trend which can be discerned today, with the spread of distributed computing resources, is the growth of 'do-it-yourself' programming. Increasingly, professionals in other fields do not want to call in software specialists every time they want to do something on their computer terminal. They prefer to have the facilities available to enable them to program their own applications, or to tailor a general-purpose package to their own specific requirements.

Application software systems, like declarative languages and CASE tools, represent the move away from lines of procedural code and towards more flexible ways of utilising computer resources. They provide a general capability to a professional user in a particular area (for example, an engineer or an accountant), in contrast to application programs which are designed to solve one particular type of problem.

For example, application software systems help engineers to use the computer to design cars, bridges, and most especially complex micro-electronic circuits. They provide tools for accountants to do their financial modelling on the computer, for artists to prepare their finished artwork on the computer and for process control engineers to program the computer to control various processes.

These capabilities are commonly known as *application languages*. In contrast to general purpose languages such as Basic and Cobol, they are specific languages, in which the vocabulary clearly reflects the application area for which they are intended.

Compilers and Interpreters

As we have previously illustrated, ultimately the instructions that the processor carries out must be drawn from its instruction set. But its instruction set only exists as a set of binary codes, and although it is feasible to program in machine code (at least, within smallish limits) it is not usually desirable.

In order to be executed by the processor, the high-level language statements have to be translated into machine code. This is done in one of two ways. The simplest is to translate the statements into machine code every time the program is run. This is done by passing them through a program called an *interpreter*, which acts much like a human interpreter, expanding each high-level command into its (usually many) low-level equivalents. Using an interpreter is simple for the programmer and is a particularly good method when a program is in development and not yet finished. The major drawbacks are that the interpreting process markedly slows down the computer's speed of operation and that the cumbersome work of interpreting has to be done, not once only, but every time the program runs — indeed, every time a statement in it is executed, which may be many times even during a single program run.

The other way is to interpret the program once only, and transform the original high-level statements (known as *source code*) into their equivalents in low-level machine code statements (known as *object code*). This is done by processing the original language statements through a program called a *compiler*.

It is important to recognise that compilers and interpreters are programs just like any other programs. Their input is the source code statements in a high-level language; their output is the object code statements (either compiled or immediately executed) in machine code.

These are general-purpose programs, in as far as they can translate any valid source code in the relevant language into correct object code. For any non-trivial, practical piece of source code there are usually several alternative equivalent sets of object code possible: that is, there is no unique translation from source code to object code. For this reason, the object code resulting from a compilation may be relatively inefficient, as compared to what would be possible if the problem had been coded directly in machine code. (Inefficiency is usually measured in terms of cpu time taken to execute the particular piece of code.) In some applications, where fast execution is paramount (typically on-line, real-time systems such as airline reservation systems) coding will be done directly in Assembler to ensure as efficient a code as possible.

A different compiler or interpreter is needed for each high-level language to be implemented on a particular machine. The compiler/interpreter is tied to one particular machine (or more precisely, to one particular instruction set); but a high-level language is potentially more general, since a program written in such a language can theoretically be run on any machine on which a compiler or interpreter is available for that language. (In practice, there is little standardisation of languages,

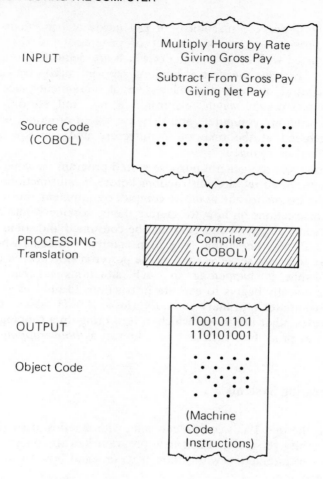

INPUT

Multiply Hours by Rate
Giving Gross Pay

Subtract From Gross Pay
Giving Net Pay

Source Code
(COBOL)

PROCESSING
Translation

Compiler
(COBOL)

OUTPUT

100101101
110101001

Object Code

(Machine
Code
Instructions)

Figure 4.4 *The Compilation Process*

and the features supported in different 'dialects' may vary markedly,
reducing this theoretical portability of programs from machine to
machine.)

System Software

It is crucial to appreciate that in the absence of any instructions our
computer equipment would not function at all. This is because what we
are primarily describing in this book is, strictly speaking, termed a
general-purpose, stored-program, digital electronic computer system. It is

a general-purpose machine — it can tackle any problems for which we can provide an appropriate set of programs and data. This can be contrasted with other computers which are dedicated to a single specific task — perhaps the best example is seen in microprocessors devoted to the control of some particular item of equipment, such as a washing machine, digital watch, electronic game, and so on. These micro-processors are computers and they are stored-program; but the program is included at the time of manufacture and subsequently cannot be modified or changed.

However, the general-purpose stored-program machine with which we are concerned requires instructions before it can function. If we switched on the power to our items of computer equipment, but did not provide any instructions on how to operate them, nothing would happen, except that some electrical energy would be consumed and some heat given off. But you may be saying, 'I've seen computer systems which do become active in a user sense as soon as the power is switched on to them'. True, but what is happening in such situations is that the processor automatically begins to execute instructions located in a specific area of the computer's primary memory (in a ROM) which itself loads and executes other programs, which in turn bring up a running system for the user. A procedure such as this is known as *bootstrapping*.

Operating Systems

Until the mid-1960s computers came with a series of special applications and utility programs. Each new program had to concern itself with the effect of interaction with other programs and how to store data on the filing system.

When IBM introduced their 360 range they introduced with it a new concept in organising the computer. The IBM 360 came with an operating system (DOS/OS 360), which was a program that managed the operating environment, thus taking that requirement away from each application program. Quite rapidly all other computer manufacturers adopted the same approach. Though 'operating system' is now the usual term, operating systems are sometimes called 'executives', 'supervisors', and 'monitors'.

The capabilities of an operating system vary, depending upon the size, type and applications of the computer system on which it is used. There are a number of components, however, which are common to all operating systems, large and small.

Operational Control

It is important that today's computers should be enabled to operate as automatically as possible. The speed of even the most routine and instinctive human intervention is painfully slow when set against the computer's speed at handling operations, and any human involvement at all dramatically slows down the entire process. So the operating system tries to ensure that the computer handles all routine events (and quite a few less-routine ones) automatically. The human computer operators of a generation ago have largely been displaced in today's computer systems. Nowadays the role of the operator is confined to a few purely mechanical tasks which are difficult to automate, such as swapping magnetic tapes or discs, or taking paper off the line-printer. Otherwise the system itself manages its own operation, scheduling its resources to meet the tasks imposed on it, with the objective of maximising the utilisation of the cpu on application programs. In all but the very simplest computers, this involves some kind of *multitasking*: interleaving different tasks so that cpu time not required by one task (for instance, time while the user is slowly typing in a response) can be applied instead to a second task. Different tasks may be allocated different priorities, and there is generally a system of *interrupts* so that — for instance — a message from a remote computer, or a warning from a sensor being monitored, can be handled immediately, whatever the computer is currently doing.

Control of Integral and Peripheral Devices

Every computer depends for its operation as a system upon peripheral devices: secondary storage devices such as magnetic disc drives, communications devices such as modems and printers, and so on. An essential part of the computer's operating system are the software and hardware components required to utilise these devices automatically. These are referred to as *drivers* or *controllers*.

A magnetic disc controller, for instance, will (among other functions) determine where space is available on the disc, will control the movement of the read/write head and the actual reading or writing of data to/from the disc, and will automatically maintain a directory of files on the disc.

It is also important for the cpu to maintain control over devices which form more integral parts of the system. It is necessary to control what appears on the video screen, for example, and a video driver handles this function, dealing with the necessary refreshing and updating of the screen data.

Utility Routines

The operating instructions of the processor chip tend to be very general and simple, as we have seen, covering simple arithmetical operations and the transfer of data from one memory location to another. Included in the operating system are routines, typically written in machine code or Assembler which produce relatively simple 'utilities' built up from these basic capabilities. These utility commands or programs can then be used by higher-level programmers working with the computer.

Typical utility programs (for example, display directories of files on disc on the video screen, or print out hard copies of them) format hard and floppy discs and perform 'housekeeping' operations such as deleting unwanted files, setting up a file structure of directories and subdirectories, and allocating parts of the computer's memory for use as 'buffers' (special 'waiting' storage areas) or for other purposes.

Network Control

When a number of computers are linked together in a local area network (discussed in detail in Chapter 10), the demands for operational control are much more complex. Special operating systems designed for use in network environments handle the elaborate protocols that enable the computers in the network to share information and resources with each other.

Network management systems are one of the fastest-growing development areas within the systems software, and are of critical importance to many innovative users.

Types of Operating System

Many of the features of the computer's operating system are required almost continually while the computer is in operation. The software that performs these functions must be permanently available in primary memory. In some computers, the operating software is encoded in ROM memory. In others, it is held in secondary memory (for instance, on a hard or floppy disc), and is loaded into RAM on every computer start-up. Today, as a rule, this is done automatically. A small portion of the operating system is always resident in ROM, and this loads the rest, in an operation known as *bootstrapping* (i.e. the system pulls itself up by its own bootlaces).

Where RAM space is at a premium, however, the size of a very complex operating system with many capabilities and utility programs can be a serious disadvantage. In order to ease the problems of memory congestion, some parts of the operating system are not loaded automatically. These utilities are held in secondary memory, and when the user wishes to make use of them he/she has to load them, just as any application program is loaded.

A large number of operating systems are available today. Historically, each computer manufacturer developed his own proprietary operating system in order to exploit fully the capabilities of his own systems, to deliver more functionality to the user, and to bind the customers closer to the supplier. However, today many large customers recognise the high costs of being tied to one operating environment, dependent upon the hardware of the manufacturer (and thus locking him out of advances made by other manufacturers). Hence there is a growing trend towards more open systems, which in essence means common, standard operating and network environments capable of implementation on a variety of manufacturers' hardware.

The general trend is towards the predominance of a small number of systems, sometimes implemented in different ways to suit the precise operating requirements. This trend tends to enhance the 'portability' of programs, since programs written to make use of a single operating system's utilities can be transferred comparatively easily to a different model of computer which uses the same operating system.

In the personal computer world, the predominant operating system throughout the early 1980s was MSDOS, the Microsoft Corporation's operating system developed for computers like the IBM PC and its IBM proprietary version, PCDOS. With the introduction of the PS/2 generation of personal computers in 1987, IBM began a move to a different operating system, OS/2. (Both MSDOS and OS/2 are in effect standard operating systems, running on hardware from several manufacturers.) Among the main features of OS/2 are its ability to address large quantities of memory (up to 1 GByte for those with suitable microprocessors), its virtual memory management, and improved methods of data transfer between primary memory and disc. The operating system supports multitasking and can handle large numbers of data files simultaneously. OS/2's user-interface is called the 'Presentation Manager', and uses the concept of WIMP: windows, icons, mouse-pointers and pull-down menus (discussed in more detail in Chapter 14) in order to improve its user-friendliness.

On larger computers, the operating system with the widest range of support today is S/370, the derivative of S/360, used on all IBM mainframe systems. Essentially this is an unofficial standard because of IBM's dominant market position. Similarly, the operating system for IBM's S/3X range has set unofficial standards in smaller systems.

However, the first truly portable operating system (across several manufacturers' hardware) is UNIX.

UNIX is a multi-user operating system developed by Bell Laboratories, the commercialisation of which was sponsored chiefly by AT&T. It runs on computers from mainframes downwards, and is available in networked versions. It has been confidently forecast that by the mid-1990s the computing world will be dominated by only three operating environments, S/370, UNIX, and MSDOS/OS/2.

Digital's VAX minicomputers primarily use the proprietary VMS operating system.

The PICK operating system, once regarded as a major rival to UNIX, has never received quite the same degree of support. But by 1987 it had nearly 1 million users, and was implemented on over 100,000 systems worldwide, so it retains a significant slice of the market.

Operating systems developed specifically for networking applications include the Cambridge Distributed Computing System (developed in conjunction with the Cambridge Ring), and V, a distributed operating system developed at Stanford University in the early 1980s.

Modes of Computer Operation

The various hardware components of a computer system function at very different speeds: the cpu is by far the fastest, and input/output peripherals are the slowest, especially keyboards with human operators.

The first operational computer systems in the 1950s handled one job (that is, one program) at a time. Transactions to be processed (for example, orders, invoices or time sheets) were gathered together in a batch, and at fixed intervals, or when the batch reached a suitable size, the entire batch would be processed at once. Once the program finished, the computer would pass on to the next job. This form of operational organisation is known as *batch processing*. It has steadily been superseded by more flexible methods, but many computer systems still work on a basis similar to this today.

Originally, all peripheral devices (card readers, printers, etc.) were connected directly to the cpu, which spent most of its time working at well below peak capability while inputting or outputting data to/from a slower device, or simply waiting for the operator to initiate the next job. Cpu utilisation was improved when this direct connection was broken, and the input/output processes used a tape file as an intermediate destination. So input typically went from the card reader to tape while the computer was doing another job, then from tape to the cpu; and output went from cpu to tape, then on to a printer while the cpu had passed on to the next task. Queues of work to be processed would build up on the tape files, and each job in succession was initiated automatically once the previous one was completed. This *spooling* process significantly improved the throughput of work.

Multiprogramming

Even with spooling, though, the cpu was only working on one job at a time, and its utilisation rate was low. Most commercial computer processing involves the transferring between primary and secondary memory of large data files. Whenever this takes place a separate controller takes over, and the cpu is left idle in a 'wait' condition until the data transfer is completed. A natural next stage was to enable the processor to switch to a second or subsequent program as soon as it encountered a 'wait' on the program which it was currently executing. This process is illustrated in Figure 4.5.

In this system the processor begins by executing program 1, the first in the input queue. If, as is likely, execution is suspended for a file transfer, the cpu transfers to program 2 and begins executing this. If program 2 now requests a file access, it too is suspended; the operating system checks to see if the file access for program 1 is complete, and if so resumes its execution; if not it begins to execute program 3, and so on. This process is known as *multiprogramming*.

For multiprogramming to take place, the operating system must be able to suspend and resume execution of a program, and the computer itself must have sufficient resources to keep several programs concurrently in memory. Though these requirements have generally been met by mini- and larger computer systems for some time, it was only in the mid-1980s that multiprogramming became common on personal computers.

In the simplest multiprogramming systems, execution is transferred between programs at a 'natural break' in the execution of one program, and chance plays a part in determining the speed at which individual program runs are completed. More sophisticated multiprogramming systems set priorities for the different programs under execution. In the case outlined above, if program 1 had the highest priority then the operating system would *interrupt* the cpu's other activities and return control to program 1, as soon as its file transfer was completed.

Interrupt capability was crucial to the development of the next phase of development: on-line interactive systems.

On-line, Interactive, Real-time Systems

In the above methods of operating system organisation, the input/output peripherals are deliberately not connected to the cpu, but are spooled,

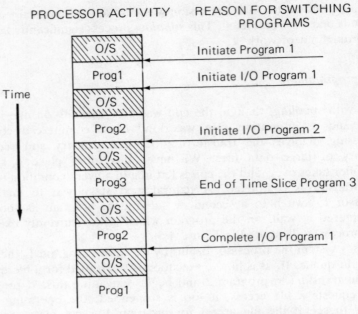

(a) Processor activity over time (O/S indicates operating
system overhead switching between programs)

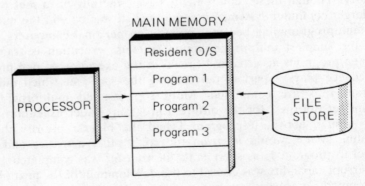

(b) Allocation of main memory in multiprogramming
environment

Figure 4.5 *Operation of a Multiprogramming System*

off-line devices. This gives the user (or programmer) no chance to communicate directly with the computer while the program is being executed. This is often regarded as an unacceptable drawback today, when the trend is towards more flexible user-oriented systems, where users expect to be able to exert some control over the course of program operation.

For example, on-line data entry by originators (or 'owners') of the data can greatly contribute to overall data accuracy (and identifying and correcting data inaccuracies once some processing has been undertaken is often a difficult, time-consuming and expensive operation). Most forms of computer modelling are significantly more effective if the modeller can interact directly with the system; and an increasing number of systems, such as automatic bank-teller machines, include direct communication with the end-user as a basic part of their design philosophy.

The term *on-line* indicates that the user can directly submit data or instructions to the computer and receive the results without the data passing via any human intermediary. If the user has no opportunity to interact with the program, then this mode of operation is known as *remote job entry*. However if the user can influence the program once it starts to execute by entering data, selecting options, specifying the results required, etc., then that is called *interactive computing*. Obviously interactive systems must be on-line. The difference between this approach and that of batch processing is illustrated in Figure 4.6.

The term *real time* indicates that the system will respond to some transaction within a given (short) time, and that this response time is a critical performance parameter of the system. Typically these systems run only a single application, and are optimised to support a large number of terminals. The term is also used in process control systems to indicate that the system must respond to a given signal within a critical time, e.g. by shutting a valve.

Time-sharing Systems

A slightly different situation occurred with the proliferation from the late 1960s of systems which incorporated a single computer (sometimes a mainframe, but this development grew most particularly around mini-computers) to which a number of terminals were attached.

As each terminal user required access to the computing resources, it was necessary to devise operating systems which shared these out in a generally acceptable way. The *time-sharing* philosophy takes advantage of the relatively slow speed of terminal input/output when compared to the cpu, and shares cpu time between the terminals in a simple 'round robin'

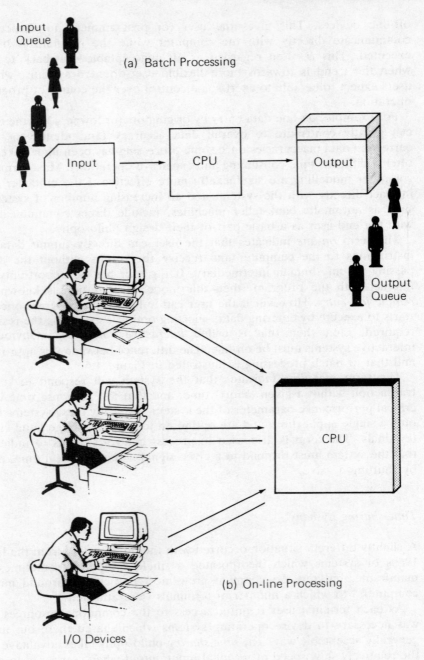

Figure 4.6

fashion. Thus user 1 gets, say, 20 milliseconds of cpu time, then it is user 2's turn, then user 3's, and so on in turn back to user 1, who hopefully hasn't noticed the interruption! Each user apparently has personal use of the whole computer, though it soon becomes evident that this is not the case when the number of users grows too large, and the response time deteriorates. Time-sharing systems grew in popularity and availability throughout the 1970s.

'Virtual' Systems

One of the problems encountered with multiprogramming operating systems, including time-sharing systems, was that they required all of the programs being run (and much of their associated data) to be in primary memory at the same time.

In practice, primary memory in such systems was divided into a small number of partitions (initially of fixed size, but in later versions variable), with different priorities on each partition and, in effect, separate job queues for each partition. However, this approach demands ever-increasing amounts of (relatively expensive) primary memory. To circumvent this difficulty, the 'virtual memory' approach and the concept of a 'virtual machine' were developed. This involved breaking both the applications program and its data into small *segments* or *pages*. Only a proportion of the pages are kept in primary memory at any one time. Code segments can be shared between several users. All other pages are kept on a high-speed secondary memory medium such as a hard disc. A 'memory manager', a special part of the operating system, determines which pages are held in primary memory at any one time, on a basis such as frequency of use, next in sequence, or according to a priority structure. In some systems a large part of the operating system is also paged in this way, with only the core being permanently resident in primary memory.

The process of switching pages between the two memory media is known as *swapping* or *paging*. It was first made available on the Ferranti Atlas in the early 1960s but became widespread practice only in the late 1970s, when large primary memories and fast, reliable disc drives were basic components of most large computer systems. An example of this process is shown in Figure 4.7.

In effect a multiprogramming, on-line, interactive, virtual memory operating system is the culmination of all the developments in operating system design described above. Its all-round flexibility ensures that the cpu's resources are properly utilised, and that the user's requirements are met as fully as possible. Most new-generation operating systems, including UNIX, are based on some form of implementation of this concept.

MAIN MEMORY   SECONDARY MEMORY

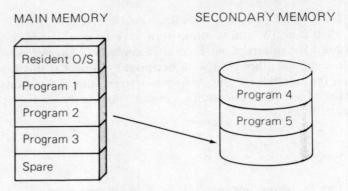

Operating systems require Program 4 for execution which is currently not resident in main memory. There is insufficient spare space to load Program 4, therefore some resident program(s) must be swapped onto secondary memory.

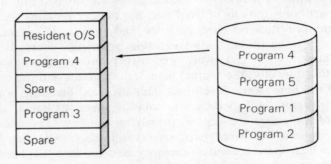

Figure 4.7 *Illustration of Swapping*

System Performance

These improvements in operating system effectiveness and efficiency are not without their cost. An operating system is a set of instructions, a program just like any other, albeit usually somewhat larger and more complex than application programs tend to be. It too requires system resources, processor time and memory, and it runs all of the time, so these requirements form a permanent overhead on system operation.

As operating systems have become more sophisticated and complex, so their demands on system resources have become greater and greater. It is not uncommon in large multiprogramming systems for the system software physically to take up somewhere between a third and half of primary memory, and to consume as much as half of total cpu time. Thus the throughput of the system, measured in terms of productive user work, may well be lower than might have been judged likely from the improvement in hardware specifications.

There are major differences in operating system efficiency between typical mainframe, minicomputer and microcomputer systems. A typical mainframe operating system has gone through most, if not all, of the development stages mentioned above, and the end result can be a large unwieldy beast. In contrast, minicomputers developed out of real-time control systems used for process control, instrumentation and weapons control, and were designed from the outset as on-line, interactive systems which, to a significant extent, could be tailored to the individual characteristics of each user's environment.

This is even more true of microcomputers, but — with the growth of user expectations, of user-friendly interfaces (where the computer presents, for example, a screen full of 'icons' indicating options available, instead of a blank screen with an uninformative system prompt) and of networking — microcomputer operating systems too have become much more complex over recent years.

Open Systems

Historically, a computer's software platform (that is, all its software, including the operating system and networking software) has ultimately been tied to the hardware upon which it ran. Hence each manufacturer developed his own proprietary operating systems (plural — most manufacturers developed more than one, since most also developed multiple hardware platforms) and networking software. Apart from any technical rationale, this policy was also in the business interest of the manufacturer, since it 'locked in' his customers.

Any applications that the user developed functioned within the operating environment, provided by the operating system and networking software. If any elements of this operating environment were changed (for example, if the user made a switch to an alternative manufacturer) then elements of the application software also had to be changed.

For many manufacturers and users, this situation has become increasingly intolerable, though in general the motivations for change amongst users are stronger than amongst manufacturers. The users have to bear the considerable costs (both tangible and intangible) should they change from one manufacturer to another; typically they have to maintain expertise in several operating environments and the capability to develop applications within them; and they have to maintain environments that are used by their existing applications, but are no longer an active choice for new systems. For the smaller manufacturers, too, the costs of developing and maintaining multiple proprietary operating environments have become prohibitive.

Thus in recent years there has been an accelerating trend towards what is known as an 'open systems' approach: standardised operating environments and network architectures capable of being implemented on hardware from several manufacturers. Some of these standards are informal, and have been established by sheer market presence. Thus, for example, IBM's proprietary operating systems are *de facto* standards, especially S/370 for mainframes, and PCDOS (known in non-IBM versions as MSDOS) and its recent derivative OS/2 for personal computers. In both cases other manufacturers produce hardware platforms on which these operating systems can run.

On the other hand, UNIX is the subject of formal standardisation efforts, through the organisations X/OPEN (European based) and POSIX (US based). Although UNIX had a single origin in the work done at AT&T, various dialects and extensions were developed subsequently to tailor it to particular needs. The standards bodies are now codifying the core, and some of these extensions, to develop a standard version of UNIX. This pressure towards greater standardisation has been increased by the decision of several governments to make UNIX a requirement in their systems procurement. Most of the world's computer systems suppliers are members of these standards bodies, and several are very active in developing and adhering to the standard, and in contributing their own extensions to the public domain to move the standard forwards in terms of capability. For example, Hewlett-Packard contributed its extensions to UNIX to cope with languages other than English.

In the networking area, standards have emerged by similar processes. The IBM architecture, SNA, is a *de facto* standard to which most manufacturers have built interfaces. OSI (Open Systems Interconnect) is the formal public standard to which all suppliers subscribe in ·varying degrees. Enthusiasm for the standard varies from manufacturer to manufacturer. Some suppliers such as Hewlett-Packard are committed to fully implementing each OSI level as the standards are agreed, but others, including DEC and IBM, depend upon evolving their proprietary systems towards OSI standards.

The combination of standard operating systems and networking software — an open systems environment — offers the customer the potential of establishing a common operating environment across hardware from different manufacturers.

5

File Organisation and Processing

In this chapter we will examine how the processing of transactions may be organised, and how the files of data associated with this processing are structured and managed.

File Organisation

An electronic file in computer technology is exactly analogous to a paper-file file in an office context. It is a collection of logically-related material grouped under a single heading — for example, a personnel file, a customer file, a stock file, and so on. A file consists of a number of records or entries, each of which contains all of the data for each entity in the file. Thus, in the personnel file, there would be a record for each employee; in the customer file, one for each customer; in the stock file, one for each product; and so on. A record contains the data for that entity as a set of fields or data-items. Thus, each personnel record might have as data-items works number, employee name, address, hourly wage rate, tax code, deductions code, bank sort code, bank account number, and so on. Similarly, each record in the customer file may contain a customer code, the customer name, invoice address, delivery address, credit rating, contact name, and so on.

The hierarchy of data storage is thus as follows:

database is a collection of related files

files are collections of similar records, organised in some sequence

records are collections of logically related data-items, to be treated as a single unit *data-items* are the individually representative items of data

bits/bytes represent the characters and numbers in the data-items.

An example of the data hierarchy for a sales order system is shown in Figure 5.1.

Such files may of course be very large — the personnel file for a large company may have several tens of thousands of records, whilst the stock file may have hundreds of thousands of records, most of which are active each day. As we have seen earlier, such files have to be stored in secondary memory, and records (either in blocks or individually) retrieved and copied to main memory for processing. For large files considerable care and effort has to be given to the logical organisation of such files, the way in which they are to be stored in secondary memory, and the way in which transactions pertaining to the contents of the file are to be processed. Although we will be discussing these points as separate items, it is important to recognise that in practice they are highly interrelated and the decisions about file organisation, storage and processing are joint ones.

In practice there are two main alternative ways of organising and processing data files — either sequentially, or using some form of direct access. Each method has relative economic and technical advantages and disadvantages, depending upon the needs and characteristics of the specific application. For example, characteristics having a significant impact on the choice of file organisation and processing method are:

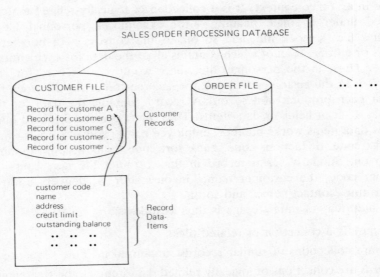

Figure 5.1 *Example of Data Hierarchy*

Response time, defined as the time which elapses between the request for processing and its completion; in some applications, response time is a critical parameter.

Activity rate on the file: that is, within a given time, what proportion of total records in a file are accessed. The economics of the processing methods are significantly affected by this rate.

Volatility measures the rate at which records are added to or deleted from the file; again, this can have a significant impact on the economics of alternative processing methods.

The *size* of the file, measured by either the number of records or the total number of characters in the file, can have a major impact on the type and capacity of the physical media used to store the file.

Finally, the degree of *interdependence and sharing* of a file can have a major impact on both organisation and processing. Files used by several different applications have to be organised and managed in some commonly agreed manner, and may well lead to their implementation using some *database management system* (*DBMS*).

It should be recognised that the basic record management operations on a file are common to all files, irrespective of their organisation. For example, in general all files will require:

procedures to *create* a new record;

procedures to *delete* an existing record;

procedures to *retrieve* the contents of a specific record;

procedures to *update* the contents of a specific record;

procedures for *backing-up or archiving* some or all records, and corresponding procedures to *restore* records from an archive.

These are some of the basic operations. In any specific application there may well, of course, be others (for example, transaction logging, or audit trails). We will now examine the major file organisation and processing methods in the light of the characteristics and procedures described above.

Sequential File Organisation

In a sequential file all of the records are stored in a specified, known order. The order, or sequence, is determined by the value of some particular field or data-item within each record, usually referred to as the *key field*. For example, in the personnel file the records could well be stored in ascending works number sequence. If the works number

```
PERSONNEL
   FILE

Record 1
   works no.        00352
   name             Smith J. R.
   address          13 Acacia Drive
                    Little Bishwick

Record 2
   works no.        00473
   name             Jones F.J.
   .. ..            .. ..
                    .. ..

Record 3
   works no.        00487
   name             Allen A.B.
   .. ..            .. ..
                    .. ..

.. ..  ...          .. ..
.. ..               .. ..
.. ..               .. ..
.. ..               .. ..
                    .. ..

End of file
```

Figure 5.2 *An Example of Sequential File Organisation: Personnel File with Records in Ascending Works Number Sequence*

included, say, a two-character department code followed by an employee number, then the records might be sequenced by department, and by employee number within department. This is illustrated in Figure 5.2.

In a customer file, the sequencing key might be the customer code, whilst in the stock file it could be the product code. Note that the field used for sequencing need not be just numeric. Typically it includes alphabetic characters as well (i.e. it can be composed of any alphanumeric characters — usually any of the characters from the standard character sets mentioned in Chapter 3, though often excluding most of the special characters). However, it is usually necessary for such key values to be *unique*. As all retrieval and processing is based on the key value, non-unique keys would give retrieval problems. Thus, in our example of the personnel file the key field would be the assigned works number (which is presumably unique), rather than using, say, the employee name (which, for a large file, almost certainly won't be unique).

A sequential file ordered by one field will in general not be in any particular order if any other field is used. This may pose major constraints on the way the file is used. For example, if the personnel file was sequenced by works number, but for company records a list of employees in alphabetical sequence was required, then this could only be achieved by sorting all the records in the personnel file such that they were now in sequence by employee name — in essence, creating a new file with exactly the same contents as the existing personnel file, but with the records ordered in a different sequence. Clearly this would appear to be a wasteful exercise (in both processing time and storage capacity needed) if it had to be done at all frequently.

Sequential File Processing

Retrieval of a specific record from a sequential file involves starting at the beginning of the file, reading each record in sequence from secondary memory into primary memory and then comparing its key field with the key field of the required record until a match is found; or until the value of the key field on the file is bigger than that of the desired record, in which case the record doesn't exist on the file (assuming the file is in ascending sequence). If there is only one record to be processed, then this is a very time-consuming and relatively expensive operation in computer terms. Because of this, transactions to be processed against a particular master file are usually accumulated in a batch over some period. The length of period may be determined by the operational necessity of the business — such as producing a payroll each Friday, or having an up-to-date stock file available at the beginning of each working day, or simply by waiting until a large enough volume of transactions has been accumulated to make a processing run economic.

As we saw earlier, initially the only form of secondary memory available for computer systems was magnetic tape, on which all files are sequential simply because of the nature of the media itself. Thus the original method of processing in commercial computer installations was almost invariably some form of batch processing. It is still true today that a majority of business data processing involves sequential files (typically stored on disc) in a batch-processing environment. Batching together a number of transactions to be processed against a specific file means that the entire batch can be processed in a single pass through the file, assuming that the batch of transactions has first been sorted on the same key sequence as the master file. The basic logic of a sequential processing run is shown in Figure 5.3a and 5.3b.

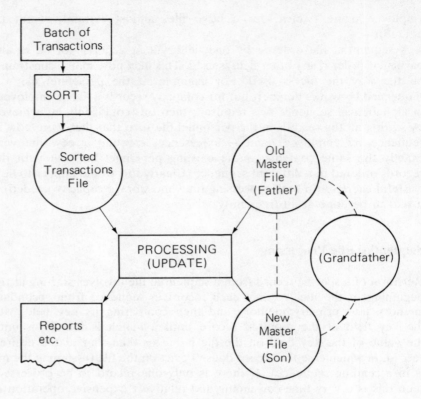

Figure 5.3a *Sequential File Processing*

The run begins with an *old master* file which is to be updated (this file is the file that results from the previous processing run). The batch of *transactions* to be processed is *sorted* into the same *key sequence* as the master file to form a transactions file, in which the records are ordered in the same sequence as the master file. This transaction file is then processed against the old master file (by comparing key field values until a match is found) to create a *new master* file and produce any reports that are required. As a result of the processing, the fields in the records processed on the master file have been updated. For example, in the personnel file the fields containing gross pay to date and tax paid to date will have been updated as a result of a payroll run. All records are read from the old master file and copied to the new master, even if they are not updated. Thus problems of back-up and archiving are simply organised with a magnetic tape-based sequential processing system, since

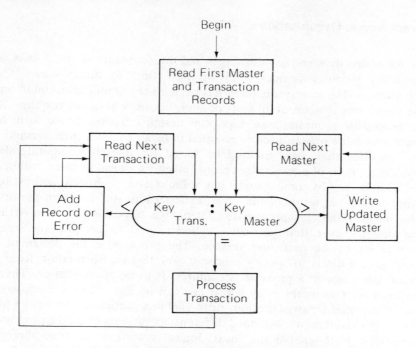

Figure 5.3b *Basic Logic of Sequential Processing*

old master files (usually referred to as 'father', 'grandfather' etc., with the new master being 'son') can be retained, together with the most recent transactions file, so that a particular set of processing runs can be repeated if necessary (i.e. the clock can be put back).

On average the response time is slow where sequential processing is involved, since on average the required record will be half-way down the tape, and all previous records must be read and compared before it is retrieved. The file can only be sequenced on a single key, so that in cases where the file has to be shared by several applications, either they all have to use the same key, or duplicate copies of the file are kept, sorted by another key. For a volatile file, creation and deletion of records is easily accomplished as a part of a normal processing run. If the activity rate is high (i.e. a typical transaction file contains a high proportion of the total records on the file) then sequential processing is very efficient, since most records need processing, and all of the records in the file are accessed in a single run. However, conversely, if the activity rate is low, then sequential processing is relatively inefficient, since all records are accessed, but only a few require processing.

Direct Access Organisation

We have already seen the advantages and disadvantages of using discs as secondary memory devices, and we now turn to direct access file organisation. In recent years there has been a very rapid expansion in on-line interactive systems in all sorts of applications, where fast response to file processing requests is an important design criterion. Some form of direct access file organisation is essential in order to meet such demands. This requires that some method be found for directly computing the physical location of a particular record, given its logical position within a file, as indicated by some specific key value. Given a physical address on a disc surface, in terms of the drive, cylinder and surface, then the disc drive incorporates the appropriate control logic to position the read–write arm directly over that particular cylinder, and to activate the head appropriate to the particular surface. The problem in the design of a direct access file is to specify precisely how this transformation from a record key value to a physical disc address is to be accomplished. There are basically two methods by which this can be done; either *random* or *index-sequential* file organisation. Both enable a particular record in a file to be retrieved directly, but have different operational characteristics and economics. Both enable the 'next' logical record to be read directly without having physically to read the (sequentially) following records.

'Random' File Organisation

This method of file organisation uses what is known as an indirect method of addressing the physical records on disc. Some simple procedure is used to transform the key field value of the record into a physical address. An area of the disc is set aside for storing the file, and then some addressing procedure is devised which will evenly distribute the records over the area of disc. To retrieve a record under this method, the value of the key field for the required record is used by the transformation procedure to calculate the disc address; this is then used to retrieve the record directly. It may happen that two key values give the same disc address (this is known as a *synonym*). As two records cannot exist in the same physical location, one has to reside in a designated overflow area. Thus when a record is directly retrieved using this method, the value of the key must be checked and if incorrect then the overflow area is searched (usually sequentially). This procedure is known as 'random' file organisation since the transformation procedures are usually chosen such that the logical records are randomly (evenly) distributed over the disc addresses, and such that the expected number of synonyms (i.e. overflow situations) is also known. This randomising is often referred to as a *hashing algorithm*.

With random file organisation and processing, records can be retrieved in any sequence. Indeed, even if they are to be retrieved in logical sequence (i.e. key value sequence), they still must be retrieved individually since they are not stored in any physical sequence on disc, and there is no way of going directly from one record to the next in key value sequence. Thus, batching or sorting transactions to be processed against a random file does not provide any advantage. The elapsed time and cost of retrieving a record from a random file is roughly constant — response time can be very fast. However, if activity rates are high, processing may be very expensive compared with a sequential file, since processing cost per transaction on a sequential file decreases as the activity rate increases. If the file is highly volatile, then it is likely that a large number of synonyms will be generated. Also, deletions may well leave records in the overflow area when their synonym has been deleted. Thus a volatile, randomly organised file will need very regular reorganisations (usually referred to as 'garbage collection'). Integration of several applications requiring multiple file accesses for one transaction is straightforward and easily accomplished with a random file organisation, since for each transaction the disc addresses in the relevant records and files which it impacts on can be computed, and multiple files immediately updated.

However, the overwhelming advantage of a randomly organised file is that it can provide very fast response times (within relatively narrow margins) to file accesses on very large files. It is typically used where these are on-line enquiries onto a large file, where each enquiry initiates relatively little processing, but speed of response is vital. Seat availability on particular airline flights would be an example where such organisation may well be used.

Index-sequential Access Method (ISAM)

So far we have two forms of file organisation which are best suited to very different types of processing and application needs: sequential organisation and processing gives the lowest cost per transaction for files with high activity rates and is simple to implement — however, the application must not have a critical response time factor; random organisation and processing is ideal where fast response is essential, and especially where activity rates are low. However, for a large number of applications, some method combining the characteristics of these two methods is required. The problem with the two methods as they stand is that it is an either/or choice — a file organised randomly cannot be processed sequentially.

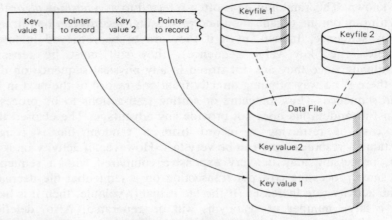

Figure 5.4 *Index-sequential Access Method (ISAM)*

The ISAM method (sometimes referred to as KSAM: Keyed Sequential Access Method) is an attempt to provide the best of both of the previous systems. ISAM allows for high-activity economical sequential processing, as well as direct access, rapid response processing when required. The way it does this is to provide a set of *pointers* in a *chain* to indicate the next logical record in sequence (usually both next in ascending and descending sequence) relative to some specific key value. These pointers are stored as a part of the record, so that retrieval of a particular record also produces the disc addresses of the records logically adjacent to it in sequence. It is possible to store more than one set of pointers with each record (though this naturally increases the storage used), so that it is possible to access records in the file according to several different keys. Usually, in a situation where multiple keys are used, one key is designated as the primary key, and the file is often physically organised as a sequential file on this primary key. This is illustrated in Figure 5.4.

Thus sequential processing is possible on any of the keys by simply retrieving the first record in the sequence for that key, and then following the chain of pointers, retrieving each record in sequence. If this sequential processing is on the primary key, it will be relatively efficient, since the file will be physically in this sequence. In order to be able to undertake direct access processing on such a file we have to have some method of entering a chain close to where the desired record is located, rather than starting at the beginning and working sequentially through it. The way this is done is to form one or more hierarchical indexes to the file. Each index is relatively short and is accessed sequentially. In practice they are usually kept in primary memory to facilitate rapid access. The highest-level index provides a broad categorisation of a file, the computer sequentially searches this index to find which category the desired record is in and this in turn points to a second index, divided into further sub-categories which the computer also searches sequentially. The computer may search one or two more indexes of this type, and is then pointed to a record in the file which is close (within a known number of records) to the one being searched for. This record is retrieved and compared with the desired key value — if the desired key value is higher than the value of the one retrieved — then the computer follows the pointer chain sequentially 'upwards' through the file until it finds the one it wants. If the desired value is lower, then it similarly follows the chain 'downwards'.

As might be expected, the economics and characteristics of ISAM files lie between those of sequential and random files. Compared with either sequential or random files solely carrying out sequential or direct processing, ISAM processing will appear relatively inefficient and more costly. However, the user is in essence paying for the ability to carry out both types of processing on the same file if necessary. Naturally, as far as possible, it is a good thing if the user can ensure that the high activity transactions are processed sequentially, and the low activity ones directly. ISAM will not provide such a fast response time as a randomly organised file, as it must search one or more indices, and perhaps retrieve several records, before finding the desired record. Because of the indexing and the ability to use multiple keys, ISAM files are relatively flexible — for example, often the primary key is used for sequential processing, and one or more of the secondary keys used for direct processing. The user pays for the flexibility through lower efficiency. Because ISAM files are totally dependent upon the indexes and pointer chains, they are potentially more susceptible to software and design problems, and secure back-up and archiving require much more care. Through the ability to cope with multiple keys, ISAM-organised files also facilitate the sharing of such files between different applications. Again this tends in practice to make them potentially more unreliable. Nevertheless, it is probably true to say that by far the majority of on-line processing is undertaken using some form of ISAM file organisation.

Database Processing

However, all of the file organisation and processing procedures that we have discussed have left the choice of method and implementation to the designer of the particular application system. Thus, in many installations, the specification of file structures and organisation was locked into a specific application program, making modification, or use by anyone else, very difficult. The same data were often stored more than once, giving consistency problems. In addition it was very difficult to specify or implement common standards for file structures, data accuracy, and so on; and there was a danger of each application re-inventing the wheel in the form of developing particular software to perform standard functions involved in file maintenance — creation, deletion, updating of records, and back-up and recovery procedures. Allied with a realisation of the growing importance of data as a corporate resource, these problems and issues lead to the acceptance of the concept of a *database*, and the development and implementation of specific *database management systems* (*DBMS*).

The database concept breaks the direct link between the data files and the application programs by inserting some software, a DBMS, between the two. All requests for file access from an application program are now made to the DBMS. The DBMS has incorporated tools enabling it to meet these requests, whilst also undertaking all of the usual file management and maintenance tasks. Schematically Figures 5.5a and 5.5b illustrate the differences between a more traditional file organisation and the use of a DBMS.

As a part of, or closely associated with, the DBMS will be several other pieces of software. A 'data dictionary' will maintain a record of each data-item held in the database and its characteristics (i.e. type and length); thus the DBMS 'knows' about all the data-items in the database. The DBMS itself will know the logical structure of the records in each of the files within it, and the relationships between them. It would reduce, if not totally remove, duplication of the data in different files, and enable data to be much more easily shared where necessary. Requests for access required (e.g. either read-only or update) can be controlled. Back-up and archiving can be undertaken automatically at specified times, and transaction logs and audit trails generated as a part of normal processing. For input of data, a screen-handling utility is typically provided which will generate screen formats, and undertake some verification of the data provided, as well as interfacing with the DBMS. Usually, the utility can be used directly by the users to create and modify their own screen formats. On the output side, an English-like query language allows for *ad hoc* enquiries against the database, handling queries such as:

FIND CUSTOMERS FOR REGION = NW AND

BALANCE-OUTSTANDING > 10000

On the other hand a report generator would facilitate the design and production of more regular and formal reports. The relationship between a DBMS and these utility programs is shown in Figure 5.6.

A DBMS and its associated utility programs are large, complex pieces of software. From the schematic diagram shown in Figure 5.6, it should

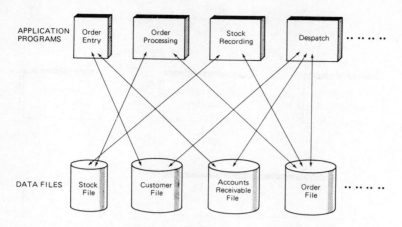

Figure 5.5a *Relationship between Application Programs and Files using a Traditional dp Approach*

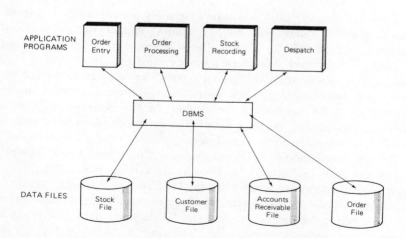

Figure 5.5b *Relationship between Application Programs and Files using a Database Approach*

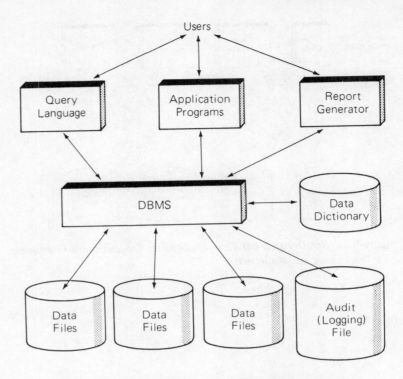

Figure 5.6 *Functional Components of a Database System*

be apparent that the DBMS will be extremely heavily used, and from the user's point of view will have a major impact on overall system performance. DBMSs do consume large amounts of computing resources — both primary and secondary memory, and processor time — and in general will impose some additional system overhead as compared with a more traditional approach. However, these additional costs are generally considered to be more than outweighed by the benefits of DBMSs as outlined above, and, perhaps above all, by the flexibility and ease with which new systems can be developed.

DBMSs were originally developed for large mainframe computers during the early and mid-1970s, both by the computer manufacturers and by third-party software houses. Today DBMSs are available for all of the major large-scale computer systems: from the computer manufacturers — DL1 (currently the market leader) and IDMS from IBM, and DMS from Univac, for example; and from software houses — for example, ADABAS from Software AG, IDMS from Cullinane, Focus from Info Builders, and TOTAL from Cincom.

DBMSs on smaller scales are also available on most minicomputers;

indeed one of the major reasons for the success of Hewlett-Packard in growing from an instrumentation and measurement company into a more broadly based computer manufacturer was the availability of its DBMS, Image, as part of the standard software for its range of minicomputers. On personal computers, too, database packages have become big business, with the leader being Ashton-Tate's dBaseII and its successor, dBaseIII.

DBMSs come in three varieties: hierarchical, networked and relational. In a hierarchical structure, the data are accessed in a sequential fashion via a primary key (or attribute) — in a personnel file, for instance, these might be the employee name or works number. In a networked structure, each data record is linked to the others by sets of pointers linking those with common attributes: for example, for a personnel file, all those working in the same department. In a relational structure, the data are organised as a set of tables specifying the relationships between the data and their attributes. So instead of looking up a single key field for each data record, it is possible to access the data record at any point — for example, not only by checking on an employee's works number, but also by requesting information on all employees at a certain salary level, or with a certain length of service. Increasingly, relational databases are required to satisfy the relatively unstructured needs of the professional users of systems.

Few organisations would consider developing new dp applications without using some form of DBMS. The problem lies with the management, maintenance and possible conversion of the existing, more traditionally organised application programs and their associated data files. This is a topic to which we will return in Chapter 14, in the context of software development problems.

Part III

THE ADVENT OF THE MICROCHIP

In the previous part we reviewed the fundamentals of computer systems — both the characteristics of the hardware components and the nature of the software and its critical role in providing a relevant application system to the user. The prime reason for the rapid development of information technology has been the phenomenal technical progress seen in microelectronics over the past 30 years or so. One of the most significant results of this progress is that the computer has become a low-cost, reliable component in an immense range of products — in many instances a component that the user is totally unaware of. It has become an all-pervasive bearer of intelligence to an ever-increasing variety of products. It is this low-cost, pervasive computer as a component which is providing much of the driving force in the development of the information technology industry.

Any products or processes involving measurement or control, together with those doing signal or data processing at some point, are now potential candidates for microelectronics-based design. Microelectronics can cram the processing power of a major computer into components so small and at a cost so low as to have been incomprehensible two decades ago. (Indeed if Neil Armstrong had found a 1988 wristwatch calculator on the moon he would have been staggered by the capability contained in such a small space.) Chips, the product of microelectronics, have been likened to the crude oil of the 1980s as the critical national resource, and it has been suggested that microelectronics lies a close second to the wheel in terms of social, commercial and industrial significance. Few spheres of human activity and few sectors of industry are likely to remain untouched by the application of this technology.

So in this part we will try to explain 'what is a microchip' by discussing:

the major technical developments in microelectronics;

the basic economic characteristics of the production process;

the major product categories;

the development and exploitation of the market for the products of the industry;

the present and prospective applications of this technology.

6

The Technological Base

The Development of Microelectronics

Valves

What we term microelectronics is the current state of a continuing evolution in the development and manufacture of electronic components. *Passive* components, such as resistors, capacitors and coils provide electrical friction, storage and inertia, while the *active* components have two functions — amplification and switching. Most signals in the real world vary continuously in amplitude and frequency. The obvious example is sound: it is either loud or quiet, high pitched or low. If we wish to capture this signal electronically, then the easiest way to do this is to take an electrical *analogue*, i.e. a voltage or a current which mirrors the signal exactly. This is exactly what a microphone does. Similarly, a loudspeaker reverses this process.

Most signals, once in electrical analogue form, need amplifying. How accurately the amplified signal represents the original will depend on the linearity of the amplifier. The other role in the active component is switching. The key factors here are speed and 'cleanliness'. Speed will depend mainly on the electrical inertia — it is like the difference between closing a barn door and a cupboard door. Cleanliness is the ability to switch accurately from one state to another without overshooting.

The basic building block of all electronic digital devices is an electronic switch or 'gate', which allows the passage or otherwise of an electrical pulse, depending upon the instruction of some control unit. Originally, all electronic devices were assembled using *valves* (vacuum tubes) to form these electronic switches, the characteristics of which were as follows:

Individually they were relatively large components.

They required large amounts of power for their operation.

They generated considerable amounts of heat.

They were very unreliable in operation.

Thus the early computers and other items of electronic equipment were extremely bulky, needed carefully controlled physical environments and were very expensive to purchase (since the computer or other electronic device had to be assembled by hand from tens of thousands of individual components) — yet the average time between breakdowns for such early computers was usually measured in minutes!

Transistors

The successor to the valve in forming electronic switches was the discrete *transistor*, originally invented in 1946 but, because of technical difficulties, not in mass production until the mid-1950s. Initially the first transistors were made individually by hand and were much more expensive than the corresponding valve equivalents. The relative advantages over the existing current valve technology were:

much smaller physical volume;

much lower power requirements (enabling batteries to be used as the power source);

much greater robustness and reliability.

These led to their initial use in a few products where these characteristics were sufficiently important to overcome the higher cost penalty — for example, domestically in hearing aids and for the military in missile guidance systems. Subsequent reductions in cost then led to the boom in products such as transistor radios, where portability, small volume and reliability gave the transistor-based product an unassailable advantage.

Development thereafter followed a familiar pattern and one that has been repeated on several occasions since: increased volume of production led to lower average costs, which were then passed on to the consumer, thus expanding the market, lowering costs still further, generating further expansion of the market, and so on. Each step in technology has ultimately lowered the cost per circuit to the end-user, and has consequently ruthlessly .wiped out its predecessor. For example, the response of the valve manufacturers to the mass-produced transistor was to try to automate the production of valves; the result was that, of the top ten valve manufacturers in the 1950s, only one survived to be a major transistor manufacturer of the 1960s.

Integrated Circuits

The next major technological jump came in 1957 with the development of the planar transistor (i.e. a transistor manufactured as an integral part of the flat surface of a piece of material), about a ¼ inch square, and 0.015 of an inch thick. Since this date there has been continuing progress in the search to squeeze ever more and more circuits into a given surface area. Hence the overall generic term for what we are discussing is literally *microelectronics*: the design and manufacture of ever smaller electronic devices, each incorporating many electronic circuits. The basic unit is the '*chip*', typically a rectangle of a *semiconducting* material (usually silicon, hence silicon chips), in which are manufactured many tens of thousands of electronic circuits. The industry which manufactures these devices is similarly known as the *semiconductor industry*.

Any device in this industry consists of a set of circuits to perform a certain function which, when combined with other devices, forms the final electronic product (which itself is normally only a component of the final consumer product) — for example, the memory and arithmetic components of an electronic calculator; the sensing and control circuits for an automatic washing machine; and the signal decoding circuits for a hi-fi tuner. The trade name for chips incorporating more than one circuit is ICs (*integrated circuits*), and the scale of integration is indicated by the use of the following mnemonics:

SSI   Small Scale Integration (1–20 gates);

MSI   Medium Scale Integration (20–100 gates, or 1-Kbit memory);

LSI   Large Scale Integration (100–10,000 gates or 16-Kbit memory);

ALSI   Advanced Large Scale integration (10,000–20,000 gates or 32-Kbit memory);

VLSI   Very Large Scale Integration (20,000–200,000 gates, or up to 1-Mbit memory).

Note the measure: bits, not bytes; it takes (for instance) eight 16-Kbit chips to hold 16 KBytes of data. You may also sometimes encounter the term ULSI, or Ultra Large Scale Integration. The relationship between these terms is illustrated in Figure 6.1.

Today we are in an era of VLSI, or Very Large Scale Integration. All the circuits of a large-scale computer system can be manufactured on a handful of chips.

The difference between integrated circuits and what went before is not one of kind, but one of degree. Previously each transistor, diode or whatever had to be manufactured separately, and they were then wired together on a board to form the required circuits. On a chip, tens of

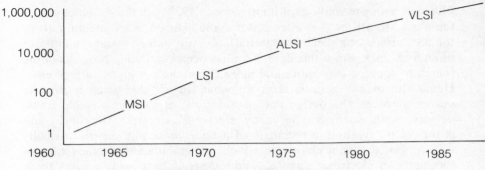

Figure 6.1 *Packing Density*

thousands of circuits are manufactured at the same time — the components themselves, and their interconnections. Greater and greater degrees of integration mean that more and more circuits are mass-produced jointly and simultaneously.

In the next two sections of this chapter, we explain exactly what chips are, and how they are made.

Manufacturing Process

Chips are typically manufactured using as a base a semiconducting material (usually silicon) which can be impregnated with impurities so that it will function as an electronic switch, being moved electronically from one state to another in a few millionths of a second, either allowing an electronic pulse to pass through or not, as the case may be.

Basically this is achieved in two steps. First, the silicon is 'doped' by different chemical compounds. The two common variants are: 'n-type', in which, typically, arsenic (or phosphorus) is introduced to bond with the silicon atoms to leave a free electron (which can be induced to move); and 'p-type', in which, typically, boron is introduced to bond with the silicon atoms leaving them one electron short, i.e. leaving a 'hole' into which other free electrons may be induced to move. The circuits to be formed on the silicon (transistors, resistors, diodes, capacitors, etc.) are manufactured as a series of n- and p-type regions. The second part of the production process is then to provide the necessary electrical insulation and connections between these circuits.

This is a description of what is known as a *Field Effect Transistor* (FET), which is manufactured using a metal-oxide on silicon process, referred to as MOS. The other major approach to circuit design is known as *bipolar*. The basic difference between the two approaches is in power

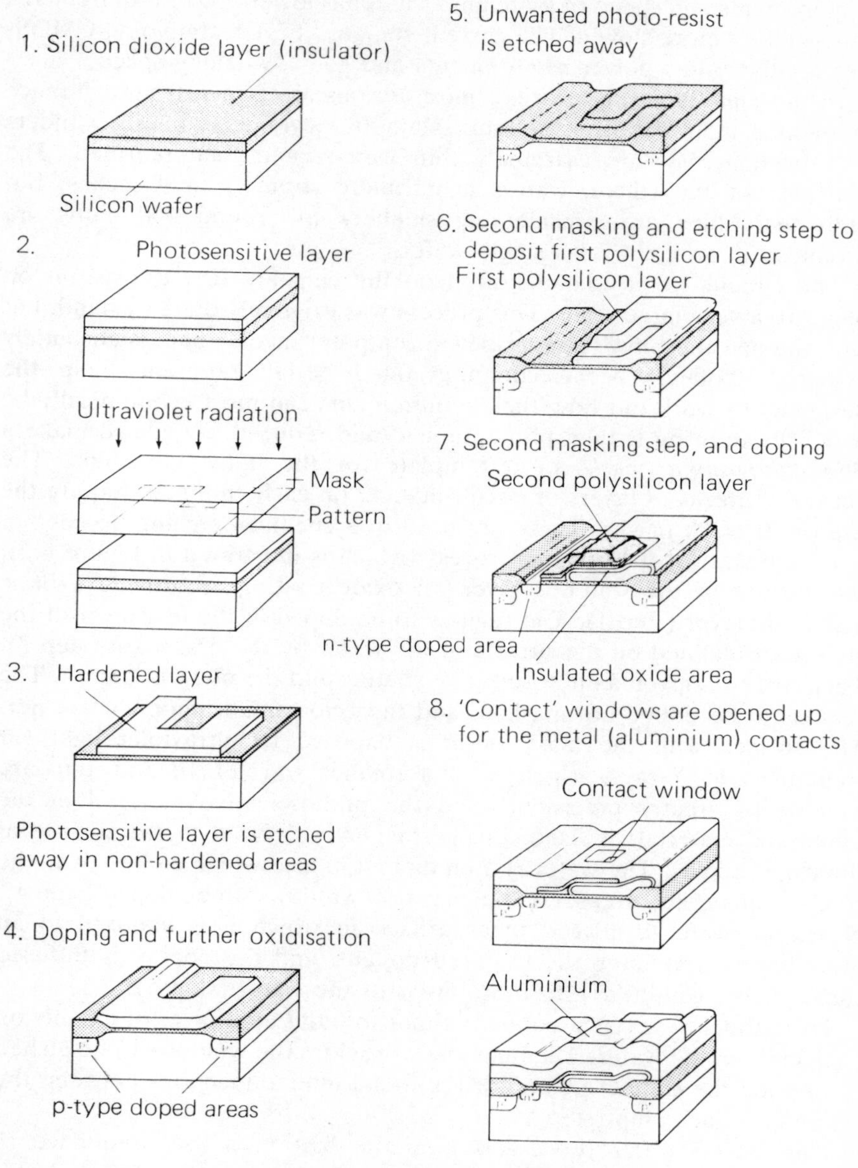

1. Silicon dioxide layer (insulator)

Silicon wafer

2.

Photosensitive layer

Ultraviolet radiation

Mask
Pattern

3. Hardened layer

Photosensitive layer is etched
away in non-hardened areas

4. Doping and further oxidisation

p-type doped areas

5. Unwanted photo-resist
is etched away

6. Second masking and etching step to
deposit first polysilicon layer
First polysilicon layer

7. Second masking step, and doping
Second polysilicon layer

n-type doped area
Insulated oxide area

8. 'Contact' windows are opened up
for the metal (aluminium) contacts

Contact window

Aluminium

Figure 6.2 *Stages in the Chip Manufacturing Process*

requirements and speed of switching. MOS has lower power requirements but switches more slowly. The current standard FET technology, CMOS, has relatively low power requirements and good switching speed.

In the manufacturing process, pure crystals are grown from a furnace containing molten silicon, as long salami-like cylinders. These cylinders are sliced across into extremely thin *wafers*, and then polished. The diameter of the silicon wafers is normally about 3 to 4 inches, but individual chips are considerably smaller, so around 400 chips are produced in an array on a single wafer.

The circuits to be manufactured on the chip are first drawn out on paper to a very large scale. This process was originally done by hand, but with the densities now being achieved computer involvement is absolutely essential. Today, special computer-aided design programs help the designers to work out how their requirements can most economically be met. The drawing is then photographed and reduced in scale to make a *photolithographic mask*, or a template for the individual chips. The various patterns of layers of circuit making up each chip may require the use of 20 or 30 masks. These are used in a chemical etching process.

At the start of the etching process (which is illustrated in Figure 6.2), the surface of the wafer is given an oxide coating to provide a basic insulation layer (step 1). The regions to be doped in the first layer of the circuit are defined on the surface of the wafer by the first mask (step 2). This surface is given a photosensitive coating and the mask is laid on. The regions to be doped are masked, and those to remain undoped are not. The surface with the mask on it is exposed to ultraviolet light (or sometimes to X-rays, which have a smaller wavelength and thus are capable of greater precision), and the photosensitive material in the unmasked materials is fixed, i.e. permanently bonded to the surface of the chip (step 3). The wafer is then dipped in acid which etches away the soluble, unmasked areas, creating a set of 'windows' to be doped (step 4). Next, the wafer is placed in a furnace in which it is exposed to an atmosphere containing the required dopant, and the dopant is diffused through the 'windows' into those areas of the wafer (step 5).

This sequence is repeated many times to build up a layer of circuits on each chip on the wafer. The final mask provides the windows to be etched to provide the contact points for the metal interconnections between the circuits on each chip (step 8).

This silicon wafer process is only the first in a long sequence of processes to be undertaken before an end-product is produced. Next, each chip must be tested to ensure that its circuitry functions correctly. This is normally done before the wafer is broken up into its constituent chips. This complex process is almost totally automated. Chips are tested as early as possible, so that the subsequent costs of mounting and connecting are borne only by the good chips. For really complex chips, it is impossible to test every conceivable circuit combination, because the number of possible combinations is so vast. The standards of testing actually carried out vary quite markedly, and premium prices are routinely charged for more highly tested chips with better guarantees.

Then each wafer is broken up, and the individual chips are mounted in casings, and fitted with connectors. At this stage the chip can be handled relatively easily, connected up to power supplies and other chips, and assembled into the final component or product.

Chip mounting and testing were originally basically manual operations, and in the 1970s and early 1980s their manufacture was concentrated in the Far East, typically in Singapore, Korea, Taiwan and the Philippines. Today, however, much of the process has been automated, and this situation is slowly being changed.

Packing Density

The major design and technical challenge facing the semiconductor companies has been (and still is) to increase the number of circuits that can be 'packed' on to each individual chip: that is, its *packing density*.

The first chip, containing a single transistor, was produced in 1957. In 1964 it was suggested that the future packing density would continue to double roughly every year. As illustrated in Figure 6.1, this prediction held true up to about 1975, but since then the rate of improvement has slowed to less than half the rate, and because the process is approaching some fixed scientific limits, it is not feasible to expect much of a further reduction in the density achievable through CMOS and similar technologies. Future improvements are perhaps more likely to come from a switch to other technologies, as we describe below.

Though some improvements in packing density can be achieved by optimising circuit design using computer-aided techniques, the main improvement comes from reducing the scale of the circuits, and most particularly, from making the individual circuit lines narrower and reducing the width of the gap between components. In 1980, a typical width for the metal wires providing the electrical contact between transistors was 5 microns (also known as micrometers). (Contrast this with the typical thickness of a piece of paper, at around 75 to 80 microns, and you will see how very tiny this is!) Today that width has been reduced to about 1.2 microns in volume production, and less in experimental production, and there is talk now of reducing it still further, to perhaps 0.5 microns within the next decade.

Light in the normally visible spectrum is no good for the type of photolithographic process involved at this scale, because its wavelength is far too long, and it is too easily diffracted by dust particles. Even ultraviolet light has its limitations, and an increasing amount of research has been done into the use of X-rays instead. X-rays are not very powerful, though, and this can mean that long exposure times are required (and production is correspondingly lower) or that it is necessary to use special synchrotons in order to intensify them.

In the early 1980s it was regularly predicted that the practicable limit to line reduction using photolithography would lie at around the 1-micron mark, and that in order to achieve densities greater than this it would be necessary to switch to electron beam technology (in which the masks are dispensed with, and an electron beam writes a pattern directly on to the chip). Electron beam technology still has only minority applications, though, because it is much slower and more expensive than photolithography, and the packing density improvements to date have come largely from increasing accuracy in the art of optical lithography.

Production Control

A major problem facing semiconductor manufacturers has always been how to increase production *yield* by reducing the number of defects introduced during the manufacturing process. The smallest particle of dust is sufficient to wreck a chip. It need not even land on the surface: if it distorts the beam of light during the etching process then the damage will have been done.

The environment in which chips are produced needs to be many thousand times cleaner than the best hospital operating theatre — an expensive state to maintain. In the early years of the development of a particular chip design, the defect rate from an integrated circuit production line has been as high as 90 per cent, or on occasions even 100 per cent. For established chips that are not at the very experimental edge of the practicable, it is normally at least half that rate, and sometimes lower still. The defect rates for each new chip follow a curve, starting high and declining throughout its life, so the name of the manufacturing game is to reduce the initial height of this curve.

One result of the occasional difficulties in producing good chips has been the tendency for chip design to be sublicensed to various 'second source' manufacturers: that is, a number of different semiconductor companies produce what are effectively identical chips. If one company runs into a bad patch where sufficient acceptable chips are not produced, its customers do not suffer corresponding delays, but can instead turn to one of the alternative sources of supply.

Semiconductor Products

Logic Circuits and Memory Circuits

The basic components of electronic circuitry — transistors, resistors and so on — can be combined in a variety of ways to produce circuitry which performs different functions. Often a variety of different functions are carried out by circuits on different areas of the same chip.

A basic distinction is between *logic* circuitry and *memory* circuitry. Logic circuitry is made of combinations and variations on three different types of 'gate' design. These are patterns of circuitry through which one, two or more electronic pulse signals can be sent, and which convert the signals in different ways. An AND gate, for example, transmits a '1' signal only if it receives all '1' signals as input; an OR gate transmits a '1' signal if only one of its inputs is a '1'; a NOT gate reverses a signal. By combining these simple building blocks in complex ways, the logic circuitry which enables the processor to do its data manipulation is created.

Memory circuitry is not designed for data manipulation: it is designed simply to hold data. There are two different types of memory circuitry. One is *read-only* or fixed-pattern circuitry. The data stored in this circuitry are permanently embodied in the circuit pattern, and cannot subsequently be changed. Known as ROM, for Read-only Memory, this circuitry is typically used to hold patterns of instructions: fixed programs which the processor uses. The other is generally known as RAM: *random access*, or 'read/write', memory. (The latter term is more correct, though far less frequently used, not least because read-only memory is also generally random access in its organisation.) The data are stored dynamically in this circuitry, in the pattern of electrical charge which the circuit holds while it is in operation. Data in this circuitry *can* be changed. It is used to hold data required during a processing operation, or to hold variable program instructions.

'Memory' chips generally contain *only* memory circuitry: they do not incorporate any logic circuitry. Usually they contain either all read-only memory circuitry, *or* all random access memory circuitry. Microprocessor chips, and other chips described as 'logic' chips, do contain logic circuitry, though they frequently also contain a sizeable proportion of memory circuitry.

Programmable and Non-programmable Devices

Every microprocessor, when in operation, follows a *program*, in the sense that it carries out specific operations from the range of potential operations which it is capable of performing.

Some devices have a fixed program. The instructions which the device follows are encoded within it, in the pattern of its circuitry, and it always reacts in the same way to the same pattern of input. The program may be very subtle and complex, but it cannot be adapted by the end-user. The advantage of a fixed program is that it renders the device's responses automatic. There is no need for (indeed, no possibility of) user input and there is therefore no delay while the user provides his/her input, and no risk of user error. Because the program is effectively encoded in fixed circuits, there is no danger of its contents being 'lost' when power is accidentally lost to the microprocessor, as does happen with variable-program devices. The major disadvantage is the lack of flexibility of such devices. When circumstances or requirements change, the device cannot change to meet them; if errors in the programming are discovered, they cannot be corrected.

These fixed-program devices are sometimes also known as *non-programmable devices*, and they are indeed non-programmable in the sense that the user cannot program them, though they have of course been programmed by the manufacturer.

With a *programmable* device, the user has the ability to determine which instructions the microprocessor carries out, when it should do so, and on what data. Usually the program which determines this is written in advance and is fed into random access memory, so that the microprocessor can follow it semi-automatically. Sometimes the user has the opportunity to provide additional input during program operation.— for example, by pressing buttons or by giving instructions on an alphanumeric keyboard.

The simplest microprocessors have always been basically non-programmable. They are designed for simple control operations which they perform automatically: for example, in simple electronic toys and calculators. More complex, general-purpose microprocessors, of the kind that form the central processing unit in large and small computers, *are* programmable; it is the computer programmer's job to program them. But there is a growing market today for complex devices which are *not* programmable.

When an electronic device is being designed to perform a specific task, there are two general approaches to the design task: the bespoke approach, and the off-the-peg approach. Using the off-the-peg approach, the designer takes general-purpose programmable devices and writes a program that causes them to perform the specific function for which they are needed. Using the bespoke approach, the manufacturer commissions the chip manufacturer to produce special-purpose devices which automatically perform that function (or, with complex devices, range of functions) and no others. Thus the customer has to be sure that the design is correct, and since the chip has only very specific application it is usually economically worthwhile to produce such chips only when the volume required is very large. As the user is in effect having a chip made to his specific custom design, the user may well have to bear all of the design costs, which for a complex chip can be extremely large.

The prime benefit to be gained from using such components, rather than the cheaper general-purpose microprocessors, arises from their purpose-built design: it is usually speed of operation, although low power consumption or a wider operating environment are of particular importance in some applications. For example, a purpose-built microprocessor, tailored to a specific processing application, might operate ten times faster than would a general-purpose machine programmed for the same application.

The major penalty that has to be paid for such performance is typically design lead-time. The whole point about devices such as these is that they are special-purpose, explicitly designed with a particular application in mind, so that the design lead-time is usually a minimum of one year, and more typically two. In contrast, it is perfectly possible to design an application using a standard off-the-shelf microprocessor in well under a year.

Memory Chips

The largest market for the products of the semiconductor companies (well over half the total production) is in the provision of memory chips: both RAM chips (random access, or read/write memory) and ROM chips (read-only memory). RAMs form by far the largest part of this market.

If you were to examine a microprocessor chip under a microscope, there would appear to be little regularity to the pattern of circuits on the surface. If in contrast you were to examine a memory chip in similar fashion, the pattern of circuits on the chip would be seen to be very regular. Each individual piece of circuitry that can hold a binary 1 or 0 is effectively identical. Only the addresses given to the different memory locations distinguish them from each other.

Designing memory chips does not present the fearsome challenge that is presented by the design of complex, tightly packed microprocessors. Instead, the constraint on the amount of memory that can be packed on to a single chip is purely technical: the size and accuracy with which circuits can be laid down. Thus logic chips sell on processing performance and particular design characteristics, and have very individual markets, whereas memory chips sell on the basis of cost per bit stored, and share a generic market (or, rather, a small number of generic markets depending upon the precise sub-species of memory provided).

RAM is typically *dynamic*. The memory contents are held in the form of a pattern of electrical charge, which is sustained only for as long as electrical power is applied to the chip. When power is switched off the contents are all lost, so that data that are to be stored in RAM must be reloaded on every computer start-up. Many large computer systems incorporate a battery back-up capability which will maintain power supply to RAM if the mains power is lost, typically for a few hours only. Increasingly, personal computers, especially portable models, have battery power packs which permanently maintain power to the memory circuits, even when the rest of the computer is switched off.

It is possible to manufacture static RAM (that is, RAM which maintains its data contents without requiring power) but this is more expensive than the dynamic type, and the additional cost can be justified only for specific applications.

1975	1977	1979	1981	1983	1986
1 Kbits	4 Kbits	16 Kbits	64 Kbits	256 Kbits	1,024 Kbits
(= 1,024 bits)					(= 1 Mbits)

Figure 6.3 *Capacity of Generally Available Memory Chips*

The state of the art in memory chip production is determined by the capacity of the chip, as measured in terms of the number of bits stored. An indication of the technical advance over recent years is given in Figure 6.3. Remember that the measure here (for dynamic RAM) is in *bits*, not *bytes*: it takes (for instance) eight 16-Kbit chips to hold 16 KBytes of data. The dates indicated for each chip show the year in which that chip technology started to appear generally in end-user products (typically, in primary computer memory). As the rate of advance continues, so semiconductor companies proceed to prototype chips with densities that cannot yet be regularly sustained in routine production. So, although 1-MBit dynamic memory chips can now be mass-produced today, chip companies are predicting that samples of 4-Mbit dynamic RAMs will be available in 1988, and they are exploring technologies which may enable them to produce chips which can contain 16 Mbits of data. Indeed, Nippon T&T prototyped such a chip in 1987, using CMOS technology.

Programming ROMs

Whatever is stored in a ROM is fixed (usually permanently) at the time of manufacture of the chip. ROMs are typically used for holding program instructions and associated data which are needed for fundamental operations every time a microprocessor is used: for example, the program for a control operation, or parts of a computer operating system, or the program for a standard end-user application such as word processing.

By incorporating appropriate instructions in ROM, either on a microprocessor chip or on a memory chip that is to be used in conjunction with a microprocessor, a software house can produce a system for addressing a specific end-user problem. The instructions in ROM are in a form which only the processor can understand, and they cannot be altered by the user, so that the investment by the software house in writing the instructions is protected.

Virtually all computer systems today include some ROM, and so do many other microprocessor-controlled products. To avoid the uneconomic nature of very small production runs in manufacturing ROMs, what are known as Programmable ROMs (PROMs) are widely used, both for small-market products and for testing purposes before the program fixed in the ROM has been completely debugged. PROMs are user-programmed once only using a machine known as a PROM Blaster, which creates, or more typically destroys, some of the connections on the chip in order to turn an initial regular circuit pattern into a specific one incorporating the required data. A more sophisticated version of the same principle is used in the Erasable PROM, or EPROM. The user-programmed pattern of connections in the EPROM can be erased a limited number of times through exposure to ultraviolet light, and reprogrammed.

Naturally both PROMs and EPROMs are more expensive than straight ROMs. As a general rule, each additional letter in the mnemonic increases the price by an order of magnitude. However, the price when compared to the total cost of the end-product is often still very small.

General-purpose Microprocessors

Most microprocessors are *general purpose* in that their instruction set (that is, the set of data-manipulating functions which their circuitry can perform) is very general. By combining their basic add/subtract/compare and data-moving functions in specific ways, through a program, they can be used to control a wide variety of different applications. So the same microprocessor might, for example, be used to control the timekeeping and display functions in a digital watch, to control the wash/rinse/spin cycles of a washing machine, or to act as the central processing unit of a word processor.

General-purpose microprocessors have a number of great advantages. First, they are mass-produced in such vast numbers that in spite of the hugely expensive design and production effort that lies behind each one, the individual chips are extremely cheap. Second, they are flexible. Third, their widespread use means that they are well supported by both hardware and software. Programmers write thousands or even millions of different programs to run on popular models of microprocessor; chip manufacturers support them by surrounding them with complete 'families' of other chips that handle a wide range of support functions. For example, various input/output controller chips interface the processor to a variety of instruments, sensors and actuators, video display screens and so on; specialist supplementary processor chips provide, for example, more sophisticated mathematical abilities. This support means that it is relatively cheap and easy to create an end-product around the microprocessor. In contrast, planning and interface between a special-purpose processor and its host product can take a very great deal of design time and effort.

Different models of microprocessor vary greatly from each other. The microprocessor chips have none of the in-depth regularity of memory chips. On each one, the designer has made specific decisions about the capabilities to be provided and the ways in which they can be fitted together. All 1-Mbit dynamic RAM chips are effectively identical; the same is not true for any two different models of microprocessor.

Each microprocessor has an individual instruction set, reflecting the choices made by the designer in creating its logic circuitry. Each will have slightly different arrangements for storing data, and for communicating with other devices. Some microprocessors have more on-chip memory than others; some have considerably more support circuitry (e.g. peripheral device controllers) on the chip than do others. This makes it relatively difficult to compare two microprocessors with each other and indicate which is 'better': each will have its own strengths and weaknesses.

From a production viewpoint, it is possible to gauge the advances in microprocessor production by counting the number of gates (that is, separate AND, OR or NOT logic circuits) that can be packed on to a chip. Today's technology packs around 50,000 gates on to a single chip. In terms of component parts, that may represent up to 300,000 individual transistors.

From the user viewpoint, two other measurements are more meaningful. One is the word length of the microprocessor: that is, the number of adjacent bits that can be processed or transmitted in a single operation.

Even this is not always a simple measurement, because many micro-processors use different word lengths for different purposes, so that they may transfer data to and from memory using 16-bit words but carry out logic operations using 8-bit words. And the other is the speed at which the microprocessor operates. This can be gauged roughly by its 'clock speed': the time each single operation takes to perform. In an era in which parallel-processing microprocessors, which can perform more than one operation simultaneously, are coming on to the market, perhaps more useful is a measurement in instructions per second, or ips.

The original microprocessors were 4-bit processors. The limitation to four bits made them difficult to use for any but very simple computations, so they were suitable primarily for simple control functions. Eight bits is the minimum word length necessary to store one character (alphabetic, numeric or special); therefore these processors could not be used for text processing applications. However, though 4-bit devices are not suitable for use as computer central processing units, they are still employed today in some simple toys, games, cheap calculators and so on. These devices are generally not user-programmable.

The next product up the line, the 8-bit processor, is the component which led to the original boom in personal computing and small business systems. Today the 8-bit processor has largely been superseded in this market by 16-bit devices, and some popular microprocessors operate at least partially in a 32-bit mode. Processors with longer word lengths have considerable advantages: they are able to function more rapidly and flexibly, and they can directly address the much larger amounts of memory needed for today's sophisticated multiple applications.

As an indication of the current state of the art, around 60,000 32-bit microprocessors were marketed in 1985, at a premium price for use in high specification engineering work-stations and similar computers and terminals. By 1991 it is estimated that the 32-bit microprocessor will be the mass-market standard for cheap computers, and that around 4.7 million of these devices will be sold. Among the latest generation of widely available devices is Intel's 80386 chip: a largely 32-bit chip which is made in CMOS at a scale of 1.5 microns. It incorporates about 275,000 transistors and can process up to 4 mips — that is, 4 million instructions per second. This microprocessor, and others in the same range, are being used in IBM's latest PS/2 series of personal computers. Motorola's broadly competing device, the 68030, is the latest in the series of chips that have been used in the Apple Macintosh range of personal computers. It has a slightly higher specification, being made in 1.2-micron high-performance CMOS, and containing around 300,000 transistors. This is the equivalent of the processing power of a medium-sized mainframe computer of the 1960s or 1970s — on a single chip! The phenomenal power packed into minute devices such as these has caused havoc with the original distinction between small computers of limited power, and larger computers with much greater power.

Such measurements, though, can give only the crudest idea of the different strengths and weaknesses of these chips. Choice of one or the other by computer manufacturers depends not only upon their own estimation of the quality of chip architecture, but also on the support provided in terms of peripherals, and most crucially today upon the take-up by other manufacturers, particularly major manufacturers, and thus the software support provided. The overwhelming success of Intel in the 16-bit microprocessor field, for example, was very largely underwritten by IBM's choice of Intel's designs as the processors in their first generation PCs.

In personal computers and similar products, the processor chip is usually accompanied by a bank of memory chips together with probably at least another half-dozen logic chips, some of them off-the-shelf designs, and sometimes some of them specially designed chips for use in that particular product or manufacturer's range of products.

Custom Logic Devices

Though general-purpose microprocessors have always taken the major share of the processor market, there has always been a complementary market for made-to-measure microprocessors; for *custom logic* or special logic chips. Custom chips of this kind, where the logic circuitry itself is designed to fulfil specific applications, should be distinguished from ordinary microprocessor chips that are limited 'o a single application by being controlled by programs fixed in ROM form.

Because custom chips are optimised for a particular end-use, they are more efficient than standard devices: they may be smaller; they may consume less power; often they are faster in operation, which may be a crucial design criterion; frequently they can perform operations beyond the capability of a software-programmed general-purpose microprocessor. These advantages meant that they found early application in products designed to fulfil crucial control functions: for example, in missile guidance systems, signal processing, process control and telecommunications equipment. Their comparatively high cost limited their application outside these specialist areas. But today, with advances in design and production technology making it feasible to produce relatively short runs of custom logic chips, the balance is tipping in their favour, and they are predicted to take an increasingly large share of the microprocessor market in the late 1980s and early 1990s. In 1983 the proportion of custom chips was around 6 per cent; by 1990 it may have risen to, say, 25 per cent.

Custom chips can be produced in either of two general ways. They can be designed from scratch to contain the precise mix of circuits that is best for the intended application; or an off-the-shelf general logic device can have a particular pattern fixed on it, much as a ROM is programmed once only to hold a certain pattern of information.

The off-the-shelf designs consist of regular patterns of logic gates. These are known as *uncommitted logic arrays*. Sometimes they are manufactured without any electrical connections at all between the gates: these are called *gate arrays*. The user determines what pattern of connections is required, and these are added at a final manufacturing stage — for example, by using an electron beam wiring technique. Sometimes they are manufactured with a comprehensive set of connections, and unwanted connections are 'burned out' in order to customise the circuits. These are called *programmed array logic* chips. In either case, once the particular logic pattern has been fixed in such a device, it is permanent and cannot be subsequently altered. Because of the technologies involved, gate arrays contain many fewer gates than the latest generation microprocessors described above: typically, less than 10,000. Semi-custom chips on these lines can be designed and manufactured in only a few weeks, and can be economic for production runs of only a few thousand.

To custom-design a chip from scratch is a much slower and more expensive business. It may take a year or more, and because the design cost has to be spread over a smaller unit base, each chip will be far more expensive than a mass-produced microprocessor (perhaps ten times more expensive, or even more so). Full designing is generally only practicable when the user requires at least 50,000 chips. However, it is possible to partly simplify the process by using standard 'building blocks', patterns of logic circuitry which can be fitted together to produce a semi-custom chip. A program called a *silicon compiler* helps in this more automated design process. Standard-cell chips can be designed in three to four months, and are generally produced in runs of from 20,000 to 50,000.

Other Technologies

Although most of the popular discussion about microelectronics is in terms of silicon chips — that is, those using silicon as a semiconducting base on which circuits are fabricated — it is important to appreciate that other semiconducting materials can also be used. For example, several companies are working on manufacturing chips using gallium arsenide as the base material. Chips fabricated on this base have lower power requirements and operate at much higher switching speeds than silicon-based circuits, and are thus of great interest to companies attempting to design faster processors.

Japan's ERATO (Exploratory Research for Advanced Technology) project has begun to develop a device called the *static induction transistor*, a gas device which channels electronic signals between the atoms of the crystal. The advantage of this approach is that the electrons move very rapidly, and little heat is generated. It could become an important technology in the next phase of technological development.

CISC and RISC Architecture

Although computers today have a vast range of applications, their capabilities are still, as always, limited. A typical microprocessor provides an instruction set of perhaps fifty different instructions involving the movement and simple manipulation of data. Full application programs are built up in layers: basic instructions are combined to make routines that can perform more complex tasks, and so on. In today's thinking, though, this basic instruction set is under siege. There is a divergence of philosophies, with some organisations working on developing CISC — the Complex Instruction Set Computer — and others working on RISC — the Reduced Instruction Set Computer.

The CISC philosophy is based on the proposition that as many operations as possible should be transferred from software — from the program of instructions — to hardware. As each instruction becomes more complex, so less of them are needed to make up an application program. This philosophy proves particularly appropriate when the time the microprocessor takes to execute instructions is much less than the time it takes to obtain data and instructions from primary memory. But though this was once generally the case, it is increasingly less true today: the speed of memory transfer, improved by special techniques such as the use of a 'cache' memory, now approaches that of microprocessor operation. In order to speed program execution to the utmost, it appears increasingly viable to shift the load not from software to hardware, but vice versa: from hardware to software.

The RISC philosophy reduces the number of instructions in the microprocessor's instruction set to a bare minimum, and concentrates on designs that enable each individual instruction to be carried out very rapidly: far more rapidly than the complex instructions of a CISC design could be performed. Even though RISC designs demand longer programs, computers designed and programmed on this basis can now outperform computers of more conventional design.

RISC initially came into its own in applications where speed of processing is of paramount importance: complex scientific applications and the like, involving supercomputers capable of performing hundreds of millions of instructions per second. Even so, today some individuals and organisations believe that RISC may be the way ahead for mainstream computing as well. The philosophy has been adopted most wholeheartedly by Hewlett-Packard, who are developing their Precision Architecture, or PA, RISC approach across their entire range of computers.

The Transputer

Until recently, all microprocessors followed much the same general pattern of architecture, based upon *serial processing*: that is, carrying out logical operations one after another, in a series. But much of today's research into supercomputers has focused on the alternative approach of *parallel computing*, and, with this development in mind, INMOS have developed a series of microprocessors which work in a parallel fashion, the *transputers*.

INMOS was originally set up by the British government as a high-technology venture to give Britain a toehold in the semiconductor industry. Today it is owned by Thorn–EMI, and its short-term future is uncertain because the success to date of the transputer is counterbalanced by continuing losses in more conventional semiconductor business.

The transputers operate on a reduced instruction set theory — RISC, the supercomputer architecture described above. Also they are optimised so that they can communicate easily with other transputers, thus opening the prospect of linked banks or *arrays* of these special microprocessors.

7

The Semiconductor Industry:
its Economics and Characteristics

In the last chapter we examined the basic technology of the semiconductor industry and reviewed the major types of circuits that can be manufactured in a chip. In this chapter we consider the consequences of the nature of the manufacturing process, in terms of the economics of production faced by the semiconductor companies, and review the resulting significant characteristics of the industry. First we examine the technical and economic consequences of making electronic circuits smaller and smaller.

Small is Beautiful

As has been suggested for economics in general, so definitely in the economics of microelectronics, smallness brings beautiful economic benefits! The primary consequences of making microelectronics even more 'micro' — that is, increasing the packing density — are illustrated in Figure 7.1.

There are four primary areas of benefit. First, the circuits manufactured into the chips are concerned with manipulating and storing electrical pulses representing binary digits. If the packing density increases, then the circuits on the chip are closer together, so that the time taken for the electrical pulse to travel from one circuit to another is less, and therefore the component on the chip will function faster (since the electrical pulse spends less time travelling between circuits). An indication of the increase in speed over the past thirty years is shown in Figure 7.2.

Second, as the circuits on the chip are now smaller and closer together,

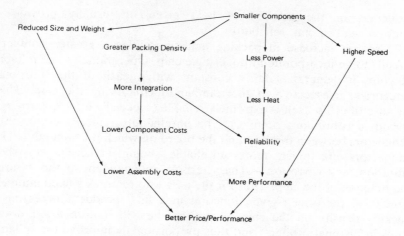

Figure 7.1 *Benefits of Microelectronics*

their power requirements are less, so that, for example, operating from batteries is feasible for a wider and wider range of products. In an electronic component there are no moving parts, so that all of the electrical energy used to switch the circuit from one state to another is given off as heat — lower power requirements mean less heat to be dissipated. This is of direct and indirect benefit: adequate dissipation of heat is a major constraint on the designers of both the chip and the product that it is used in (for example, even today the cpu's of many of the world's most powerful computers are liquid cooled). Also, heat (too much of it) is a significant influence on the reliability of a chip, so that a

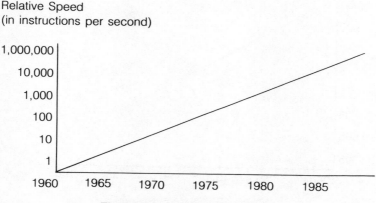

Figure 7.2 *Increase in Speed*

reduction in the amount of heat given off usually provides an improvement in chip reliability.

Third, an increase in packing density enables a greater number of circuits to be incorporated into a single chip. Operationally, the reliability of chips in general is fairly constant within each of the four major categories, irrespective of the number of circuits on the chip. This is because the chip itself is extremely reliable (especially after a 'burning-in' period of continuous running). The unreliability typically occurs in the connectors between the chip and the board on which it is mounted. These connectors are much more unreliable, being vulnerable to shock, vibration, and corrosion — characteristics independent of the nature of the function of the chip. Thus for the user who requires a fixed number of circuits to perform a given function in a final product, increasing the packing density on the chip means that he will require fewer discrete chips in his final product, and thus proportionally improve the reliability of his product.

The final benefit of increasing the packing density is that the customer gets all this, and at lower and lower prices. More circuits on a given chip means that the cost per circuit falls, since the manufacturing costs of a chip are largely independent of the contents of the chip. Also, for a given function, the user will require fewer discrete chips, so that the cost to the user of providing a given function falls dramatically. The decline in cost is illustrated in Figure 7.3.

In the chip manufacturing process the costs of all four hundred or so chips on a wafer are shared as joint costs until the break-out stage. The manufacturing process up to the break-out stage is highly automated (and capital intensive). Establishing a new chip production facility entails

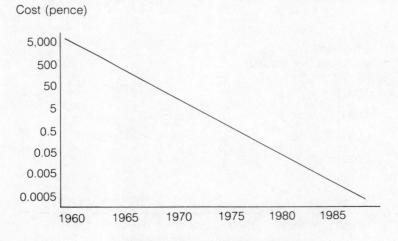

Figure 7.3 *Cost per Component*

heavy investment in specialised equipment (e.g. clean rooms, doping ovens, photolithographic facilities), such that roughly 90 per cent of the costs are incurred before a single chip is produced. Hence, it is a mass production business, and most chip manufacturers aim to produce hundreds of thousands of chips per week.

Up until this point, the costs of the multi-stage etching and lithographic processes are borne by all the chips on the wafer, good or bad (hence the importance of production yield mentioned earlier). It is only after break-out that each (good) chip carries its own handling and mounting cost. This is illustrated in Figure 7.4. Recent developments in automated testing, and now progress towards automated mounting of the chip in its carrier and on the board, have served to heighten and emphasise this characteristic.

Shared Costs	wafers photolithography (masks) multi-layer etching testing and break-out
	yield = percentage of good chips
Individual Costs	mounting assembly on boards

Figure 7.4 *Economics of Production*

An illustration of how the benefits arising from the economics of chip production are brought to the user is shown in Figure 7.5. This shows the scale of chip technology employed, the number of components necessary, and the total cost of 1 MByte (i.e. approximately 1 million characters) of primary memory, using the latest generally available RAM technology. As can be seen, the packing density for memory chips has doubled roughly every year, so that the number of chips required to make up a

	Bits/Chip	*Chips/MByte*	*$/MByte*
1975	1K	8,192	95,528
1977	4K	2,048	37,198
1979	16K	512	14,924
1981	64K	128	6,100
1983	256K	32	2,532
1986	1,024K	8	240

Figure 7.5 *Cost per Megabyte of RAM Primary Memory*

megabyte of memory has halved every year, with proportionate improvements in reliability. (The pace of improvement has slowed, but only marginally, very recently.) And at the same time the final user price has fallen even more dramatically, till today RAM costs a tiny fraction of a cent per character stored.

These figures indicate roughly the cost for *latest technology* chips, but in fact the cost for previous-generation technology chips is often much more competitive, so that (for instance) once 256-Kbit chips were widely available, the price of 64-Kbit chips fell to distress levels. However, use of larger-scale integrated chips reduces assembly time and costs, and improves product reliability because there are fewer vulnerable connections on the circuit board.

Given these economic and production characteristics of the chip, how has the semiconductor industry developed? And what are its dominant characteristics?

Historical Development of the Semiconductor Industry

The original stimulus (and the massive R & D funds) necessary for the manufacture of the first microelectronic components came from the American military authorities, particularly for missile control and guidance systems, where compactness, low power requirements and reliability were paramount requirements. Initially systems made up from individual transistors were used, but the development of the capability to manufacture integrated circuits led to an explosive growth in their subsequent development and application. Roughly the same period (the 1960s) saw major growth and developments in computing, and in particular the widespread application of computers in commercial data processing. The rapidly growing defence and computer industries formed the major markets for the products of the semiconductor companies until the beginning of the 1970s. By then the industry had entered a pattern of explosive growth in output and reduction in cost.

The original companies in the semiconductor industry were those engaged in instrumentation and precision engineering, such as Texas Instruments, Hewlett-Packard, Fairchild and Motorola. Subsequently they were joined by most of the computer companies, and by several totally new companies such as Intel and Mostek, most of which were founded by people leaving one of the original manufacturers and setting up to exploit their own engineering or design flair. Throughout the 1970s the semiconductor industry was characterised by its dynamism, competitiveness and entrepreneurial flair, especially in the creation and exploitation of totally new markets for its products.

However, profits in this new field were never certain, even when companies succeeded in developing and manufacturing the right products at the right time. The 1974 recession in the American economy left many semiconductor companies with excess capacity and large stocks, and certainly throughout the 1980s the industry has been jittery about the prospects for future growth. Many of the early markets for semiconductors — for example, the electronic calculator and digital watch markets — are over saturated, prices of end-products have fallen to a level that barely covers costs, and it has not always been easy to develop new markets at the required pace.

The special nature of the semiconductor industry brings it unfamiliar problems. Enormous sums must be expended in start-up costs, capital equipment and research, while the end-products sell for relatively trivial amounts. This high start-up barrier now tends to exclude all but the most heavily backed newcomers from entering the market. At the same time, the necessity to obtain some return on the massive investments has often meant that competitive selling has brought the prices of all but the most leading-edge technology down to extremely low levels.

Though chip design is a highly complex business requiring refined technical and scientific skills, the actual chip manufacturing process demands much less expertise. Throughout the 1970s there was a great deal of demanding, but essentially routine, work involved — for example, in chip testing, and in mounting chips and adding connectors. The rapidly developing economies of the Far East proved to have workforces well suited to this work, and a great deal of the semiconductor business moved to this part of the world — to Malaysia, Korea and Taiwan, for example. To some extent this process has been reversed with the increasing automation of these parts of the production process, but still there are new entrants to the industry among the sunrise economies. India and China are likely to be among the next generation.

Though manufacturing capacity is spread relatively widely, the ownership of dominant firms is, in contrast, heavily concentrated: in Japan and the USA. These two countries currently seem destined to continue their fight for dominance of the mass-produced semiconductor market until the end of the 1980s at least. Together, firms based in these two countries account for about 90 per cent of all sales. In 1985, sales of semiconductors were at a level of about $30,000 million, of which around $5,000 million went on discrete components (e.g. single transistors or resistors) and $24,000 million on integrated circuits.

In 1986–7 by far the most successful microprocessor supplier was Intel, who marketed over a quarter of the microprocessors used in micro and minicomputers. Intel's success with its 8,000 series of 16-bit microprocessors seemed set to be carried through to its 80,000 series 32-bit products. The second largest supplier was Motorola. The market for memory devices was dominated by Japanese companies — NEC, Hitachi,

Toshiba, Fujitsu, Matsushita and others — who overwhelmingly supplied the indigenous electronics industry, and exported around 30 per cent of their output. In 1986 accusations of 'dumping' by these firms on the US market led to the imposition of very high (100 per cent) tariffs; but this, together with a recovery in the trade after the bad years of 1985 and 1986, helped to ease the problem, and by 1988 the tariffs had been lifted. Indeed, early in 1988 prices for most mass-produced chips were *rising* through shortages of supply. Semiconductor companies had not invested in new capacity during the recession of 1986–7, and problems in getting large yields of the new 1-Mbit DRAM (Dynamic RAM) chips exacerbated their production difficulties.

The European presence in the chip market is relatively small. UK chip companies such as Plessey, Marconi and Inmos accounted for only 1 per cent of world production in 1986, though the percentage was increased by the continuing investment of foreign firms in British-based plants: among others, NEC, Motorola, National Semiconductor and Texas Instruments have established new microelectronics manufacturing facilities in the British Isles. The indigenous industry is becoming increasingly concentrated in the custom chip field, where comparatively new entrants such as Mietec and European Silicon Structures have an opportunity to establish themselves in leading positions.

Vertical Integration and Added Value

Increasingly in recent years, partly as a result of deregulation policies and partly as a result of the economics of the business, there has been a tendency for companies to integrate their activities vertically throughout the information technology field. The same massive conglomerates control organisations which are active at every stage of the industry, from chip design and manufacture to software production, support and even end-user consultancy.

Vertical integration makes a great deal of sense to both semiconductor and computer manufacturers. The semiconductor companies are assured of a market for their products that is relatively insensitive to the degree of market competition, and they are no longer made vulnerable by their near total dependence on a single customer whose activities they cannot control. The computer companies in turn are assured of the supply of a vital component, at times of shortage and glut alike. Both parties are able to collaborate closely over design philosophies and requirements, an essential strategy in this era of rapidly changing technology. Almost all of the major telecommunications and computer organisations have at least some captive chip manufacturing capability today, including AT&T, IBM, ITT, NEC and Philips.

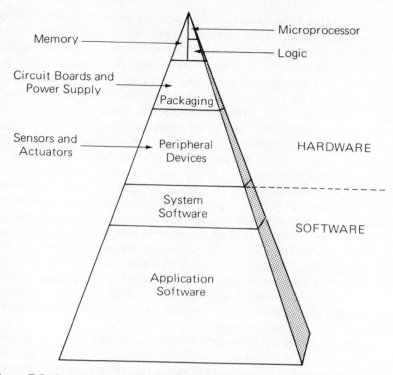

Figure 7.6 *Relative Costs in Producing Microelectronics Based Systems*

The desire of the semiconductor companies to enter consumer product markets is reinforced by the fact that the value added in these final products is much higher than in the production of chips. For the semiconductor companies and the companies using chips in their products, the world looks something like Figure 7.6, where the area of each part of the diagram is roughly proportional to the work done and value added at each stage in building up to the final system. Although this diagram was originally formulated in the context of computer system applications, it does have equal relevance to the incorporation of microelectronics in products. If we examine Figure 7.6, we note that the microprocessor with which we are concerned comprises the small top right-hand triangle: that is, the microprocessor is an extremely small proportion of the final cost of most systems. To this are added some memory and logic circuits (typically, to handle the input and output of information to and from the processor), and it is then packaged, perhaps only on a printed circuit board or in a rack, together with some power supplies to give the system builder an operational computer.

Several other items are also necessary in order to produce a finished end-product. It is necessary to use peripherals to enable the processor to communicate with the outside world — sensors, actuators, keyboards, displays, and so on — and in the case of information processing applications, some form of secondary memory device is required, such as a disc drive. This can constitute the complete hardware of a computer system. However, the system also requires some software, i.e. instructions on how to operate on the information input.

As we saw in Chapter 4, software is basically of two types. System software is concerned primarily with the internal functioning of the computer, and the way in which its resources, including peripheral devices, are managed. It is usually supplied with the computer. Application software is the specific instructions telling the computer how to deal with the data input in a specific application. In a general-purpose computer system these instructions will vary from task to task, and will normally be loaded into the processor as required. In simple or mass-market dedicated applications, such as calculators, watches and machine controls, they may be permanently embodied in the pattern of circuitry.

The final cost is the operation and use of the final system. In a commercial data processing context, this will often be the largest cost element in the entire operation.

All the way down the triangle shown in Figure 7.6 the value added (in general) increases, obviously not in precisely the same proportions for every application, but usually following this broad overall pattern.

Pacing Technological Change and Application Technology

To improve chip manufacturing technology so that last year's 256-Kbit RAMs become this year's 1-Mbit RAMs is, however, only half of the challenge. There is no point in making technological advances in *component* capability unless there are corresponding advances in the capability of the *products* in which microelectronic components are incorporated.

Though the semiconductor industry has changed its technology rapidly throughout its relatively short lifespan, the same is not true of most end-product sectors. The watchmaking industry, for example, has existed for centuries and evolved its technology at less than a snail's pace. Left to itself, it would doubtless have taken many years even to absorb 4-bit microprocessors. It is difficult to envisage how it might have generated any demand for an improved semiconductor product every year or two. This is the other major reason for vertical integration into product areas: the simple need of the semiconductor manufacturers to force-feed the

market for their products. Watch manufacturers evaluated microprocessors only slowly, so new companies, often allied to the semiconductor companies themselves, began to develop digital watches from
scratch, and soon many of the older generation of companies were forced
out of business.

Microelectronics companies have been remarkably successful in finding
markets for their output, and the list of products in which microelectronics is incorporated grows almost daily. But even so, the push is
difficult to sustain. Every time a microprocessor is incorporated into a
product, the product must be redesigned, and the microprocessor
programmed to control it correctly. It simply is not practicable in many
fields for this redesign process to be started again from scratch every time
the semiconductor manufacturers come up with new devices with
ever greater capabilities.

This is true even in the computer industry — indeed, perhaps
especially so. In some areas there *is* an undoubted demand for new,
improved technology. Advances in RAM packing density are eagerly
greeted, and the new sizes of RAM quickly incorporated into all but the
cheapest of computers. But advances in microprocessor technology are
taken up much more slowly.

One major reason for this is simply the immense difficulty of taking full
advantage of the power of the latest technology. Programming a complex
computer, even a personal computer, containing a 16- or 32-bit processor
and various other support chips, is an incredibly demanding task. Even the
best programmer cannot hope to take full advantage of the power at his
or her fingertips. To produce a highly complex program can take many,
many man-years of programmer time. Even when large teams of
programmers work together, it takes months or even years of calendar
time too.

Take, for example, the IBM PC — IBM's first generation personal
computer. The PC was first launched in 1982, and even then the
technology it used was not at the very leading edge: the Intel 8080 chip
around which the original PC was built was a well-established 16-bit
device launched some time earlier. Though the PC was an immensely
successful product, it still took many months for a large user base of PCs
to grow up. It took many more months for software houses to study the
PC's architecture, come to grips with its capabilities, and write, document
and sell programs which used those capabilities to anything like their full
potential.

It was a full five years before IBM launched what were intended to be
their next full generation of PCs, based round a more advanced
microprocessor architecture, in 1987. By this time the original PC line
had evolved, some of the low-end machines had become redundant, and

other machines with better specifications had joined the range. The user base had grown to massive proportions. The PC programs available were numbered in their tens of thousands, and this generation showed immense advances in sophistication from the first products.

Technical computer buffs had complained for years that the PC was outdated, its architecture barely better than antique, and its days long past. But things looked very different to the end-user, who typically had built up a substantial investment in PC know-how and a large library of floppy discs in PC format, and who would have seen many, many signs that the PC support market was thriving. So, after five years, the original PC was far from dead. And yet microprocessor architecture enters a new generation, at present, every two years. How many computer users want to swap to a new machine every second year, to transfer their files to a newer, denser format, to learn a cadre of newer, more sophisticated programs? There is always some cachet in acquiring the very latest product, but the real demand for advances in PC technology has come not so much from the users, but from the chip manufacturers who want and need to see new machines being designed around *their* new chips.

At the same time, the cost of a single chip becomes an ever-decreasing part of the overall cost of a computer system — not only because of the reduction in semiconductor costs, but also because of the *increase* in the demands for software and overall support, as the technology becomes ever more complex and powerful. Typically today, the budget of a data processing department shows around a third of the total cost devoted to personnel — a proportion that is slowly but steadily rising. Around 40 per cent of the cost goes on hardware, including peripheral devices such as printers. This proportion is slowly falling. About 10 per cent of the cost goes on bought-in software, though this has to be considered in conjunction with the in-house personnel cost of writing special software or tailoring packages to meet specific requirements. And another 10 per cent or so goes on overheads, supplies and so on. In spite of attempts to automate the program-writing task, and a general tendency away from software written in-house and towards bought-in software packages, it looks increasingly likely that these trends will continue for the foreseeable future.

The inevitable outcome of all these developments is that the time taken to fully exploit each more complex generation of technology, and the investment made in each generation of computer equipment, will grow; and though there will always be room for change and growth, it looks as if there is no real *need* for the extraordinary growth levels of the 1960s and 1970s to be sustained indefinitely. Indeed, there is no real *capability* to make use of this pace of technological advance, even if it were sustainable.

R & D and Innovation in the Semiconductor Industry

In an industry whose product declines in price by 25 per cent each year, the motivation for undertaking research and development is obviously very high. An R & D programme giving a company a year's advantage in launching a new product can give it a 25 per cent cost advantage over its competitors. Similarly, a year's delay can put it at a severe disadvantage.

Each new product is first available to potential customers in prototype form. Mass production generally follows as much as 9 to 15 months later. As early as this prototyping stage, the manufacturer is also expected to quote fairly firm prices at which the product will eventually be available (in lots of up to 100,000 or more) — prices which, by the very nature of the industry, are typically at least 25 per cent below current prices, and usually below current production cost.

The manufacturers of a new processor chip design also enter into what are known as *second sourcing* agreements with one (or more) other semiconductor companies. Basically this means that the originating company provides a set of chip production masks to another semiconductor company, who can then make the same chip under licence. This reassures the customer that the chip can be mass-produced by another company, thus providing some guarantee of supply in the event of difficulties at the original manufacturers. For instance, Hitachi has produced microprocessors following Motorola's designs; Fujitsu produces Texas Instruments microprocessors.

For all companies in the semiconductor industry, continuous product development is a fact of life, R & D expenditure typically takes at least 10 per cent of revenue, and rapid product obsolescence is the norm. In the light of these comments about pricing policy it is interesting to note that the problems of some semiconductor companies have been in the area of cash management rather than circuit design. Up to the end of the 1970s the industry was typified by young companies — very successful, or very dead!

With the levels of interest rates seen in recent years, one of the major concerns of the semiconductor companies was how to finance their growth. Each new chip design generally proves more expensive to design and develop than its predecessor, in spite of the developments in automated design aids. The capital expenditure required to get the design into mass production is also enormous, and there is no guarantee of large sales, particularly for microprocessors whose design may not find favour with the standard-setters, such as IBM. It was difficult for small independent companies to expand themselves under such conditions, and ever since the 1970s there has been a steady stream of takeovers of young, thrusting microprocessor companies by larger conglomerates.

Some of these have been conglomerates already firmly established in the IT industry (thus leading to the kind of vertical integration we discussed above), while others have been end-users of chips. Companies such as General Motors have moved into the field, not only to ensure supplies, but also to buy technical know-how. This is a process of backward integration, rather than the forward integration by semiconductor companies mentioned earlier.

These developments have been viewed with concern by some commentators because of the potential loss of engineering and entre-preneurial flair when relatively small, and very personal, companies are absorbed by much larger, and perhaps more impersonal, organisations. In much of the semiconductor industry, corporate financial questions now predominate over creative drive and design flair. It is perhaps sympto-matic of this that the early supremacy of the US companies has been lost to the more methodical Japanese, with their particular skills in corporate innovation and in slow but steady technical advance.

On the other hand, it has sometimes proved to be true that large companies can afford to carry out research into esoteric fields where the return is so uncertain that an independent one-product company would find it difficult (or impossible) to obtain financial backing. In the recent past, for instance, major attempts by firms such as IBM and Texas Instruments to create commercial technology out of such concepts as the Josephson junction and bubble memory have been consigned to the scrap-heap. Fortunately both organisations were so large and diversified that the resources spent down such blind alleys of research, though they undoubtedly depressed overall results to a small extent, did not drag them into disaster.

Many predictions have been made that the rate of innovation in the semiconductor industry is certain to slow down shortly; but, in spite of some wrong turnings, research and innovation have continued at a very high level. Even if current channels of research lead to little or nothing, enough has already been accomplished to fuel the carrying through of the revolution in both product and service industries. We turn our attention to these applications of microelectronic technology in the next chapter.

Applications of Microelectronics

In this chapter we will be reviewing the application of microelectronics, and of the microprocessor in particular, in products. We will exclude from the discussion those products which come from the traditional computer and telecommunications industries, as we will be looking at them in greater detail in Parts IV and V. From the point of view of the semiconductor companies, the whole point of the markets for the application of chips is that they must be big — preferably very big! — and the primary means for stimulating and developing application markets has been an aggressive pricing policy. If necessary the semiconductor companies themselves have been willing to develop new markets if the existing firms in the market have been slow or uninterested.

Personal Products

Products for individual people obviously represent a very large market. The difficulty lies in discovering the kind of product that everybody will want. The two best-known examples are digital watches and the electronic pocket calculator.

Calculators and Watches

In both instances the original firms in these industries appeared blissfully unaware of the fate that was about to overcome them. It was the semiconductor companies, hungry for mass markets, who were the leading revolutionaries, following the familiar pattern of aggressively pricing a technically superior product to achieve maximum volumes as rapidly as possible.

Electronic calculators were first introduced as desktop machines in the mid-1960s at prices in excess of £1,000 each. Even at those levels their advantage over the existing mechanical or electro-mechanical calculators was so great that within a very few years they had totally swept the market. The availability of a technically superior, cost-effective product led to a rapid increase in demand. This in turn led to more technical developments in chip design (permitting calculators to be designed with more functions and providing a marketing edge for the manufacturer), a better product, even more demand, higher output, lower prices, more technical developments (in the manufacturing process as well as calculator capabilities), and so on — stimulated and fuelled by the aggressive marketing stance of the companies initially involved, which were largely Japanese.

The customer as well as the manufacturer (of the calculator, not the chip) has benefited from vast increases in productivity. The price/performance improvement in the product has been dramatic. From highly expensive office machines, calculators have become give-away devices. Only the packaging and retailing mechanism keeps the price level at pounds rather than pence.

Although there were UK manufacturers of mechanical calculators, they completely missed out in the electronic calculator revolution, and this particular battle was fought out between the Americans and the Japanese. The Japanese share of the market peaked at 45 per cent in 1971; after that, vertical integration by US semiconductor companies such as Texas Instruments, Rockwell and National Semiconductor enabled the Americans to expand the market. It is several years now since this market reached saturation point. Few households in the industrialised world can fail today to possess at least one calculator, or a pocket computer which functions as a calculator. The market now is for replacements (the product life of a cheap hand-held calculator is very short) and for more gimmicky or specialised devices: calculator wristwatches, calculator radios, toys incorporating calculators, and so on.

Twenty years ago, how many people would have seriously believed that nearly every person in the Western world would come to possess an electronic calculator? Even if they had believed that it was technically possible, they would surely have asked what these myriad calculators would be used for. Well, strange to tell, nobody knows what they are (or perhaps are not) used for. This is one dramatic illustration of the difficulty in forecasting the likely consumer demand for new types of electronic goods — or for old goods, transformed so totally by price and technology that they can tap entirely new markets.

Toys and Games

Toys and games are prodigious consumers of chips. This too has been a difficult market for manufacturers to forecast, not least because of the varying fashions in toys. One year's runaway success can be the following year's disastrous failure, and manufacturers need to rely on considerable ingenuity to keep semiconductor-based toys in the running for Christmas after Christmas.

The early chip-oriented toys were relatively simple devices: for example, Texas Instruments' 'Simon' game (a simply copy-the-tune device); it was a considerable success. Subsequently there have been developments in overtly educational games, in robots which can be programmed to move in complex patterns, produce noises and even speak, and in more traditional toys with new capabilities. One new successful line, for instance, is a doll which listens to its owner speaking, and then repeats the words.

Domestic Products

The home contains a large number of specialised appliances, many of them covered by the term 'white goods', such as devices to cook, wash, clean, mix, dry, polish, etc. Virtually every device which contains an electronic motor has been rethought over the past few years, and often microprocessor control has been incorporated into the latest models.

Domestic Appliances

One of the first companies to try microprocessor controls was Servis with their top-range washing machine. Washing machines were prime targets for the incorporation of electronics, since their relatively complex electro-mechanical controllers tended to be inflexible, somewhat unreliable and relatively expensive.

Incorporating microelectronics has proved to be a fairly difficult process, but today the advantages have become obvious. The mechanical parts of the machine (motor, drum, etc.) can be treated more kindly, for example, by implementing more controlled start-up procedures. The general state of the internal parts can be continuously monitored, and warning lights can indicate the need for maintenance. Some machines now incorporate limited self-testing features, though the washing machine has some way to go in comparison with (for example) the photocopier. Greater levels of safety are possible, and washing programmes are more flexible. At the same time, electronically controlled devices are actually cheaper to build than their electro-mechanical predecessors!

Microelectronic control on microwave and conventional ovens enables them to monitor temperatures more precisely, and to implement much more complex cooking programmes. It has also revolutionised the part played by the automatic timer. Microelectronically controlled sewing machines offer very extensive ranges of automatically produced stitches; and there are now electronic mixer-blenders, vacuum cleaners, electric drills and many other devices.

Environmental Control

Another major application in the home is controlling the heating, air-conditioning, lighting and security. Most recently designed central-heating controllers are microelectronics-based, and the old 'time clocks' are giving way to much more sophisticated and flexible programmable devices. Some advanced devices incorporate intelligent features: they estimate how long it will take to warm up the house to a chosen temperature, and start the heating process at the right time, using feedback information to recalibrate themselves day by day. By ensuring that heat (or cooling) is provided only when it is required, and to the exact level required, these devices can bring about considerable energy savings.

Digitally coded switches are now on sale, which can be programmed to switch on and off electrical appliances at pre-set times. As well as anticipating the householder's waking-up requirements, or his or her arrival home from work, these devices can be invaluable burglar deterrents, ensuring that lights, television sets etc., are switched on to simulate occupancy even when the house is deserted.

The latest home security systems incorporate microelectronically controlled sensors, programmed to detect intruders. When the doorbell or the telephone rings, a message can be flashed on to the television screen (or in some versions, a closed-circuit camera takes a picture of the visitor and superimposes this on screen), thus ensuring that the door is opened only to authorised callers.

Integrated Home Systems

Just as the trend in the office today is towards integrated systems, so the trend in home automation is towards a carefully planned and integrated approach. This even has its own jargon names. The preferred European term is 'domotics', while the Americans prefer to call it the 'smart house' approach, and the Japanese speak of 'home automation'.

Central to this approach are two elements. First is a network of conventional cables, fibre optics, infra-red and other communications channels designed to carry digital data from room to room. A central computer can then be used to control home security and to monitor and control domestic devices such as freezers, television sets and washing machines. The second element is a gateway linking the internal home network to the external telecommunications network. This paves the way towards everything from home banking and shopping to working at home (with close computer links to a central office) and to warning systems — for example, the computer might telephone the householder and give a warning of fire, earthquakes, burglaries, freezer breakdowns, and the like.

Technically much, if not all, of this is possible today, but because many homes are ill-adapted to a networked approach, it may be some years before the domotics market reaches its peak. However, research into this field is now being carefully co-ordinated, particularly with a view to ensuring some European participation in the market-place, which might, it has been estimated, be worth £8 billion a year by the 1990s. Esprit 2, the second stage of the EEC-wide research project on information technology, has shifted its emphasis from the office automation focus of Esprit 1 partly towards home automation; and another research project — Eureka Integrated Home Systems, in which Philips, GEC, Siemens, Thorn EMI and other European manufacturers are co-operating — is investing £12 million towards the development of home information networks.

Leisure Products

As we are being made painfully aware, leisure is becoming an occupational hazard. The demand for aids to help cope with the problem is on the increase, and this is an area in which the application of microelectronics can really demonstrate some of its virtuosity.

Hi-Fi and Television

Digital sound for domestic hi-fi systems became a reality in 1982, with the launch of the Sony/Philips compact disc: a smaller, audio-only version of the videodisc. In spite of the initially high prices of the discs themselves, while manufacturing capacity fell far behind demand, the systems quickly established themselves in the market-place, and now look set to replace conventional hi-fi.

Progress in digital tape recording has been slower, largely because of political problems. Many major manufacturers are determined to agree on standards for digital tape only if and when 'spoilers' are incorporated in the tapes, to prevent unauthorised copying, a major problem with today's cassette systems.

The colour television has over recent years reached something of a plateau in its development, and the slow spread of teletext (and even more halting progress of videotext) has done little to revitalise the market. It looks probable that two divergent tendencies will shape the future market. First, there is a trend towards truly portable televisions, though the availability of portable sets has not yet snowballed. And second, there may be an increased interest in TV projection systems, long popular in the US but never as successful in Europe. These systems blow up the TV picture to about four feet square, and project it on to a wall or screen.

Video

The early existence of three incompatible recording standards did little to slow the explosive market growth of video tape recorders in the early 1980s. Initially these devices were used for a mixture of (strictly speaking, illegal) recording from domestic television sets, and playing rented feature films, but with the decline in cost of video cassettes the rental market soon began to give way to a retail market.

While videotape is well established, videodiscs have failed to make their mark in the UK. Though discs are much cheaper to produce than tapes, the discs and their players have failed to establish a sufficient market base to make them cheaper in the market-place. And the video cassette recorder has an immense advantage in its ability to act as a 'time shift' machine, allowing viewers to record programmes to be watched not at the scheduled time, but as suits their own convenience.

Over 30 per cent of British households now possess a video recorder, and the early peaking of this market has now passed. Today the product which is receiving the full thrust of promotional advertising is the camcorder: a device which combines video camera and recorder, enabling home (and business) users to shoot their own film on video cassette, and to play it back almost immediately.

In Chapter 3 we explored the way in which laser disc technology is being used as a computer secondary storage medium. It has many other potential applications — in education and training, for the distribution of telephone directories and mail order catalogues, and so on — but few of these have been developed in any significant way as yet.

Industrial Products

Instrumentation Sensing and Control

Industrial controllers and sensors have, in a sense, reflected much the same dramatic technical and application changes that have been seen in the watch and calculator markets. The instrumentation industry has had to redevelop almost its entire product range over the past ten years, making its products 'smart' and heralding the era of truly automated measurement. Demand for sensors has risen dramatically.

Today's smart instruments automatically carry out what were formerly the functions of a technical or laboratory assistant. They can run tests, analyse the data obtained (or transmit it to a computer which performs the analysis) and link to controllers which automatically adjust processes in response to the results.

Microelectronic 'intelligence' has proved particularly beneficial in the latest generations of testing and diagnostic equipment. These are easier to use than earlier generations of instruments, they do not require graduate operators and they can carry out a much wider range of tests in a much shorter time. The trend has been towards self-checking and diagnostics: systems which are able to identify their own faults, and to point the way towards repairing them quickly and cheaply.

Robots

The word robot was coined by the Czech Karel Čapek in his play *R. U. R.* (*Rossum's Universal Robots*) in 1920. In Czech the word '*robota*' means forced labour. Since then it has come to have some quite specific connotations. Science fiction writers have explored the possibilities, none more than Isaac Asimov with his 'laws of robotics'. A robot is a general-purpose programmable machine that can replicate some types of human actions. It should be distinguished from a programmable machine tool, which has more specific, and unhuman-like, functions. A robot is best defined by looking at the kind of robots that have been developed so far.

'First generation' robots are relatively crude, *unintelligent mechanical arms*. They typically perform fixed repetitive tasks in conditions that would be dangerous or unsuitable for human beings: most common applications are in paint spraying and arc-welding, often of car bodies. Other applications are in handling castings from furnaces, feeding metal presses, and taking products from moulding machinery. In all these applications the robot blindly follows a set programmed routine, but has no awareness of the environment in which it is operating, or of the material that it is manipulating.

The first robots typically cost between £25,000 and £60,000, but even at those prices, and with very limited capabilities, they found an increasing number of applications in industry. The reasons are not hard to find. For example, if a typical robot for welding car bodies costs £50,000, can handle two-shift operation and has a five-year life, this works out at a cost of about £2.50 per hour. Contrast this with a rate for human car assembly-line workers that today is three, four or more times higher.

These first generation robots have been described as 'one-armed bandits — blind, daft, dumb devices screwed to the floor'. The simplest are pick-and-place robots, capable of moving an object from point to point. Another class specialise in a particular task, e.g. paint spraying. However, the trend is towards general-purpose robots.

The main problem for people working with robots is that the robots work to much finer tolerances and are currently unable to cope with any degree of disorder.

There are three different ways of programming a robot. First, an operator directs the robot through remote controls, thus 'teaching' the robot a sequence of actions. Second, the robot is given an example of what to do, in a task like paint spraying, by physical manipulation, and translates these physical movements into a programmed series. Third, the robot can be programmed entirely by instructions from a software library. Only in this final way (where the robot has a library of instructions, and follows different instructions in order to carry out different tasks) can it be made rapidly to switch from one task to another.

Second generation robots show improvement in dexterity, sensory powers and flexibility, thanks to the greater degree of processing power incorporated in them, and to greater programming sophistication. Smaller and cheaper circuitry enables the robots to handle and manipulate relatively small and delicate objects, and to assemble precision equipment (which was impossible with first generation robots). These robots are used, for example, to assemble electrical motors and alternators.

Much research and development effort has gone into improving the sensing capability of robots — giving them the ability to 'see'. This is done by linking the robot to a television camera (itself a product of microelectronics) and a computer with pattern-recognition capabilities. Pattern recognition is an excellent example of a computer application which requires considerable processing and memory resources, and thus becomes economically viable in a wider area of application as the cost of electronic components falls. But it presents a difficult problem, because the robot ideally needs to be able to identify components at any angle, and at various distances from its camera. Though considerable advances have been made, they have proved less rewarding then was once hoped, and even the latest robots fall very far short of human capabilities in this field.

The UK has been backward in both the development and the application of robots. The number of robots in use in the UK has steadily increased from around 125 in 1979 to 1,000 in 1982, and to approximately 5,000 in 1987, but this increase has not been sufficient to close the gap on overseas industrial rivals. In Japan, for instance, there are now 35,000 robots; in the USA there are approximately 15,000. Although the UK itself produces a small number of robots, it is insufficient to provide a positive balance of payments: in 1983 the value of robot imports was more than four times the value of exports, and the scale of research funding in this area is miniscule compared to that of some of its foreign competition.

CAD/CAM

The robot is only one element in the factory of the future. Manufacturing a product involves a whole range of activities from conceptualising, through design, analysis, simulation and drafting, to materials handling, forming, cutting, joining and processing, and to quality and inventory control. Computers have long been associated with design, analysis and simulation, but often as a series of unrelated activities. Using a CAD (*Computer Aided Design*) system the process can be co-ordinated using a series of common files or a database.

CAD starts with the design process. The designer typically works on a video screen, using the computer's processing power to enable him or her to try out new options and dispense with them quickly if they prove not to work; to draw with total accuracy, and envisage the object in three dimensions (good CAD systems will switch, on demand, from one 3-D view to another); and to make necessary calculations, and ensure that the design is as economical as possible.

CAD greatly speeds up the process of product design and redesign, and allows the designer to spend more time on exploring alternatives and optimising his work. The proposed item may be visualised and simulated in operation, and it is quick and easy to obtain estimates of production cost and materials requirements for many alternative designs. Once the product is designed, plans and drawings optimised for each stage in the subsequent production process can be produced rapidly, and to very high standards, on an automatic drafting machine. Drawings are only necessary, however, when people are involved in the production process. Today this is less and less often true. When computers control the process, the CAD computer can deal directly with them, providing them with all the information they require.

In the first phases of computer-controlled production automation, machine tools were equipped with their own individual *numerical control* (NC) systems, which enabled them to function more automatically and to far greater degrees of precision than is possible under hand and eye control. In a next stage, these machines are linked together with a data transmission network, making a process called *direct numerical control* (DNC). Using a computer to control the entire network, and to integrate the action of the machine tools, was known as CNC.

CNC, together with CAD, makes the basis of a CAM, or *Computer Aided Manufacturing*, system. The only missing ingredient is a facility to move materials from machine to machine. This step too can quite simply be automated, using a transfer line if the production volume is high, or by using robot-controlled transport, to create a *Flexible Manufacturing System*, or FMS. Using the FMS approach it is economic to produce small batches of products and to mix the type of product being produced at any one time. There are, as yet, only a few proper FMSs in existence; Japan has always led this approach to manufacturing.

Today's technology is passing beyond CAD, past the stage when the computer *aids* manufacturing and towards a stage when it will control every phase of the manufacturing process. This new concept is known as CIM, or *Computer Integrated Manufacturing*. It envisages a stage when all machines and people in a factory will be supplied with information from a single database, when supplies, orders and manufacturing operations will be fully integrated and optimised under production control. CIM should prove most beneficial in contexts in which the products are produced not in long identical runs, but with regularly changing specifications. It could be used, for instance, to control the customisation of motor cars, so that each buyer's specific requirements are met automatically; or for even shorter-run products such as aircraft. Though some high-technology firms are working on this concept, it is not yet a reality, largely because of the immense problems of producing the very complex and sophisticated software required.

General Motors have pioneered a standard known as MAP, or *Manufacturing Automation Protocol*, for use in industrial environments. This is very similar to a local area network, in that it is used to connect different computer-controlled devices, but its protocols are specifically designed for use in a manufacturing context. Using MAP, it is becoming possible to create networks that link robots, computers and programmable machines from a wide variety of manufacturers.

Just-in-Time Systems

Manual stock control systems depend upon a large amount of leeway for error, late ordering, late supply and so on. Because of the limited responsiveness of the system, a large amount of stock is usually kept in store.

The same need not be true of a computer-controlled system. When an organisation's manufacturing facilities are linked by computer, it is possible for a central system to know precisely what the stock situation is in every different factory and warehouse. There is no reporting delay, and less risk of error than with a manual system. The computer can then calculate what new stocks are needed, and where.

Just-in-Time, or JIT, systems work on this principle. They aim to improve cash flow by reducing stock levels to a practicable minimum. Similarly, they can schedule manufacturing and delivery so that the right goods are produced to meet customers' orders at the right time. JIT is a fast-developing concept, at present more widely found among large companies than small. Increasingly, large organisations are linking their computers to those of their suppliers and customers, so that the computer not only ascertains what stock is needed, it also orders it automatically; and customers are able not only to place their orders by computer, but in some instances they can even search the inventory of their suppliers and discover whether the goods they require are currently available from stock.

Personal Computers

The identifying feature of a personal computer is that it is intended for use by one person only. This might be a child playing a computer game; a student performing advanced calculations; a professional person using a business-oriented applications program; a designer using a graphics program; or any other single computer-using individual. Though the personal computer may be linked to other computers in a network, it is capable of functioning independently. In this it must be distinguished from a *terminal* or *work-station* which provides computing power to one individual, but derives much or all of that power from elsewhere in a network.

Personal computers grew up around microprocessors, and typically today the personal computer has a single microchip acting as its processor, though it will generally contain other support chips as well as memory chips and other components. The best personal computers today use leading-edge technology which (in 1987–8) means 16/32-bit microprocessors and sizeable internal memories, typically over 1 MByte in total. (A 16/32-bit chip is one with a 16-bit register — that is, it processes data in 16-bit words — but its data paths are 32-bit, so it can transmit data quickly.) However, cheaper models are invariably on offer too, taking advantage of last-generation technology (for instance, 8- or 16-bit microprocessors) and selling at a very substantial discount.

The IBM PS/2 Range

IBM's first generation personal computer, the PC, established an industry standard in terms of operating environment (based on the MSDOS operating system) that prevailed for five years or more. It is still too soon to know whether IBM's recently unveiled successors, the PS/2 range, will reach the same predominant position in the market-place. These machines do, however, provide a good example of the current state of the art in personal computers.

It is typical of today's approach that a whole series of basic machines should be available, each with options that allow the user to customise his/her personal computer to his/her own budget and requirements. Internal card slots are provided into which users can slot circuit boards which provide additional capabilities.

The lowest-end PS/2 machine is little different in power from its predecessors, so the mid-range Model 60 provides a better example of the new generation technology.

This microcomputer is based round an Intel 80286 microprocessor, one of Intel's new range of chips originally used in the IBM PC/AT, the upmarket version of the original model. IBM used Intel chips in the original PCs, and their decision to stay with Intel allows a limited degree of compatibility between the old and new machines, though by and large they will run quite different software. The 80286 is a 16/32-bit chip and can handle up to 16 MBytes of internal memory. (Compare that with the 640K of the original PCs: it is a more than tenfold advance.) 1 MByte of RAM is provided as standard. The 80286 chip in the Model 60 runs at a clock speed of 10 MHz.

On the original PCs, graphics capability was an optional extra, and one not taken up by many customers, though many IBM-ulators (producers of copycat machines) offered graphics as standard. Today, graphics is seen as more of an essential, however, and the PS/2 machines all offer monochrome graphics capability, with colour available for those who select a colour display screen. Also inbuilt is the capability for the computer to handle a *mouse*, a small device which is run across the desktop, to move a pointer on screen.

With these machines, IBM has made a transition to the 3.5-inch floppy disc format, from the 5.25-inch floppies used on earlier machines. The Model 60 comes as standard with one double-side drive, on which each disc can hold up to 1.44 MBytes of data, and a hard disc drive which can hold up to 44 MBytes. Capabilities for adding to this secondary memory provision are provided.

IBM has also moved to a new operating system for this range of machines. OS/2, the new offering, was not available when the machines were announced, however, and they are also capable of running PCDOS, the operating system (a specific variant of Microsoft's MSDOS) used for the first generation PCs. The full potential of the 80286 and 80386 processors in the new machines will not be fully realised until OS/2 is available, and software has been developed to make full use of the capabilities of the hardware and the operating system. When this has happened, the Model 60 should be a *multitasking* computer, enabling the user to keep several applications in memory at once — for instance, a spreadsheet, a word processor and a diary facility — and to switch at will from one to the other. It should provide a user-friendly 'front end': a graphics-oriented display which makes it easy for the non-expert user to find his or her way around the software on offer, and to make selections and carry out housekeeping tasks with the minimum of effort. And it should be able to cope with the latest generation, memory-hungry programs such as graphics packages, desktop publishing packages, and expert system builders.

Typical prices for a full working system based round a Model 60 are around £4,500 to £5,000.

The Non-IBM Market

Standards emerge by practice rather than by formal agreement in the microcomputer market, simply because the software producers have to work to reasonably common protocols in order to spread their development costs over a wide market. Machines that do not meet the prevailing standards generally have less software available, and today this puts them at a crippling disadvantage.

The IBM PC and subsequently updated AT ranges established the standards for business-oriented microcomputers during the 1980s, and the majority of successful machines in this era followed their standards. This often caused difficulty, because there were legal problems in determining which features of the machines were open-market standards, to which other manufacturers could properly adhere, and which were IBM-patented, and not open to free copying. A number of outright 'pirate' machines, copying IBM's proprietary software on ROM chips, were produced, especially in the Far East, and this led to a series of international court cases by IBM in its attempt to protect its developments.

Of the manufacturers who closely followed the IBM lead, the most successful has been Compaq, who have specialised in 'luggable' computers. Compaq have established an enviable reputation for reliability and for high-quality products, causing many corporate buyers to favour them over IBM. Many other manufacturers have produced significantly cheaper copies, but doubts over their long-term ability to support and service their machines, and over the finer points of their compatibility with software written for the IBM, made it difficult for them to establish themselves.

The only large-scale rivalry to the position of the IBM and IBM-ulated machines today comes from Apple Computers. They introduced what was, at the time, an entirely different design philosophy in their powerful and innovative 'Lisa' computers. The Lisas had excellent monochrome graphics capability, and came complete with an integrated range of application programs which were multitasking in an era when personal computers generally ran only one program at a time. The operation of these programs was co-ordinated through an operating system which provided a graphic-oriented front end, using a mouse as a pointer and the concepts of *windows* and *icons*.

A window is a screen within a screen: a 'virtual' display area which can be interleaved with other windows on the same video display unit, thus allowing several programs to be used simultaneously (or one program, e.g. a word processor, to handle several files simultaneously). Window handling features allow windows to be resized, to be moved around the screen, and to change their priority, rather like shuffling a sheaf of pieces of paper. The icon is a small graphic symbol which may represent a file, a 'trashcan' or a process, e.g. an application program. The user selects a file or program by pointing at it with the mouse pointer. This windows/icons/ mouse/pull-down menus (or WIMP) philosophy was pioneered by Xerox, but Apple were the first to bring it to the commercial market-place.

Unfortunately the Lisa range was too expensive, and too little proven, to appeal widely, and it was not a commercial success. Apple recovered from the disaster, however, to launch the more downmarket Macintosh, using much the same philosophy, which has enjoyed a steadily growing success, and caused a resurgence in their fortunes. Indeed, the basic appeal of the Lisa-type design philosophy has also been proven by the appearance of many programs for IBM-type machines which make the IBM appear to work in a Lisa-like way!

Though the Macintosh has not achieved IBM's penetration into the large corporate market, it has proved especially successful with independent personal computer users, particularly as next-generation Macintoshes have remedied some of the practical shortcomings (slow operation and lack of storage among them) of the first generation. Apple have more recently launched the MAC II: a new generation of machines which will, like the earlier MACs, use Motorola's chips in contrast to IBM's Intel-type dependence. The MAC II is based around the 32-bit 68020 chip operating at a nifty 16 MHz, with a Motorola co-processor to add still more power. Like the IBM Model 60, it comes with 1 MByte of RAM as standard, with a high-capacity floppy disc drive (MACs have always used the 3.5-inch standard), and a hard disc too. Unlike the earlier Macintoshes, the MAC II has full colour graphics capability.

In the early days of personal computing, Commodore Computers also maintained a strong position, but internal difficulties, and an over concentration (at one stage) on the home computer market, led Commodore into severe difficulties from which they have not yet fully recovered. Though their Amiga computers have been widely praised, they have not established themselves in the corporate market, and in the UK at least they are too expensive to be widely acceptable as home computers.

Atari too have a powerful range of non-IBM computers in their ST range. They have produced a cheap, powerful computer which, though not as technically innovative as the Amiga, appeals to the technical, educational and recreational market. While it is unlikely to make a serious challenge on the IBM-PC standard, the ST may well establish a significant market niche.

Laptop and Luggable Computers

'Traditional' personal computers are not portable machines. Though their size and weight have been reduced markedly over the years, they are still large and heavy, with sizeable 'system units', large display screens and big, easy-to-use keyboards (typically with a numeric keypad and a wide range of special function keys as well as a full qwerty layout). The delicate circuitry of their disc drives makes them vulnerable to movement, and transporting them at all requires careful preparation and a strong pair of hands! Yet many users have a requirement for a portable computing resource. Businessmen want to use their computers on planes, in trains and at home in the evenings. Salesmen, engineers, doctors, journalists and other professionals want to use them when out in the field. Virtually every computer user travels on occasion, and it inevitably causes difficulties when his/her computer cannot travel too. There is a sizeable market, therefore, for computers that *can* travel.

The move to supply this market has taken two different directions. First came a movement *upwards* from pocket calculators, towards slightly larger, but still compact, machines which have much wider capabilities. And second came a movement *downwards* from desktop personal computers, towards smaller and lighter machines with much the same capabilities. Pocket computers have been available since the 1970s, with pushbutton-type alphanumeric keyboards (sometimes qwerty, sometimes arranged alphabetically), relatively small internal memories and, typically one-line liquid crystal displays. The small size of these machines limits their capabilities even today, however: though microprocessors and memory chips are tiny, disc drives are not, and pocket-sized displays and keyboards are not easy to use except for short periods. Pocket computers are still aimed primarily at a note-taking market, at calculator users who have a smallish requirement for wider capabilities.

The smallest computers which emulate the full capabilities of today's desktop machines are the so-called *laptop* computers. These are typically a little larger than a fat paperback, at most around the size of a portable typewriter, with a liquid crystal type screen that folds down to protect the keyboard when the machine is not in use. They work on batteries, usually with a mains option, and incorporate a floppy disc drive (or, on some of the transitional models between this and the next class, a hard disc drive). Communications facilities are frequently excellent, enabling users to link up with larger computers back at their base. Though laptops do not have the full power of a good desktop personal computer, they are capable of running broadly the same programs, so that it is possible to transfer discs between a desktop and a laptop, and to continue working on the same projects when away from the office. Some transportables have software built in, in ROM chip form.

The development of laptops has received much impetus from the development of LCD technology. Today's laptops often have full-sized screens, or, at the very least, eight or ten lines of display, with displays that, though they do not rival the best monitors in clarity and ease of use, are at least readable in a wide variety of light conditions. Several are back-lit to improve visibility. Prices vary, depending upon the features offered, but are typically in much the same range as desktop computers offering the same power.

Portable computers in larger packages are known as *transportables* or as *luggables*. Though these machines can be carried around, they comprise a heavy piece of luggage in their own right, rather than a small item to be slipped into a briefcase. Typical weights are up to 30 lb. Some transportables are around the size of a briefcase; others are around the size, and weight, of a large portable sewing machine.

Compaq pioneered the luggable concept for IBM PC-compatible computers (though there were earlier, less powerful machines) with essentially the same features as IBM's machine in a portable package. The system circuitry was much the same size, but instead of a full-sized video monitor, the Compaq had a small screen at one end of the system box, next to the inbuilt disc drives, over which the keyboard clipped to form a lid. More recent Compaq models have narrowed the gap between the luggable and the laptop portable computers. The Portable III, for instance, has come down in size to around that of a large ghetto blaster, and in weight to 20 lb; it has a full-width gas plasma screen, and high capacity hard and floppy disc drives. It is not possible to use a machine like this on your lap, but it can be set down on a table, the lid folded down, and used just like a desktop computer. Many Compaqs are indeed used regularly in office environments, but even on the newer models the small screen size makes working with this kind of computer for several hours each day a rather wearisome prospect.

The Home Computer

In the early 1980s, the UK saw an explosion in the sales of 'home computers'. Some of these were really no more than video games machines, programmable as an afterthought, if at all. Others were intended mainly for educational purposes, and others still were genuinely general-purpose machines.

General purpose — but what purpose? It was an era in which every up-to-date family seemed to think that it should have a computer, and then found itself asking, what for? Often, no good answers came to mind, and the computer was thrust to the back of a cupboard.

Computer games have evolved into an art form of their own, and the ingenuity that has gone into pushing the capabilities of a very limited home computer like the Sinclair Spectrum to (and, it often seems, beyond) its limits is amazing. But few adults enjoy playing games on a computer more than very occasionally, and the average child has a short attention span when it comes to games and crazes. Even when children do become strongly attached to computer game-playing, there are worrying implications. When children play games with other children, less than half the time is spent on actually playing the game: the rest is spent negotiating rules and (in an informal way) practising the arts of social behaviour: learning how to co-operate with other people, adapting one's performance so that one's companions will win at least occasionally, and so on. When a solitary child plays a computer game, in contrast, the skill of the game is everything. There is mental stimulation in working out how best to play; the child gets practise in physical co-ordination from fast-moving action games. Many children acquire a burning desire to beat the machine, or their own previous top score. But there is no human contact, no opportunity for negotiating or social skills practice.

It is only a short step from the game-crazed child to the hacker: the adolescent or adult programmer who retreats from human contact into an all-absorbing relationship with the machine. Many hackers show remarkable technical ingenuity but, for all that, they are often not particularly good programmers, because their grasp of end-user requirements tends to be limited. Obsessive hackers are not well-adjusted, rounded human beings, and most parents do not wish to see their children take this route through life. Intelligent interest in the technology is fine; but the technology should be there to *aid* people in their interactions, not to replace human–human interaction with its poverty-stricken human–machine equivalent.

Many software houses have made strenuous efforts to extend the home computer to serious, business-type applications: to word processing, financial budgeting, cheque-book balancing, programs that keep track of share portfolios, and so on. These endeavours initially had only limited success, though their prospects have been improved with the emergence of new generations of 'home' computers whose capabilities equal and often exceed those of the professional personal computers of only a few years ago. Often today the only difference in the home-oriented machines and their business-oriented counterparts is that the home machines have better provision of colour graphics facilities and of game-oriented peripherals such as joysticks and light pens, and the business machines have better secondary storage capability.

Word processing has been by far the most successful of the 'serious' home computer applications, and many individuals have doubtless justified the purchase of a home computer primarily on this basis. The other applications have rarely caught on, on a large scale. Some of the early household financial budgeting and cheque-book reconciliating programs were cumbersome and unreliable, and convinced those that did try them that pen and paper were still by far the most effective way of keeping track of personal finances; and some of the early home computer systems, with poor quality screens and cassette tape secondary storage, were so difficult to use as to render the whole prospect unappealing. Other attempts to widen the appeal of the micro included such diverse projects as biorhythm forecasting and computerised cookbooks, but these all seemed to be scraping the bottom of a very small, very empty barrel. Those who bought a home computer without any clear idea in advance of what they would use it for often found the answer to be 'nothing'.

Today the general-purpose home computer bubble has burst. The home computer hasn't claimed a permanent position in most households, as the television did so effortlessly. People have more microprocessors than ever before in their homes, but they are almost invariably special-purpose machines, even when they do the kind of tasks that it was once suggested might be carried out by general-purpose home computers. There has been a boom, for example, in intelligent telephones and telephone-answering machines: but these computer-like devices are not programmable, nor general-purpose.

One of the revelations of the home computer era, indeed, is that most people simply are not interested in programming home computers for themselves. No matter if they (or their children) learn programming at school, no matter if they could conceivably program the computer to perform useful tasks in under an hour, they simply do not want to sit down with a pile of manuals and work out the necessary coding. Although it's a theoretical advantage of general-purpose machines that they are programmable, in practice it's an advantage to end-users only if the programs are presented to them, ready written and easily usable. New models of 'home' computers are still being launched, though in fewer numbers than in the boom years of the early eighties; yet, even now, there seems to be a difficulty for manufacturers in clarifying their intended applications, and much the same mishmash of programs are still being produced.

In our experience, the successful home computers users are those who focus their use of the machine around one or more regular, 'base' applications which turn it into a 'home office' resource for daily use, with a permanent position in a corner of the living room or on a study desk. Word processing is certainly one such application. Regular educational use, regular use for financial planning, regular use to keep the records and perform the administration of a club — for all these, recourse to the computer may be semi-automatic; and they can provide a pivot around which other applications may aggregate. In a slightly different context, the French Télétel system (discussed in Chapter 10) has proved the same point, by establishing *its* regular use round its function as a replacement telephone directory.

We can anticipate today many more 'base' applications which may eventually make a general-purpose home computer an essential part of every up-to-date home in the 1990s and beyond. Some such applications look towards the era of domotics (discussed above), when many or all of the microprocessor-controlled operations in a modern home will be integrated, and a general-purpose home computer will act as a co-ordinator and overall controller of a network embracing dishwashers, washing machines, home-security systems and so on. More modest proposals along the same lines envisage the computer forming the heart of an electronics entertainment complex. But neither of these are commonplace today, and past experience suggests that the practical difficulties of fitting new integrated systems into old, discretely designed houses may make it more difficult than was once imagined to realise them tomorrow.

Perhaps more promising is the prospect of the home computer acting as an essential entry-point into a public information exchange network comprising electronic mail, public databases and the like. We discuss some of the present-day manifestations of this type of system, including home banking and videotext, in Chapter 10.

Computers in Education

Many schools in the UK acquired microcomputers in the early to mid-1980s, partly through government funding and partly through supplementary funds raised via parent–teacher associations and the like. The Department of Education and Science's original initiative coincided with the BBC's short television series, *The Computer Programme*; Acorn's BBC computers, introduced and featured heavily in that series, were one of the two ranges of machine approved for use in schools. (The other range, Research Machines' 380Z and subsequent computers, received much lower take-up.) The BBC computers were ingeniously designed machines, with (for their era) excellent capabilities for controlling, and inputting data from, peripheral devices including not only disc drives but sensors, oscillators, loudspeakers and so on. They have proved to be reliable and long-lived when compared with home computers of the same era such as the Sinclair Spectrum and the Commodore 64, and have stood up well, on the whole, to the challenge of years of hard use by sometimes rough-handed schoolchildren. But their near-monopoly position in the British educational market led to serious problems.

In an era when the prices of other home micros were dropping yearly, Acorn were able to maintain the prices of the BBC machines at a disturbingly high level, and, since school budgets were extremely tight, this led to severe restrictions in the number of machines bought. Acorn were slow in bringing out updated models in the same range, and when peripheral and extension devices, networks, etc. did eventually appear (sometimes years after they were promised) they too tended to be overpriced. It was also unfortunate that Acorn were unsuccessful, by and large, in their attempts to penetrate overseas educational markets, particularly in the United States. Though the large user base of BBC machines in UK schools and colleges made of them an effective 'standard' of their own, this was not the standard which the rest of the world was following, and neither was it a standard which received any recognition in British commercial circles. Children who learned to program the BBC Micro at school, in its very idiosyncratic dialect of Basic, had to learn different languages and different machine architectures, when they made the transition to the commercial world.

Perhaps even more fundamental, though, was the difficulty for educational authorities in coming to terms with the realities of the economics of computer use. A computer is not a one-off purchase which can effectively be used all on its own, just as it comes out of the box. It requires to be supported by peripheral devices such as disc drives and printers, and most particularly it needs software, either bought in or written by trained programmers. Frequently school computer budgets barely stretched to the machine itself. Sometimes a disc drive was not provided; often a printer was not; and only a very limited selection of software was made available. The Department of Education and Science has made some nods towards training teachers in micro usage, but all too often this has amounted to no more than a short initiation course. Special computer staff have rarely been appointed, and teachers with existing wide responsibilities generally do not have the time, the inclination or the expertise required to write educational programs from scratch. In many schools, too, there has been uncertainty as to what the computer is to be used *for*. Is it to be used for teaching programming and technology, or is it to be a more general computer-aided learning resource? Ideally, schools would have a plentiful supply of computers for both these purposes, but when a handful (at most) of machines are available for several hundred pupils to share, the opportunities for hands-on experience are either minimal or more often zero.

In theory, the prospects are brighter. Teaching machines initially gained a poor reputation and the inflexible mechanical devices that were developed twenty or thirty years ago had little to recommend them. But today's generation of computer-aided learning systems are sophisticated and effective tools, often with interfaces to recorded audio and video material, and with the capability to adapt the pace of learning to the individual student's capabilities.

For state schools, though, the immediate prospects are not bright. The BBC Micro technology has now reached the end of its natural lifespan. Though an updated machine has been launched, there appear to be no initiatives in sight for the replacement of the original machines with either this or any other contemporary micro. In an era in which 16-bit micros are the norm, and 32-bit ones are appearing daily, British schools continue to soldier on with pathetically few 8-bit machines with tiny internal memories and (by today's standards) very limited capabilities. Even these cannot be expected to last for much longer, and it is not proper to expect teachers to spend their time scouring the second-hand columns for machines they can cannibalise to keep their own functioning. Schoolbooks may last for twenty years, but microcomputers do not. Alas, this lesson has not yet been learned by Britain's educational bureaucracy.

Part IV

THE CONVERGENT TECHNOLOGIES

As we saw in Part III, microelectronics is having a major impact on many products and processes, and none more so than the information processing industry itself. This new industry is arising out of the convergence of three technologies — traditional computer data processing, especially in the development of distributed data processing; telecommunications; and office products and services. All three industries are converging to serve a common market — that of information processing. The computer companies are marketing ever cheaper products, yet with higher end-user performance, distributing processing power to the end-user. The telecommunications companies have discovered that future methods of transmission are more akin to how computers talk to each other than how telephone systems have previously operated. And the office products suppliers are being overtaken by a rash of 'intelligent' devices, much as the instrument makers have already been subjected to.

9

Distributed Data Processing

Information Processing Industry

The major operations involved in processing information are its
generation or capture, storage, subsequent retrieval, processing, transmission and display. The computer companies have long been engaged in
all of these operations on data, and find it logical to extend into the same
activities for other information media — voice, video, text and facsimile,
particularly as these media are increasingly digitised. However, the
activities of the computer companies in their existing markets, especially
the present promotion of the distributed processing concept, are
increasingly involving them with telecommunications.

The market for telecommunications services in general is rising rapidly
in all industrialised countries (and in many of the less-developed ones,
too), in all of which the services have traditionally been provided by a
publicly owned or regulated corporation. The telecommunications
companies are well aware of the expansion in interests of the computer
companies and are generally fighting back by moving into wider markets
of information handling equipment to hang on to their networks. At the
same time the office equipment manufacturers, particularly those of
typewriters and copiers, are being forced to increase the functionality of
their products to compete with the alternative approaches being offered
by the computer companies.

The point about this *convergence* is that although Intel and Motorola
may produce chips that end up performing control functions in cars or
washing machines, we don't expect them to set up in competition with
Ford or Hoover. However, in information processing, companies such as
IBM, AT&T and Xerox are all invading each other's territories, and even

complete outsiders such as General Motors have entered the field. One reason is that in the case of the car or washing machine the incorporation of microelectronics doesn't change the fundamental purpose of the product — it simply improves its all-round performance and cost-effectiveness.

But information processing is in a sense a new market which until now has not been approached in a coherent and systematic manner. The incorporation of microelectronics is resulting in products whose performance has changed so much that they can be regarded as a completely new product. A computer-controlled, electronic telephone exchange or a laser-printing, computer-driven copying machine with telecommunications capabilities are very different products for their users, compared to their predecessors.

Approaches to DDP

The term 'distributed data processing' (ddp) does not have a formally agreed meaning: it is a concept, rather than a set of equipment. It has been used to describe systems as diverse as:

Hundreds, in some cases even thousands, of terminals connected to mainframe computers in a strict hierarchy, where the mainframe is master and the terminals are slaves. This produces a 'star' configuration, as seen in Figure 9.1(a), and is the situation into which the dp configurations in many large organisations have evolved.

A number of minicomputers linked together in a network, as equals, with slave terminals linked to each mini. Each machine may perform the same function (e.g. as order-entry systems in different sales regions) or they may be specialised (e.g. one for order-entry, one for manufacturing control, one for general accounting, etc.). Figure 9.1(b) illustrates this general network type.

A network of personal computers, sharing resources such as discs and printers, and perhaps linked to a more powerful central computer facility. Figure 9.1(c) illustrates a type of local area network (a topic we discuss in more detail in Chapter 10).

The installation of stand-alone personal computers on managers' or professionals' desks. This *fragmented* approach is illustrated in Figure 9.1(d).

The only common feature of these disparate systems is the fact that the computing resources they comprise are not located in a single central computer room (as was the case with earlier centralised systems), but are widely spread throughout the work-space of the organisation.

The 1970s and 1980s have seen a steady movement away from

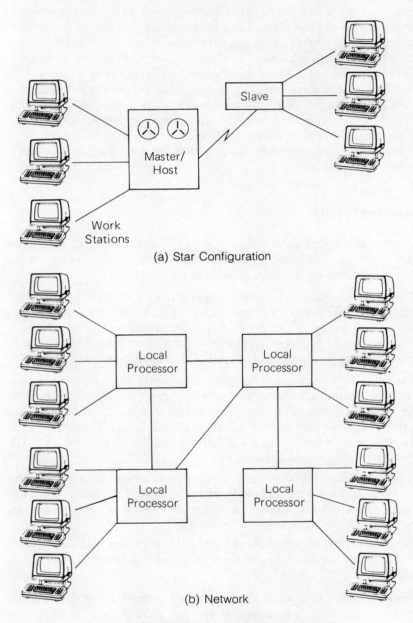

(a) Star Configuration

(b) Network

Figure 9.1 *Distributed Data Processing*

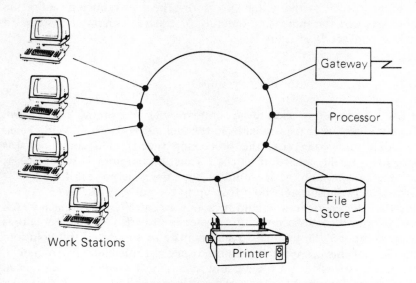

(c) Local Area Network

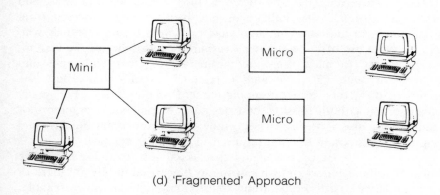

(d) 'Fragmented' Approach

Figure 9.1 (continued) *Distributed Data Processing*

centralised data processing and towards distributed systems. This movement was led by two critical pressures: the ever-reducing cost of the technology, and the increasing inability of existing computer systems to meet the real needs of users.

Cost Implications of Distributed Systems

The cost of computing used to be summarisable in a simple 'law' known as Grosch's law, after its originator in the late 1950s, Herb Grosch, which stated that the power (i.e. the processing speed) of a computer was proportional to the square of its cost. Thus, if computer B was twice as expensive as computer A, it would be four times as powerful.

Grosch's law did broadly hold true up to the early 1970s, and it is easy to see that the economics behind it favour a centralised system in which much, if not all, of the computing power is provided by one (or more) massive computer. Situational requirements also supported this solution. Computers of this era typically required special controlled environments, which were expensive to produce and maintain; it made sense to put all the computer equipment in one place. They required trained operators and programmers, and these too were most cost-effectively maintained as a centralised unit. The reliability of mainframes was open to question, and maintenance staff also operated most efficiently on centralised systems.

Things changed, however, with the dramatic decline in the cost of computing equipment. Whether or not Grosch's law is true today is almost irrelevant, since the hardware cost per transaction is minimal in any case. The vital cost statistics are those involving the time and convenience of all the individuals involved in the process, from programmers to full-time computer operators, and to professionals who need to make use of the computer's resources. Flexibility of the system, and its ability to meet users' requirements, together with ease and accuracy of entering data and obtaining output — these are the predominant factors in determining system shape today. For many applications it is both possible and desirable to put microcomputers or terminals on users' desks, where they can enter data quickly and accurately, and obtain it when required in the same manner.

Data entry is no longer a highly specialised job involving expensive punched-card machinery; now it can simply be carried out by any clerk or professional with basic keyboarding skills. Computers are more reliable, and more easily maintained when they do go wrong: modern circuit cards can be slotted out and replaced in minutes. Most of today's computers do not require controlled environments, but can operate satisfactorily on open office desks, in factories, and any other reasonably friendly environment. And they are relatively small machines, so they do not intrude unduly on other office operations. All of these factors spell the end of the dominance of the central computer room. Moreover, for IBM they pose a great strategic problem: whereas it earns most from selling large-scale computers, its customers gain most from buying small-scale ones.

User Requirements

Throughout the 1970s many organisations were faced with increased disillusionment with, and resistance to, the centralised dp operation, especially in those cases where their organisational structure in other respects was not centralised. Several reasons were suggested for this, of which the most important were:

   stagnation or deterioration in the level of service provided, largely because of the inability of a centralised dp facility to be all things to a diverse group of users;

   having to accept a general, inadequate and inappropriate level of service with little direct control, influence or priority selection, rather than a service tailored to each user's specific requirements.

In some cases, it is certainly true that centralised dp began to provide a worsening response. A shared system may be too busy for the really large jobs, too slow for interactive work, and in general too unresponsive to the differing priorities between jobs. There is some evidence, too, that in a complex shared system, interruptions in service are more frequent than in a dedicated environment.

These difficulties are the result of system complexity, rather than human unwillingness to oblige. With the maturing of dp departments, many of which had been in existence for ten or even twenty years, there often grew up, also, an increasing rigidity and inflexibility of procedures. Computer centre staff, as well as the machine itself, sometimes found it hard to respond flexibly to urgent requirements or to adapt priorities so as to satisfy all users. The operating system software has to try to be all things to all users, and to interleave a large assortment of differing demands for computing power and access to data. Operating systems of suitable size and complexity are difficult to program, and can be prone to errors. As the system size grows, so the operating system software consumes an increasing proportion of machine resources, and less computing power and memory is left free for end-users.

The difficulties of centralised data processing were also increased by the steady transition from batch processing to on-line processing. When central dp computers operated in a batch mode, work could be scheduled carefully and the load spread out over the available time. However, when on-line working was introduced this was no longer possible. For example, if a company made stock records available for enquiry say between 10–12 a.m. and 2–4 p.m., there would be a heavy upturn in workload between those times, over which dp management would have little or no control. The on-line requirements often increased the required computer power quite disproportionately to the amount of work being done. In addition, many early mainframes were unsuitable for this mode of operation, and departments using such equipment were unable to meet the demand for more direct interaction.

The reliability of data entry was a perennial problem with centralised systems. In the 1960s and early 1970s, data capture was a two-stage process: first the input data was recorded (usually by hand) on special forms, and then it was keyed from the forms on to punched cards or paper tape. Though punching was a tedious task, it was possible to keep the errors introduced at the punching stage to an acceptable level by introducing a verification stage: all data were punched twice, and the two entries checked to ensure that they matched.

A more intransigent problem arose over the recording stage. Data preparation personnel were separated from the originators of the data, and they could have little knowledge of what data were reasonable or sensible. Misreading of the input forms could cause them to key in nonsensical data, *and* to verify them correctly. This was the cause of many of the horror stories, in which this era abounded, about almost unbelievable computer-generated mistakes.

Distributed data processing means that the data capture process is taken to the originator of the data. Very often this means that recording and transcription can be combined into one process: the originator keys in the data him/herself. (Indeed, in many modern systems keying-in is dispensed with entirely, and the data are read automatically, e.g. from a bar-code reader.) The entire transaction may be processed before more data are input, and errors can be detected at this stage (for example, the computer can point out non-existent or incorrect customer numbers) and corrected with the minimum of delay or inconvenience, since the original information is still to hand. The originator is also relatively secure from making 'silly' mistakes and entering unreasonable data simply out of ignorance of its true significance.

Finally, there is the question of *ownership*, both of data and of processing resources, and in particular where scheduling and priority setting are concerned. As we have discussed above, central dp became alienated from many of its users. This is an organisational problem more than anything else. Distributed data processing is a way of allowing users to regain the feeling of ownership of their data processing capacity. This is a two-edged sword as it forces the users to become directly involved in the dp process, often for the first time.

Decentralised versus Distributed Data Processing

It is important to distinguish between distributed, or dispersed, data processing and decentralised data processing. In the former, only the hardware need be widely spread; in the latter, responsibility for its use, too, is dispersed among user departments.

With decentralised dp, responsibility for planning, implementing and using systems lies with the user, generally on a departmental basis. Where an organisation retains a central data processing department, its role is reduced to a consultancy one, at least as far as the decentralised services are concerned. The advantage of this approach is that users are responsible for taking stock of their own requirements and for acquiring systems that meet them adequately. There is no external systems analyst who can be blamed for misunderstanding what their work really involves! Where there is keen user involvement, this approach can lead to well-designed systems of which the owners make very full use.

There is a disadvantage, naturally, when users are not highly motivated to use computing resources, and when they are insufficiently guided towards suitable solutions. Another major disadvantage of this approach is that there is likely to be incompatibility between the different processing units selected by different departments, or different standards for data processing or storage procedures, or communications capabilities. In some organisations this may not be a problem, but in others it certainly has caused difficulties.

The classic early experiment in free-for-all distributed computing was that of Citibank, who decided in the mid-1970s to decentralise their dp operation in what was called 'Project Paradise'. The idea was to 'let the flowers grow': most central dp personnel were transferred to user departments, and everyone went their own way. Certainly some remarkable developments took place, with divisions having special terminals and even special minicomputers built for them. But in the end the lack of compatibility between divisions became intolerable, and central dp was reformed to tie all the parts back together again. Certainly as a result of this project, the Citibank users of this era were probably more knowledgeable and motivated about dp than were those in any comparable organisation. The missing ingredient, which was subsequently imposed, was a network which could link the different parts together, enforcing some common standards, and was maintained by the central dp department.

Distributed dp, in contrast, implies that overall responsibility for the system remains with a central department, whose role may vary from merely defining standards and authorising types of system, to having total responsibility for system development and implementation.

The precise relationship between central dp and its users normally reflects both the type of organisation and its past history of dp-user relations. Centrally managed organisations are unlikely to relinquish much control, but they do accept that it is sensible to put the processing capability where it is required. However, organisations with weak central management, or where a central department has historically failed to deliver appropriate dp systems to user management, can find ddp taking over very rapidly. This can become akin to a guerilla war, in which the user's new-found weapon is the personal computer, and the central department is left forlornly in charge of obsolete and under-used mainframe equipment.

Different computer suppliers espouse different philosophies for ddp. Most mainframe manufacturers, following IBM's lead, have favoured a large central 'host' machine with a number of intelligent satellites all under its control. On the other hand the minicomputer manufacturers favour networks of machines capable of communicating with each other as equals. This latter approach has become increasingly attractive now that internal and external networks are more flexible and easy to use. (We discuss networks in Chapter 10.) Manufacturers have historically laid much stress on the compatibility of all equipment, and on the advantages of keeping to a single manufacturer's range. Up until recently this argument held much strength, and it still has many advantages — for example, from a servicing viewpoint. The latest networks are more capable than their predecessors of linking computers from different manufacturers, with different internal operating systems, but even today compatibility and networking is a thorny subject which can lead unwary users into considerable difficulties.

It is always difficult to integrate ddp with the need for authoritative, generally available company data — for example, on a company's overall stock position. Systems must be planned carefully to ensure that all files, central as well as local, are updated methodically, and that data consistency is maintained throughout the system.

One approach, for instance, is the 'pseudo real-time' system. Consider a distribution company with a central warehouse. If each distribution outlet has its own computer or terminal which maintains data on the current stock position, then any update to the local data will need to be reflected to all the other outlets. Pseudo real-time systems achieve this on a daily basis. During the day, only the local figures are updated; overnight the data is transmitted to a central machine which collates the information from each outlet and sends out the new stock figures in time for the next day's work. Each terminal appears to be presenting current information, but in practice its data becomes increasingly inaccurate as the day proceeds. Whether this method is acceptable — and how often updating is carried out — naturally depends on the rate of stock turnover and the perishability of stock.

Alternatively, if the distribution company has regional warehouses which serve specific outlets with little or no overlap, then the data on stock availability in a particular warehouse can be maintained in a machine at that location. Communication between machines may be necessary only for inter-depot transfers and for consolidating data on stock positions and movements. However, this will involve greater communications cost (i.e. between the outlets and the warehouse). The basic point is that the concept of distributed data processing does not impose solutions: it is a flexible concept, within which each organisation can come to its own solutions.

Terminals

Progress in terminals in the 1970s was spectacular in two ways: in price reduction, and in the ever-widening range of 'intelligent' devices capable of being attached to a computer through some standard interface. Steady improvements have also been made throughout the 1980s, and now terminal technology has reached a very sophisticated stage.

The essential characteristic of a terminal is that, unlike a micro-computer, its computing power is not self-contained: it is designed to receive data from, and send data to, a central computer which processes that data in various ways. Originally, the standard terminal was an unintelligent 'KSR' (keyboard send and receive) device which did no more than this, but with the increasing cheapness of microprocessing power, there has been a steady trend towards *intelligent terminals*, with their own microprocessors, and at least limited capability to process data locally. In effect, the trend is away from terminals as such, and towards *work-stations* which combine the functions of terminal and of micro-computer. Typical of these devices are the engineering/technical work-stations developed to provide all-purpose computing power to technically oriented professionals. Today's devices are generally built around 32-bit microprocessors, running an operating system such as UNIX which can handle both their communications with the host and locally run applications. They have high-resolution graphic screens, often with colour, and sizeable amounts of local secondary storage — often up to 100 MBytes on disc. Prices for these high-specification work-stations are in the region of £5,000 to £15,000.

As well as the general-purpose microcomputer/terminal, many specialist devices are in widespread use today. Large organisations frequently find it economic to develop their own devices to suit their own specific applications. Retail point-of-sale terminals, sophisticated microprocessor-controlled cash registers, are a case in point. Today these terminals can read data on purchases directly from bar codes (with supplementary keypad entry where necessary), and print out bills with full itemised descriptions. They can communicate data on sales directly to computers which control stock ordering and accounting, and many can read data directly from credit cards, and communicate with electronic credit systems. Fully automatic bank teller machines, not only dispensing cash but also providing statements and other basic banking functions, are another example, as are airline ticket issuing machines.

Though the image of a terminal is still one of a keyboard and a screen, many other input and output media are employed today. Plotters are widespread, as are screens with full colour graphic capability. Voice output and input are both realities, though on a relatively restricted scale. Systems can read typescript, and some can even read handwriting.

10

Telecommunications

A significant part of the developments in microelectronics has been fostered by the needs of the telecommunications industry (indeed, the original invention of the transistor was made in a Bell laboratory). Two things in particular have driven these developments — the needs of the military for smallness, reliability and portability — and the requirements of the space program and satellite-based communications systems, where obviously small size and reliability are at a premium.

For many years the telecommunications equipment manufacturers have been major customers of the electronics industry — and more recently of the semiconductor industry. However, three major developments in the way the telecommunications systems of the world work will radically change the relationships between the telephone companies (and their suppliers), the present computer companies, and the semiconductor companies. These are:

the movement from analogue to digital transmission switching systems;

the adoption of new, high capacity transmission technologies, such as fibre-optic cable and microwave satellite links;

the development of new transmission protocols to improve the utilisation of the network.

Before discussing each of these developments in detail, it will be useful to review the basic characteristics of any telecommunications network.

A Telecommunications Network

It is perhaps important to realise and appreciate the scale and complexity of the world's telecommunications networks — networks which enable virtually all of the subscribers to the telephone system in the industrialised countries to dial a call directly to any other subscriber worldwide, with a very high probability of success! In many ways the world's telecommunications networks are the most complex creations of industrialised society, both technically and organisationally. A simplified diagram of such a network is illustrated in Figure 10.1.

The subscriber is connected over what is termed a *local loop* to a local telephone exchange; a local area call will in general go no further than this and be routed to the called subscriber. A business subscriber will almost certainly have his own 'in-house' local exchange, a Private Automatic Branch Exchange (PABX), which performs the functions of a local exchange for calls within a building or site, and will be linked to a local exchange for calls over the public network. A long-distance call will be routed via one or more trunk telephone exchanges to the local exchange of the called subscriber. To provide some sort of scale for Figure 10.1, the British Telecom network has 6,800 exchanges supplying 20.4 million exchange connections, and dealing with around 22,000 million individual calls each year.

Some of the basic problems seen to some degree or other in the present telecommunications networks are:

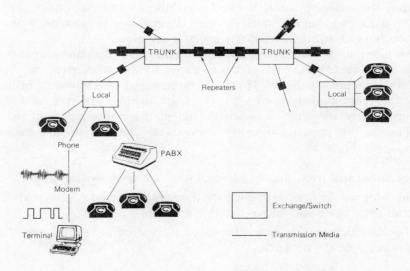

Figure 10.1 *Components of a Telecom Network*

the transmission quality is often poor, which is not of great significance for voice traffic, but is so for computer-related traffic;

the speed at which the switches in the network operate (i.e. the exchanges) is very slow;

the utilisation of the physical network is very low, since for voice traffic a subscriber rents an exclusive circuit, but doesn't use its full capacity;

the switching logic in the exchanges is fixed, so that making changes to the network is difficult;

there is no 'intelligence' in the network at the exchanges, so that provision of new facilities is difficult, and has previously meant setting up separate, duplicate networks;

the operating and maintenance costs of the present network are very high, and increasing over time.

Each of the three new developments mentioned in the introduction to this chapter addresses one or more of these problem areas, and we will now discuss each in turn.

Changing to a Digital Network

Methods of Transmitting Information

Initially, all telephone systems worked on an analogue basis. They carried only voice data, and each change in pitch of the voice transmitted was represented by the change in the frequency and amplitude of an electrical signal travelling down a wire. With the development of information technology, this basic transmission method was adapted to enable it to carry not only voice, but all kinds of data: numerical data, textual data, data on the content of visual images, and so on. This was done by converting the data, whatever it represented, into a digital pattern of 1s and 0s, or on/off states. We have already seen how decimal numbers can be converted into binary numbers made up of only two digits. Various methods are used to convert other types of information into this same basic signal pattern.

However, the telecommunications system did not carry patterns of 1s and 0s, but rather electrical signals varying in an analogue way. Therefore it was necessary to devise a code method by which the digital 1s and 0s, on-bits and off-bits, could be represented by fluctuations in an analogue wavelength. There are a number of such methods in use today. Which one is used in any particular circumstance depends on the band-width of the communications channel, the purposes for which it is being used, and of course the choices made by the system designers.

The device which converts digital data into analogue signals for onward transmission is known as a *modem* (a modulator/demodulator).

Analogue transmission does, however, have a serious drawback. As it is passed through the telephone network, the signal slowly decreases in strength, so that it has to be passed through several repeaters, each of which amplifies it. Unfortunately any 'noise' that enters the system is also amplified, along with the original message. The result is that there is a deterioration in the message quality, particularly if the message is being sent a long distance, through many repeaters. For voice communication this is not too serious: it is usually possible to infer the content of the message even if there is a sizeable amount of noise affecting it. However, in the case of other types of message, noise becomes a much more serious problem. Extensive error checking has to be incorporated into such transmission systems in order to try to negate its impact.

The alternative solution is to transmit all data not in analogue form but in binary digital form: and the modern trend has been towards doing just this. Though the onward transmission still tends to have a wave-form (whether it is sent by radio waves transmitted through the air, or by fluctuating electric current sent through cables, or by some newer method such as those we discuss later in the chapter), the data encapsulated in the wave fluctuations are coded and interpreted not in a continuously varying way but in a discrete, digital way: for example, in a pattern of on/off electrical pulses.

In a digital transmission system, the amplitude of the voice signal is sampled at (very) frequent intervals and measured as a numerical quantity (Figure 10.2). Similarly, other media for transmission such as text or images can also be coded numerically, and any messages emanating directly from a computer system will, in general, already be in binary-coded form. Thus in a digital system all the material being transmitted is numeric, and can be expressed as a sequence of binary digits.

This system is much more resistant to noise. The repeaters in a digital system do not amplify the noise along with the signal. Instead they recreate the pattern of 1s and 0s, and effectively retransmit it with renewed precision. Only if the data have deteriorated to such an extent that it simply is not possible for the system to tell whether a 1 or a 0 is being sent do error problems creep in. To ensure that any mistransmissions of this nature are detected, extra digits are added to each message as it is transmitted, enabling a check on the message accuracy to be made at the receiving end. (There are a number of message-sending protocols which use different patterns of 'check' bits.)

'Encryption' (scrambling) of an analogue signal is difficult, but with a digital signal it is much easier, and if controlled by a computer it is

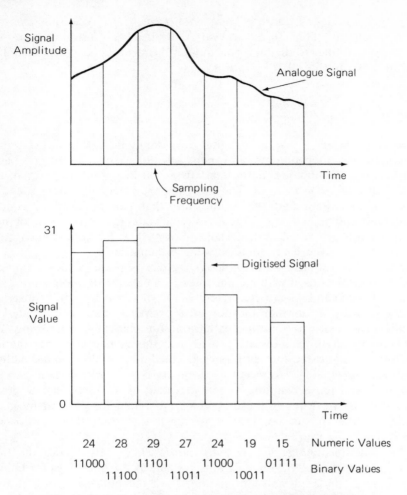

Figure 10.2 *Converting Analogue Signals to Digital Form*

potentially foolproof. Thus, in a digital system, messages may be transmitted with total accuracy and, when necessary, with near total security.

Digital systems are well suited to the transmission of data from computer to computer. Conversely, computers are well suited to the control of digital systems, since their prime activity is to process binary-coded information.

The same types of cables can be used for both analogue and digital transmission, though there have been substantial advances in transmission equipment which we shall consider shortly. But the capability of the cable (or other medium) to carry messages is exploited in a different way, so analogue and digital transmission cannot occur at the same time over the same stretch of cable. In recent years there has been a slow change-over of telephone lines to digital form, though this process is not yet complete in the UK (and in other countries).

Developments in Exchanges

Exchanges used to control digital telecommunications, based round microelectronic technology, have many advantages over exchanges based on analogue technology, quite apart from the increased accuracy of the digital transmission method. The most important are the sheer speed of switching possible, and the intelligence that can be used to control switching and line usage. This enables advantage to be taken of new transmission protocols, and, perhaps above all, it facilitates much more efficient use of the trunk lines between exchanges.

The full advantage of the new technology is perhaps most apparent today in PABXs used within companies. If a called extension is engaged, the exchange can be instructed to call back when it is free; if a subscriber is temporarily in another location, the exchange can be instructed to transfer all calls to another extension automatically; answering and message-handling facilities are provided at the exchange, rather than at each individual extension; and there are facilities for abbreviated dialling and repeat dialling. Any form of binary-coded information can be handled, and full accounting can be provided on an individual or group extension basis. Already these facilities are taken for granted by many users, so that it can be difficult to recall that they simply were not available a few years ago.

The high-technology interface to the customer often hides the fact, though, that the telecommunications system, as a whole, lags far behind this level in updating and automation. Push the buttons on a high-tech intelligent telephone today, and you can often hear the clicks (and have to suffer the wait) while an electro-mechanical public exchange sets about connecting your line. The full benefit of the new generation of technology will only be apparent when the public switched network is fully digital, and all the main trunk and local exchanges have been replaced by new-generation technology.

Virtually all the telephone companies in the world (usually referred to as the PTTs — Post, Telephone and Telegraph authorities) plan to convert their exchanges to fully digital operation before the end of this century, and with many the process is now well under way. One of the problems facing PTTs in the industrialised countries is that they already have a large complex analogue network in place, and to change over to digital operation takes enormous physical and financial resources, yet the pressure from customers for an improved service is growing inexorably, so that plans for a gradual changeover, lasting until the end of the century, are under constant pressure.

The UK Digital Network

Many old-style telephone exchanges in the UK were based on an electro-mechanical switching technology known as Strowger, after its inventor: an undertaker in the American Midwest at the end of the last century, whose business was located in a small town. The wife of his major competitor operated the local telephone exchange, and Strowger believed that he was losing business because of this, so he designed and built his own automatic exchange. This type of equipment provided the basis of the world's telephone system for the first half of the twentieth century.

Another electro-mechanical system, known as Crossbar, was developed and installed in some European countries after the Second World War, but only in a few exchanges in the UK. Development efforts in the 1950s and 1960s were focused on analogue electronic exchanges, but with little practical success. Development took much longer than anticipated, and eventually these exchanges (known as TXE) were overtaken by other developments.

Largely because of the British effort that went into developing analogue electronic exchanges, the UK missed out on the initial move to digital transmission. Another factor was the situation in the UK in which several companies manufactured equipment to Post Office (as it then was) specifications, which in some instances proved to be too idiosyncratic to enhance export opportunities and tended to lag behind technological advances. Even when digital telecommunications had been finally recognised as the coming development, as late as 1984, British Telecom was ordering more technically obsolete TXE4 analogue exchanges to replace worn-out Strowger equipment. However, the digital System X (a joint effort by GEC, STC and Plessey, to British Telecom specifications) is now available, though its development has been dogged by problems.

Figure 10.3 shows the exchanges in operation on the British Telecom network at the end of the year 1984/5. Though digital exchanges have been introduced steadily from this date, it is apparent that even in the mid-eighties Britain was operating with a fundamentally analogue telecommunications network. British Telecom's aim has been to have 5 million customers connected to System X equipment by 1990. In order to speed up the digitalisation programme, a supplementary system (System Y) developed by Thorn Ericsson, was also selected; it has been delivered and installed from 1986 onwards.

	Local	Trunk	International
Strowger	3,564	325	–
Crossbar	599	121	5
TXE	2,121	–	–
Digital	78	5	1
Total	6,362	451	6

Figure 10.3 *Exchange Types used by British Telecom (end-1984/5)*

The pressure on British Telecom has been increased by the relaxing of its monopoly position, and the competition it receives from Mercury (now a subsidiary of Cable and Wireless) on selected business-oriented services. Mercury began commissioning their largely microwave and optical fibre network in the City of London in 1983, and it will eventually extend to most major cities, as well as interconnecting with the British Telecom network. BT itself has designed the CFN, or City Fibre Network, at a cost of £70 million, to compete with Mercury in the City. This, too, will be based on fibre optics, and will contain computer-controlled multiplexers and switching nodes — the high technology described in this chapter.

In practice, the introduction of digital transmission over the network and of System X and other digital exchanges has to proceed roughly in parallel. Ultimately, one is of little benefit without the other. British Telecom has already converted parts of the trunk network to digital operation: for example, the terrestrial microwave links carry digital signals, as we describe shortly, and there is now over 60,000 km. of fibre-optic cable (designed to carry digital signals) installed. First, trunk exchanges are being converted to System X, and then local exchanges in the major conurbations. BT not unnaturally has chosen to bring the advantages of the digital network first to business customers, who are in a position to make use of it and are willing to pay for additional services.

Transmission Equipment

In recent years there have also been major developments in physical communications equipment — in particular, satellites, fibre optics and the use of the infra-red part of the spectrum. The basic transmission technologies available are as follows:

'twisted-pair' copper cable has been and still is the basic building block of most telecommunications networks. Almost all local loops (i.e. your

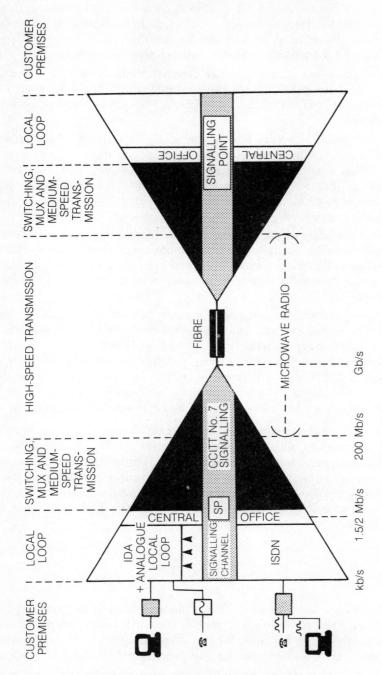

Figure 10.4 *The Emerging Digital Network*

telephone's connection to the local exchange) use this technology, and so do many local area networks. Unless quite sophisticated transmission protocols are used, its transmission capacity is very low. However, it is a cheap, commonly available, well-understood technology.

co-axial cable has a much higher capacity than twisted-pair, and is widely used for video signals (for example, the cable from your TV aerial to the set). Again, it is a cheap, available, well-understood technology.

fibre-optic cable is a very fine strand of highly reflective glass, down which pulses of light are sent at high speed, representing binary information. It has high capacity, small volume, and the great advantage that very long distances (around 50 km.) can be left between repeaters. Though a new technology, fibre optics is fast becoming established.

infra-red applications are suitable when transmission is confined within a single building. Initially used in remote-control units for domestic television and hi-fi equipment, infra-red links have subsequently been used within personal computers, and may become more widely utilised in future.

microwave transmission requires a clear line of sight between the transmission points and can be subdivided into two categories: *terrestrial*, using land towers (such as the Post Office Tower in London and similar constructions elsewhere), which provide a large proportion of the trunk-link network capacity in the UK, and also provide the basis for the mobile telephone network; and *satellite*, which is now a major technology for cross-continent and cross-ocean transmission.

Of these technologies, twisted-pair and co-axial cable are already heavily used in the world's telecommunications network. The newer technologies, satellite microwave, fibre-optic cable, and infra-red have had a sizeable impact over the last few years, and are likely to have an even greater impact in future. We now discuss these, and the technology of the mobile telephone system, the major new use of terrestrial microwave, at greater length.

Satellites

Communications satellites have to be stationed in geosynchronous (that is, effectively stationary with reference to the earth) orbit, approximately 36,000 km. above the Equator. At this point, the forces tending to send the satellite out into space and the gravitational pull of the earth exactly match.

Typically, implementation of a satellite-based service involves the construction of three satellites. Two are placed into orbit very close together — one operational, one acting as an immediate standby in case of breakdown — and the third is kept as a spare on the ground.

To station a satellite in orbit is still a difficult and dangerous business. NASA and the European Space Research Agency have the capability to perform rocket launches, but these are extremely expensive, with no guarantee of success, and there is a low limit to the size of the satellite that can be boosted up in this way. It was hoped that the coming of the American Space Shuttle would replace rocket launches, with very large satellites being constructed in near-earth orbit from components transported in the Shuttle, and then boosted into geosynchronous orbit for operational purposes. However, the 1986 disaster of the Challenger Space Shuttle set a question-mark over the entire future of the shuttle programme, which has not yet been resolved.

In a satellite-based communications system the size of the earth-based unit bears an inverse relationship to that of the satellite-based unit: that is, the bigger and more powerful the satellite, the smaller and less powerful is the required earth unit. The trend towards larger satellites is likely to continue for the foreseeable future.

Satellite communication channels are admirably cheap, not least because satellites are not limited to two transmission points, as are cables, but can send and receive from many different directions. However, there are some negative factors. The satellites themselves have a relatively short design lifetime (around eight years, compared to twenty-five years for wire or optical cables). On analogue satellite channels, noise and echoes have caused problems, but this difficulty has been surmounted by the latest generation of digital satellites. Less easily overcome is the problem of a time delay. A two-way communication involves around a quarter-second delay, which is annoying, though rarely fatal; but for a message to 'bounce' between two satellites before being relayed back to earth increases the delay to a half second, which is generally reckoned to be unacceptable.

Fibre-optic Cable

In the early days of fibre-optic development, the general assumption was that satellites would in future cater for long distance intercontinental telecommunications traffic, while increases in local traffic (and inter-organisational traffic) were likely to be catered for by the increased use of terrestrial microwave systems, and by the introduction of optical fibre systems. To some extent this has proved a misjudgement of the potential of fibre-optic technology. The disadvantages outlined above have proved limiting factors to the growth of satellite communications, and for security reasons there are advantages in maintaining a rough balance between satellite and cable capacity for transatlantic communications. So we are now on the brink of seeing the first fibre-optic transatlantic telecommunications cable.

Optical fibres are finely drawn fibres of special, highly reflective glass (about one-tenth of a millimetre in diameter) through which pulses of light, representing binary data, travel. The light beam is initiated by a semiconductor laser, and controlled by microprocessor. Transmission is at the speed of light, and the fibres have immense carrying capacity. The transatlantic cable TAT-8, planned to go into service in 1988, provides a good example of the current state of the art. It will carry 40,000 voice circuits (that is, 40,000 messages can be sent simultaneously) by multiplexing (interleaving) the signals along 8,000 different channels; and yet it will only be 2.1 cm. in diameter. Compare that to the first transatlantic cable, TAT-1, put into service in 1956 and of similar size, which had only 36 voice circuits! The transmission rate of TAT-8 will be a remarkable 557 million bits per second. The signal loss using optical fibres is much less than in systems using twisted-pair copper cable. In copper cable systems, amplifiers are required every one or two kilometres, but in TAT-8 they will be spaced at intervals of around 50 km. This decreased frequency both reduces the cost of the cable (though it is still estimated to cost a hefty $335 million), and lowers the maintenance requirement.

The glass used in fibre optics is so transparent that if you could build a window 12 miles thick, it would still be as transparent as the average window-pane. Another great advantage of optical fibres is that the fibre cables can fit into existing cable conduits between exchanges; thus considerable expansion of the system is possible by replacing copper cables by optical fibres. They are also flexible — it is possible to bend them and even to tie a loose knot in them! As the information is transmitted as pulses of light, rather than pulses of electricity, 'cross-talk' (one transmission interfering with those on the adjacent cables) is no longer a problem.

One reason why adoption of fibre optics in the public network has proceeded relatively slowly is the mundane problem of damaging repaired cables. For copper cable, reconnecting broken lines is a tedious but relatively straightforward job, but in the case of optical fibre the two ends have to be aligned with an accuracy of about 0.0001 in., and then fused together. This difficult technical problem has now largely been resolved.

Mobile Phones

A generation ago, telephones were fixed-point devices, firmly wired into the telecommunications network, and it was only in the parts of the network remote from the end-user that microwave communications were employed. Today all that has changed, with the advent of mobile telephones. They can be carried in a briefcase or a pocket, and they can be used in the garden, on a car journey, or at any point where the user is within radio range though not within reach of a conventional telephone. Their usage has exploded dramatically over the past few years.

The two rival British mobile telephone services, Cellnet (jointly run by British Telecom and Securicor) and Vodaphone (run by Racal), started service in January 1985. Cellular radio (the technical concept behind mobility) works by dividing its service area (that is, the area within which calls can be made) into small sections called cells. The area covered by each cell can vary, depending upon user density: in London, for example, the cells are a little under 4 km. in diameter, while in Hong Kong they are a tiny 1.2 km. in diameter. Each cell has its own base station aerial, and the microwave link is used to connect each phone to the base station, from which the message passes into the main telecommunications system. As a user moves from one cell to another, a central computer switches his or her call from one base station area to another.

A range of radio frequencies has been allocated to cellular radio, and they are used in a pattern which ensures that no two adjacent cells use the same frequency. Each cell has a number of different frequencies, and each user is allocated a different frequency. In the current system, there are 69 frequencies to each cell, giving a maximum of 69 simultaneous users — a number which is already proving to be a limitation and causing the system operators to beg for a wider waveband within which to operate.

Infra-red

Whilst satellites and optical fibres will handle communications over longer distances, within an individual room communications and control may be undertaken by semiconductor devices using the infra-red part of the spectrum, introducing a new era of wireless. Infra-red behaves similarly to visible light: it will travel through windows, but not walls; it can be directed or pointed like a torch, or diffused throughout a room. The initial development of these devices (which are very simple by the standards of the semiconductor industry) was for the remote-control units in televisions. At present they are rapidly spreading into the toy market, and TI has recently announced an infra-red remote-control chip set for the toy manufacturers, to go with its processor chips.

Another potential application area is where communication is required with people whose precise location within a room or building is not known. For example, some theatres in London now offer a service for the hard-of-hearing whereby they can rent a set of headphones which receive a broadcast of the play, which is diffused throughout the theatre on infra-red. The advantages are that it is not necessary to run a cable to every seat as would be required with conventional headphones, and the broadcast is restricted to the body of the theatre, which would not be the case with a radio broadcast.

However, the big application, as seen by the computer and communications companies, is as the general communications medium for the office and factory floor. An infra-red diffuser in each room, connected to a central computer (or more likely to a computer-controlled digital PABX), will provide a common shared communications path for the myriad 'smart' office products which are now being introduced — word processors, intelligent copiers, cordless telephones, data-capture terminals, and so on. This will remove the need to install communications cables to each device, so that all units become portable from office to office, and the telephone will become personalised and pocket-sized — and will be extremely difficult to get away from.

An alternative approach to the same problem (i.e. handling communications between many different devices in an office environment through some common carrier system) is provided by the development of local area networks, which are discussed below.

Transmission Protocols

Transmission protocols describe the fundamental set of rules or procedures by which messages are sent over the network. Until recently, the physical network — the cables, exchanges etc. — and the logical network — the protocols — have not been clearly distinguished from each other. Until the computer era *all* information sent over the telephone system was in voice form. This is no longer true, and in the last twenty years or so we have seen the rapid development both of different logical networks, designed to optimise message-sending in different ways, and of different physical networks, meeting the physical requirements of the different types of logical network.

There is an increasing trend towards maximising the use of the physical facilities by implementing several logical networks (often in hierarchical levels) on a single physical network. Some of the developments in the form of logical networks, and especially the generic group known as *value-added networks* (VANs), are discussed later in this chapter.

The sophistication of the protocol used can have a significant impact both on the utilisation of the network and on the quality of services provided to the user.

Types of Circuit

The standard public telephone system consists of *switched voice-grade circuits*, designed primarily for transmitting telephone conversations. As noted earlier, these were originally analogue circuits, but now they are steadily being converted to digital form. Both analogue and digital voice-grade circuits can be used for non-voice traffic, though to use analogue circuits for this purpose it is necessary to convert the signals using a modem. A drawback is that when these circuits are used for data transmission they can only operate at a very slow speed.

The speed of transmissions is measured in baud, or the number of shortest pulses required to code a single character that can be transmitted in a second. (This is approximately equal to bits per second, or bps.) The larger the baud rate, the more rapidly data are sent. However, increasing the baud rate can also increase the risk of data error. The baud rate at which data can be sent along voice-grade circuits is in the region of 300 to 2,400.

Dedicated high-speed circuits are leased from PTTs and major commercial suppliers, and run between fixed points: for instance, from one part of a large organisation to another. It is over circuits such as these that large organisations have set up their own private telecommunications networks, to a certain degree independent of the public network. As the transmission quality is higher, it is possible to send data much more rapidly without incurring an unacceptable error rate: typical rates for serial data transmission (that is, for a single message) are from 5,000 to 10,000 baud.

Message-switching networks are also based on leased lines from PTTs and other major commercial carriers, and are application dependent. These are used by private message-handling systems set up for a specific purpose. For example, the SWIFT (Society for Worldwide International Financial Transactions) is an international banking system for funds transfer, owned and operated by the participating banks, using lines leased from many different national PTTs and carriers. It now has over 1,300 member banks, in sixty-one countries.

Packet-switched networks (PSNs) can be thought of as general-purpose message-switching networks. They use a software approach to increase the utilisation level of the network. These are discussed in greater detail below.

Local area networks are designed to solve the problems of communications within a particular building or site, such that each piece of information handling or processing equipment can communicate via a common network. These, too, are discussed below.

Integrated communication systems offer sophisticated message-handling and transmission features for any type of information media (e.g. voice, text, data, video or facsimile) over a single common network. These are still developing, together with the standards necessary for implementing what is now known as the ISDN (Integrated Services Digital Network). We discuss this concept in greater detail below.

Packet-switched Networks (PSNs)

On the present public-switched network, a caller essentially rents a two-way circuit for the entire duration of the call, yet for a high proportion of this time the circuit is in fact idle. This is even more true of data transmissions than of conversations.

One technique which has been developed to increase the level of circuit usage is packet-switched systems. In these, messages to be transmitted are divided into small packets of a standard size and format, transmitted through the network at high speed, then reassembled at the point of receipt. Users require what is known as a PAD (Packet Assembler/ Disassembler) to access the system. This is a software device which typically checks the user's password, converts his or her data into the correct form for transmission, reconverts messages received, and handles the necessary billing. Charges to the user of a PSN are typically based on the length of message sent, and not on the distance between the sender and the recipient, as is the usual case for sending messages over the public network.

Packet-switched systems over the public network are now available in most industrialised countries. British Telecom's Packet Switch Stream (PSS) was launched as a generally available service in 1981. It ran into some early problems largely as a result of demand exceeding available capacity and is still a minority service, but it is now being used increasingly for electronic mail purposes — that is, for sending messages from one computer to another. Because of its very different message-sending protocols, PSS cannot use the conventional telecommunications network. It has to be set up as another network, in effect, with its own controllers and switches in existing exchanges, and naturally it has been developed in big cities initially, where the demand is highest.

In Europe packet-switching systems are being offered by the PTTs themselves, but in America this market was originally opened by the creation in the early 1970s of Arpanet, a predominantly university and research laboratory-based system. The two major American systems now available, Telenet and Tymnet, lease trunk lines and satellite channels from the network providers and can be accessed from most European countries.

A standard protocol — known as X25 — for sending messages over such packet-switched networks has been agreed internationally, and almost all computer manufacturers have available software enabling their machines to communicate over networks operating under this protocol.

Local Area Networks (LANs)

Of all the information that is generated within a large organisation, it has been estimated that approximately 50 per cent is disseminated only within its originating department. Another 40 per cent is sent to other offices in the same building (making a total of 90 per cent intra-building communication) and only 10 per cent is information destined for other parts of the organisation, for suppliers or for customers.

To this type of large organisation, then, *intra*-building transmission is in many ways considerably more important than extra-building transmission. An increasing proportion of this information is generated in an electronic form. Some of it is handled via centralised data processing networks, in which a number of terminals are connected to a host computer which can act as a message-sending and receiving centre. Much information today is generated on personal computers, however, and it is very desirable for these too to be linked together so that information can be sent from one to another without needing to be converted into hard copy. The systems developed to do this are known as *local area networks*, or LANs.

The same basic technology is used in local area networks as in other, longer-distance forms of digital communication, but because of the specific size range of LANs, there are some particularly appropriate solutions.

Of course, just as a computer in one building can send data to a computer in another building by means of the public telecommunications network, so this same method can be used to link two computers in the same building. This is regularly done, but as a long-term solution it suffers from some severe shortcomings. It is an expensive solution. There is also the major problem that each computer has only a limited number of ports — that is, devices through which it can receive and send messages. Where several computers may want to exchange messages, it simply is not possible to leave the connections open between all of them all of the time: the resources are not available. When one connection has been made, then no other user can access that computer through that port; and yet the capacity of the link is rarely being used to the full by the lucky user who has been connected. Other potential users may become frustrated by finding that the lines they wish to use are repeatedly engaged.

A local area network, in contrast, links a group of computers in a permanent (or at least, semi-permanent) manner, so that it is possible for any of them to send or receive messages at any time from any of the others, just as is done with a central computer and its terminals. Indeed, the term is sometimes used to describe systems where a number of personal computers act effectively as terminals to a mainframe computer, but it is more properly used for systems where there is no 'hub' computer but rather a number of devices of which none is functionally superior.

Though we speak here of computers, it is possible to use the same systems to link various types of peripheral equipment to computers — for example, printers and secondary storage devices — so that they can be used as common resources by the entire network. These are referred to as *servers*. A standard interface is used for each device to communicate over the network, and the addition of new devices or removal of existing ones is normally a straightforward matter. A local network of this type may be self-contained, or it may have direct links to other networks of the same type, or it may have special interfaces which enable the devices on the network to communicate with other devices not on the network, using quite different telecommunications protocols such as the PSNs we discussed earlier. Figure 10.5 shows the functional units in a local area network.

Two basic architectures are used for local area networks: the *ring*, and the *bus*. The ring, as its name suggests, is a complete-circuit loop around which messages are sent in a single direction. The bus, which is broadly analogous to the data highways internal to some computer systems, is a two-ended link along which data can be sent in either direction. These can both be constrasted with the *star* architecture of a centralised system, in which the host computer (that is, the mainframe or minicomputer at the core of the system) sits at the hub of the star, and the terminals are connected not directly to each other, but only to the host.

The ring concept originated at Cambridge University (and hence is usually known as the *Cambridge Ring*). A number of commercial systems are currently available, of which perhaps the best known is IBM's token ring local area network. Probably the most widely known of the bus-type local network systems (and indeed, the best-established local network system in general) is a system known as *Ethernet*, originally developed by Xerox in the early 1970s, but appearing as a commercially available system only in 1980. Typifying the standardisation in LAN star architecture, following standards such as the IEEE 802.3, 802.4 and 802.5, is AT&T's *StarLan*.

Regardless of the network architecture, a number of different types of cabling can be used to connect the devices in the network, and an almost infinite variety of protocols can be used to control the sending of messages from one device to another.

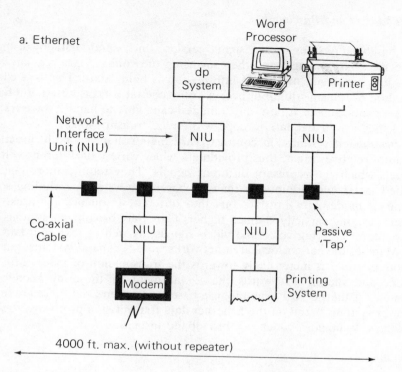

a. Ethernet

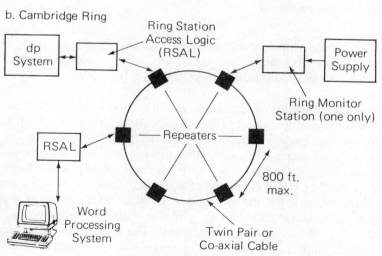

b. Cambridge Ring

Figure 10.5 *Examples of Local Area Networks*

Broadband and Baseband

A *baseband* system uses a signal carrier which sends data by using a specified base voltage, and then reversing the voltage (at a regular rate) to show when an 'on' bit of information is being sent. This is a cheap method of transmission, but because only one bit is transmitted at a time, these systems have at best only a limited capability to handle voice traffic, and they are inadequate to cope with video transmissions.

Broadband systems, in contrast, vary their voltage in both directions from a relative origin, thus providing a wider variety of different voltage levels which can represent different signals. They require more complicated interfacing equipment than do baseband systems, including some type of modem to translate bits into different frequency patterns, but their carrying capacity is much higher. Generally broadband systems are capable of carrying voice and video signals, as well as text and data.

Many of the earlier local area networks were baseband systems, but the modern trend is increasingly towards the transmission of video information, and therefore towards the replacement of these by broadband systems. Ethernet, for example, is a baseband system, but there are many newer systems based on the Ethernet data transmission protocols, such as Wang's 'Wangnet', which use broadband instead.

Message-passing Protocols

A major difficulty with LANs is to ensure that the usage level is kept high without causing too many messages to 'collide' and interfere with each other. Various different protocols have been developed for this purpose.

The two fundamental approaches are the 'token' approach and the carrier-sending multiple access (CSMA) approach. These are both forms of time-division multiplexing, which means that each station on the network is given access to its communications facilities at fixed intervals.

In a token network (there are both token rings and token buses), a special 'packet' or token is circulated about the network. When a station receives the token, it has the opportunity to attach to it a message and the necessary addressing information, and the enlarged message is then recirculated until it reaches its destination. The receiving station accepts the message, and sends back a 'message received' signal, which is effectively the same message repeated, so that the originating station can check that it was correctly transmitted. The originating station then places another token on the network, so that another station may send a message. This method is particularly appropriate to networks where there are a few stations which send frequent signals, and it is essential to ensure that each has a fair chance to use the network. It is also much used in more hierarchical communications networks. IBM's Token Ring network is an example of this protocol.

CSMA is more appropriate where there are many stations, sending messages relatively less frequently. On a CSMA system, a station wishing to send a message first 'listens out' to ensure that the network is not currently in use. The station then broadcasts its signal and waits for a returning echo that will confirm its safe reception. The difficulty arises when two or more stations attempt to broadcast simultaneously. In this case each station must wait for a short period (each station is given a different delay time) and then reattempt to broadcast. The Cambridge Ring and Ethernet use this protocol.

Sometimes the packet-switching protocols described earlier are used in a local area mode, rather than over the public-switched network. As already described, the essence of a PSN is to form a notional virtual circuit for the user, over which his message is transmitted as a multiple set of packets. Implementation of a packet-switched local network is possible (most minicomputer vendors support the internationally agreed X25 protocol) and this provides a more efficient usage of the physical network than simple point-to-point circuit connections. However, PSNs are not the most appropriate solution because in their design specification they were targeted at long-distance traffic, using existing low band-width cabling, and employing sophisticated error-checking and correction features to cope with the expected high error rates using the public network. The problem in a local area environment is that the user doesn't want to bear all of this overhead, but requires a high-capacity simple interface system.

Vendor-specific and All-purpose LANs

Interfacing problems are much eased when a local area network is designed to connect only computers from one manufacturer, or computers which use much the same software protocols. These networks are known as vendor-specific local area networks. Ethernet, The IBM Token Ring, and Wangnet, are all examples of this type of LAN.

All-purpose LANs, in contrast, are usually broadband systems and provide support for a variety of different protocols, and have the capability to transmit a variety of different types of message. Examples of this subspecies include AT&T's Information System Network, Ungermann-Bass's Net/One, and Contel's Contelnet.

A PBX-based LAN is in many ways a classic example of the all-purpose LAN. However, PBX protocol generally only proves to be a cost-effective solution if a LAN is being installed at the same time as an organisation is switching from an analogue to a digital system for straight telecommunications.

Integrated Communication Systems

It is now apparent that as a consequence of these developments, the artificial distinction between data processing and telecommunications (imposed by legislation rather than any coherent view of the market or needs of the user) has begun to disappear. We are moving towards a stage at which integrated, intelligent networks capable of handling voice, data, video, text and facsimile will become the norm. An essential forerunner of this was the deregulation of the communications industry in the USA and elsewhere, which ended the split between telecommunications authorities and data processing corporations.

The current name for this development is the Integrated Services Digital Network, or ISDN. Various standards authorities, including most particularly the CCITT (Consultative Committee for International Telephone and Telegraph) in Geneva, have been working for some time towards setting down hardware and software standards for this new generation of communications technology which will embrace all earlier separate technologies. However this has proved a long and difficult process, and it is a standing joke now that ISDN really stands not for Integrated Services Digital Network, but for I Still Don't Know!

There is considerable difficulty for manufacturers of ISDN-type equipment (which is likely to include basically telecommunications-oriented organisations such as AT&T and Ericsson, and computer-oriented organisations such as IBM and NEC) in undertaking a great deal of preparatory work before the standards are finalised. But already telecommunications authorities and PBX companies are beginning to upgrade their equipment by introducing the latest digital switches, which should be capable of handling ISDN once it becomes a reality, and some organisations — including AT&T with Centrex, and Northern Telecom with its Integrated Business Network — have introduced smaller LAN-type products which are effectively test-beds for ISDN technology.

Currently the PTTs are in the design stage of developing the IBCN (Integrated Broadband Communications Network): a public broadband network enhancing and expanding the capability of the ISDN in the second half of the 1990s.

Electronic Mail

Users access the public data networks (where these are not used purely for intra-company communications) for two basic reasons. One, for electronic mail purposes: that is, for sending short or longer messages to other computer users. And two, for information purposes: that is, for obtaining information from a database on another computer.

A bewildering variety of public data networks are available in the UK and elsewhere. Frequently the protocols used differ from one to another, and even for experts this can be a confusing field. In the next ten years we can hope for a considerable shake-out, with a few services growing considerably in size, and weaker ones falling away.

British Telecom's public electronic mail service is called *Telecom Gold* in the UK; internationally, it is known as *Dialcom* (started in 1982). Users have to join the service, and are billed (currently on a character basis) for the data that they send. Message-handling software is being developed that ties the public service directly into private networks.

It is possible to gauge the strength of electronic mail services by judging the number of mailboxes. Each user has a 'mailbox', not entirely dissimilar to a paper mailbox, to which messages can be sent by other users. The mailbox is effectively on the mail service's own computer, and when the user is ready to 'empty' it, he or she asks for the information therein to be downloaded to his/her own terminal. This means that messages can be sent even when the receiving computer is not actively linked into the network. The service, though useful, is of course no substitute for direct computer-to-computer communications, and these are far more appropriate when what is being sent is not a short message or memo, but a lengthy report or article.

The largest US electronic mail services in 1987 were Western Union Easylink, with approximately 155,000 mailboxes; Dialcom has 120,000, and US Sprint's Telemail approximately 100,000. But add on Telecom Gold's 80,000 (approximately) UK users and others in Italy, Finland and elsewhere, and Dialcom reaches a total of about 250,000 worldwide.

Users who do not have their own mailboxes can currently send messages to mailboxes by using their telex machines, with Telecom Gold's Monodata telex bureau. However, telex is much slower than normal electronic mail (the messages are sent at 50 baud instead of 1,200 baud) and the limitation to capital letters only is another drawback.

Many organisations are now building their own in-house electronic mail networks, especially those operating on a global basis, with R & D, manufacturing, sales and marketing operations in many countries and many time zones. Perhaps understandably, the equipment suppliers themselves are the leaders in this area. For example, Hewlett-Packard's in-house network encompasses 860 minicomputers, and 64,000 terminals, personal computers and work-stations for its 85,000 employees.

Public Databases

In essence there is no clear-cut distinction between public databases and private databases. A company database containing its internal commercial information is clearly private (though in the UK, at least, the Data Protection Act gives those listed a limited right to inspect it). A 'library' database which anyone can call up and access is clearly public. But many databases are more like clubs or societies: access to them is limited to a more or less tight group of members; sometimes anyone can become a member by paying the subscriptions, and sometimes the membership is limited to (e.g.) the members of a particular professional association.

A public or semi-public database is effectively the same as a company internal database. It is a collection of data, held sometimes in a file format, sometimes in a 'page' or 'frame' format (where every screenful of information is regarded as a separate unit). Much emphasis is put (though not enough, some confused users complain!) on structuring the data carefully and indexing them fully so that it is easy for users to locate the information they require.

Running a database can be a commercial activity, in which the profit is derived from the payments users make for the data they access. (Typically there is a subscription charge for joining the service, and then a unit charge — sometimes variable — when use is made of it.) It.can be a public-service activity, or it can be run on an advertising type of basis. Or, alternatively, a database may be administered for the benefit of its users, with the overheads being met by the association to which the users belong.

More than half the publicly accessible databases contain commercial or financial data; about 14 per cent contain technical information, and another 11 per cent biomedical or other scientific data, leaving around a quarter with miscellaneous contents. Roughly 10 per cent of databases are basically bibliographic, providing references from which the users can request hard-copy information in depth; the others provide relatively compressed information (statistics, etc.) in all its full form.

Users can access a computer database through any data network to which it is linked. This may be the public electronic mail service, or a videotext service (discussed below), or a widespread computer network of which the user is a part. The information obtained comes up on the user's terminal screen, and with appropriate equipment the user can then take a hard copy of it.

In recent years, databases have grown to be big business. In 1985 the worldwide database business was estimated to be worth between $4 billion and $5 billion. Of this turnover 75 per cent was in the USA, but databases are becoming increasingly common in Europe and elsewhere in the developed world — and UK users can also, of course, access many US databases. One problem with the development of European databases is the profusion of human languages and data transmission protocols across the different countries of Western Europe.

The largest firm operating databases commercially worldwide is Dialog Information Services.

In 1987 there were estimated to be about 1,000 European databases linked to the Euronet Diane network, on approximately fifty host computers. Obviously, many computers held many more than one single database.

As examples of the many databases available today, 'Wall Street Journal' (linked to the newspaper) carries financial news and similar information, and is updated daily; 'Marketing Week' caters for the marketing /media world; 'China Express' has data on business developments in China; 'InterCompany Comparisons' contains information on British companies; 'Euromonitor On-line' consists of three different databases ('Eurofacts', with comparative statistics on sixteen countries, 'Eurofile', dealing with marketing and strategic planning information, and 'Market Direction' which contains reports on consumer markets); Lexis, owned by Mead Data Central, is a US legal database which has been extended to cover English law.

A more recent development is the growth of hard-cover directories of available databases, to guide the bewildered user not merely to the right section of the database, but to the right database in the first place!

Viewdata/Videotext

Viewdata, or videotext, is a particular technique for storing, accessing and retrieving data from a remote computer using an adapted television set and a telecommunications link (usually the public telephone network). It is a combination of electronic mail and a series of public and semi-public databases.

Information is stored on a viewdata computer as a series of *frames* or *pages*. Each page consists of both content and information routing the user to the next pages. The information is stored as a massive 'tree-structure' with an initial menu page leading to other menu (routing) pages until the page containing the required information is reached. Potentially, the database has unlimited capacity, and any page can be requested directly if the correct page number is known.

The beauty of this system is the simplicity of use and the fact that it is totally content-free (i.e. any kind of information can be stored and retrieved). The disadvantage is that it can be a rather cumbersome process finding the required information. It was designed to be an electronic mail/database system for the novice user in the general population, not for the computer expert in a large company. The early systems were designed so that domestic television sets could be adapted to double as viewdata terminals, though it is also possible to access viewdata from suitably programmed computers.

The first application of viewdata was by the British Post Office (as it then was) in setting up the Prestel service in 1979. Prestel provided a variety of specialist and general information, together with a 'mailbox' facility, user clubs, and 'response frames' which enabled the user to send messages to information providers, or even to order goods and services via the system.

Though it received much attention after its launch, Prestel did not prove a success. The equipment needed to access the system was not cheap, and the information provided was itself regarded as costly by many people who were used to 'free' information from libraries, television, etc. Much of the information — horoscopes, weather forecasts, train timetables, and so on — was not critical enough, or updated frequently enough, to justify the cost of the system for many users. Prestel's text and graphics were primitive, and the volume of information per frame was very low. In consequence, as a public system it never reached a viable user level, though it continues to serve some specialist markets successfully. (It is arguable whether the system could have coped with the demand if it *had* been generated.) By 1986 it was estimated that Prestel's user base was in the region of 19,000 home customers and 27,000 business customers — a hopelessly inadequate number for the service as originally envisaged.

The French have taken a very different approach to the introduction of videotext with their Télétel service. Télétel was originally developed to replace paper telephone directories, and the 'Minitel' terminals were provided free to users, providing an enormous captive user base and a guaranteed base use for the system. Though directory look-ups are free, the other uses of the system must be paid for, and it has been estimated that the fees cover the cost of the terminals in an average of four years. By the end of 1986, around 2.5 Minitel terminals were being operated, and the number was expected to grow by 1 million a year until the early 1990s. Télétel's success can be gauged by the fact that by 1986 there were over 2,000 different services using the system, including thirty home-banking systems (see the next section).

The UK has not been the only country to get viewdata wrong. In 1986 two major US ventures, Times-Mirror Los Angeles's *Gateway* and Knight-Ridder Newspaper's *Viewtron* were both closed down after several years of difficult and unprofitable operation.

Viewdata should not be confused with *Teletext*: a system for transmitting 'frames' of information using normal television broadcasting techniques. This system was initially developed by British television engineers as a way of putting subtitles on the screen for deaf viewers. Teletext is a one-way system with a limited number of frames (a few hundred) being transmitted in sequence. The receiver has to wait for a short interval, while the required page comes around, after which it is stored in the system's memory until it is supplanted by a request for a new page.

Electronic Banking

It is in the world of electronic banking that telecommunications provides a principal agent of change. Banks have for many years transferred money 'over the wire' to other banks, and today it is estimated that up to 90 per cent of all routine transactions are amenable to automation.

The banks have set up their own telecommunications network, SWIFT (Society for the Worldwide Interchange of Financial Transactions), to facilitate this process. Using this network it is possible for, say, a Hong Kong bank to clear a cheque on a Californian bank within a few minutes. The network consists of a series of lines leased from national PTTs and commercial carriers, with small computers acting as switching nodes. It is owned as a co-operative venture by the participating banks; there are now over 1,300 member banks, in sixty-one countries. All messages on the network are routed to two large Burroughs computers in Brussels, where they are recorded for security purposes, then switched on to their destination. This is an example of a *message switching system*, and it may be classed as a *value-added network*.

However, the major banking development being spurred by telecommunications is in retail banking. The costs of handling the vast number of small transactions that make up today's retail banking have been kept high by the large number of people involved in processing them. It is not that banks have failed to invest in automation, quite the reverse, but the interface between the customer's transaction and the bank has still needed human intervention.

The UK clearing banks (like other banks the world over) are presently investing heavily in automated bank teller machines — not just cash dispensers, but machines which can fulfil several other functions, such as ordering cheque-books, requesting statements, and so on. From the bank's point of view such machines are wonderful — they use the pavement as a banking hall, kindly provided by the local authority, and externalise their labour costs, much as self-service has done in the rest of the retail business. And there is a lot of evidence that customers prefer using the machines too; certainly if you want to withdraw only a small sum it saves you from the rather condescending gaze of the teller.

LINK, a national banking network in the UK which links primarily smaller financial institutions and building societies, was completed in 1987. This initially served over 1,000 bank and building society automatic teller machines.

Already automated retail banking has moved into other locations than bank walls — factories, offices, shops, railway stations and so on — basically almost anywhere a free banking hall is available. The final logic of this process is to move much more of this right back to the home and to enable the customer to initiate financial and administrative banking transactions from his home.

The development of credit card payments has reduced the volume of transactions that the banks have to handle, but this load has been transferred to the credit card companies themselves. Each transaction generates a paper voucher that has to be individually processed. In the UK the two major organisations handling these cards, Barclaycard and Access, are finding that the possibilities of further growth are being curtailed by the volume of paper.

A new development is the *electronic financial transaction system*. These devices can automatically 'read' cards, and transmit the transaction information directly to the credit card headquarters. The device which does this is an example of a *point of sale* (POS) terminal. Similar terminals, which can read credit cards, are being installed by the large retailing organisations for applications such as stock control and cash management. Often these are not yet connected to the credit card company's own computer but rather work with the retailer's own system.

In the UK the direction of the credit card companies is dictated by the major banks, as they are the owners. In the US the situation is rather different. Visa and Mastercard have co-operative arrangements with the banks as they offer complementary services. Recently a new type of card has come into being, a *direct debit card*, which initiates a direct *electronic funds transfer* (EFT) between two parties. This in effect puts credit card companies and banks into direct competition.

The US situation is complicated by the 1927 McFadden Act, which prohibits interstate banking. Traditionally the small banks have welcomed this protection against the financial giants, but recently there have grown up regional *automatic teller machine* (ATM) networks, which allow transactions between customers of different banks. All of a sudden the small banks have realised that they can be lighter on their feet than their bigger brothers. The ATM networks, using a packet-switched approach, are considerably more economic than the Visa and Mastercard networks. Using ATMs a customer can deposit or withdraw cash and make balance enquiries, the ATMs can handle large-scale retain fund transfers, and there are increasingly widespread connections to retailers' point of sale terminals and to home banking terminals.

In America the speeding progress towards electronic banking is also being fuelled by competition between the major financial service institutions. American Express, Merrill Lynch and Sears Roebuck all now have services which compete for the same funds. Citicorp has made a major commitment to worldwide electronic banking in an effort to make the customer and the computers do the work and to reduce their processing costs.

Home banking was much trumpeted as one of the likely major applications of the videotext networks, but in fact it has been slower to take off than was anticipated. The customer has rapidly come to appreciate the volume of work required in keying-in transactions, and finds it rather a chore with the present systems, and there is a tendency for sums withdrawn or transferred to be debited immediately from the user's account, thus losing him or her the normal 'float' period before a withdrawal is debited. The failure or, at best, limited success of several early attempts at home banking has hastened the failure of several viewdata systems.

11

Office Products

One third of the industries converging in the information technology area comprises office products. Unlike the computing and telecommunications industries which are relatively homogeneous, office products comprise a wide range of products, both hardware and software, and an even wider range of suppliers.

Word Processing

Word processing is concerned with electronically processing textual information in a fashion similar to more traditional data processing — that is, entering, manipulating, editing, storing, retrieving, displaying and transmitting such information.

With the traditional typewriter, there is no intermediate stage between input and output: the typist strikes a key, and the appropriate letter appears on a piece of paper. The development of word processing began with the capability to introduce an intermediate stage: to separate input from output.

Electronic Typewriters

The very earliest machines that did this were magnetic card and tape typewriters, which stored a record of the typist's key presses on a simple serial medium: paper-tape (much like early telex machines), magnetic tape, or flat magnetic cards, similar in size to paper cards for punching. The stored record could then be reproduced as many times as required,

188

and to a very limited extent it was possible to amend it — for example, by using one card as input, adding or deleting characters, and then saving the amended record on a second card. With these early machines there was no display medium, and it was up to the operator to work from a written record of the memory contents, and to stop the playback in the right places so as to permit alterations. This was a cumbersome and demanding process.

At much the same time came the development of 'memory type-writers': devices with a small inbuilt RAM, enabling perhaps one line of text to be stored at once, and an equally small liquid crystal display. The typist would enter a line of text, hopefully catch errors on the display, and have an opportunity to correct them before pressing 'return' and seeing the entire line print out on to paper.

These two devices steadily evolved into an entire range of electronic typewriters, devices usually (though not always) with small integral displays, and with some combination of internal (RAM) and/or external (magnetic card or disc) memory.

Early memory typewriters often used the golf-ball mechanism, introduced by IBM for use in electric typewriters in 1961. Though reliable, the golf-ball was slow in operation, designed to match the pace of a competent touch-typist rather than speed along to cope with the output of an electronic memory. Subsequently a Xerox subsidiary invented the daisy-wheel, a device where the printing elements are the ends of spokes of a small wheel. This permitted considerably faster playback, and it is a very common medium for letter-quality printing today.

Memory typewriters are useful but strictly limited machines. Because of the small display and small memory, it is difficult or impossible to make large-scale alterations to a document: for instance, rearranging paragraphs, or substituting very long phrases for shorter ones throughout. The devices are really only suitable for use in the typing of correspondence and short documents where the emphasis is not on large-scale revision but on proof-reading and impeccable reproduction.

Word Processors

Word processors differ from electronic typewriters in two ways: first, the keyboard and the printer are typically divorced, instead of forming part of the same typewriter-like unit (and it is generally not possible to 'type' straight on to paper, bypassing the memory); and second, there is a full-sized video screen. The result is something very like a personal computer: a modular machine with a keyboard, processing unit, video screen, disc drive, and access to a printer (which might be shared between several work-stations).

In the late 1970s and early 1980s, a substantial industry grew up producing dedicated word processors: machines *like* personal computers, but designed only for use as word processors, with inbuilt word processing software; keyboards adapted to reflect typical word processing functions (often there were special keys for actions such as 'cut' and 'paste', or even for text units such as 'word', 'sentence' and 'paragraph'); and screens designed to appeal to typists, sometimes with black text on a white background to emulate sheets of paper, and occasionally oversized so that a full A4 sheet's worth of text could be displayed at once. IBM's Displaywriters, Wang's dedicated machines (that is, machines used only for this application), and many more were examples of this specialised technology.

In the mid-1980s there began to be an increasing trend away from this special-purpose approach. Dedicated word processors failed to drop in price at the same rate as general-purpose microcomputers, and it became much cheaper to use a microcomputer with word processing software as a word processor, than to buy a dedicated machine. The quality of the software available for micros improved to the point where the dedicated machines were no longer markedly superior; and with the growth in demand for other computer applications, the advantage in using general-purpose machines became more apparent. Dedicated word processors fought back by introducing ever wider ranges of capability in their machines, often including electronic mail, address-oriented data filing systems, and maths capabilities; but the trend now appears to be firmly set. IBM's Displaywriter is dead, for instance, and the company now promotes instead the Displaywrite range of word processing programs for micros, using similar commands and compatible document architectures.

Stand-alone and Shared-logic Systems

Networking has come only slowly to microcomputers, as we saw in the last chapter. In the more enclosed world of dedicated word processors, networking was the norm much earlier, and there is still a trend towards 'shared logic' word processing systems.

There are a number of reasons for this. From an organisational viewpoint, many large companies were quick to introduce word processors into their typing pools, where numbers of low-grade staff performing similar or identical work were tightly supervised by one or more superiors. This working fashion encouraged the adoption of terminal-based systems, where a supervisor was able to take charge of a central scheduling resource and monitor the amount of work done by each operator. Many dedicated systems included elaborate software to enable (for example) each key press to be recorded, and the day's total to be added up. The word processor was seen as a low-status tool, used intensively for routine applications by operators who often had little interaction with document originators. But today the word processor's image has changed. Senior secretaries no longer look down on wp operators; now they appreciate the value of the machines and demand stand-alone versions for themselves!

Letter-quality printers (that is, printers which produce output of similar quality to a good electric typewriter) are expensive devices: the heavy-duty daisy-wheel printers of the late 1970s and early 1980s frequently cost well over £1,000; and laser printers, when they began to be widely available in the mid-1980s, cost several thousand pounds. An individual word processor operator does not require the full-time use of a printer, except when doing specialist tasks such as form-letter generation; for a more typical mix of correspondence and report work, one printer can be shared among several operators. Word processing centres often acquired a variety of printing resources, including both letter-quality printers and dot-matrix draft printers (that is, printers using an array of dots to produce an image — working faster than letter-quality printers but producing lower quality output), which were used as communal resources to be shared among the operatives. These dot-matrix printers have now been partly superseded by ink-jet printers, which work by squirting tiny droplets of ink on to the paper to form the character or graphic. They run faster than impact printers, and are almost totally silent. The latest versions of such ink-jet printers, such as Hewlett-Packard's Paintjet, incorporate several print-heads to print full colour documents.

Networking was one efficient way in which the use of these resources could be organised. Moreover, the trend towards *electronic mail* — the generation of letters and memos sent to their destination in electronic form — also oriented word processor users towards the networking concept; as did the provision of centralised dictation systems.

Early shared-logic systems were based around a single minicomputer and a set of terminals. Each user had his or her own screen and keyboard, but processing power, memory and printers were all shared resources. Today, the trend in these systems, as in other forms of computing, is towards distributed power: either towards intelligent terminals with at least a degree of their own processing power, or towards the networking of self-contained microcomputers.

Though shared-logic systems have substantial organisational and financial advantages, they also have drawbacks. If a printer, disc, or the central controller fails, then the entire network may be put out of action. Users do not have the same feeling of ownership of their work environment that the user of a stand-alone machine enjoys. And where memory is centralised, the individual user has to rely on others to devise and implement satisfactory archiving and back-up procedures, which in a large system can become extremely complex.

Word Processing Software

Dedicated word processing systems normally have an integral word processing program, integrated with the keyboard and screen configuration, and designed specifically for that purpose. With a general-purpose microcomputer, it is possible for the user to select any one of a vast range of word processing programs, depending upon individual requirements and preferences.

Any word processor needs to provide a basic set of capabilities. Documents must be capable of being displayed on screen, and stored on disc or a similar medium. It must be possible to edit documents: adding, deleting or changing anything from a single character to several pages of text. It should be possible to 'cut' and 'paste', switching round the order of text. Documents need to be paginated, and the layout needs to be adaptable so that they can be properly set out on different sizes of paper, with appropriate margins, headers, footers, and so on.

Many other capabilities are provided by high-quality programs. It is generally possible to merge text from different files, for example to produce sets of personalised form letters. There are often sophisticated column manipulation and maths features. There is the capability to adapt type styles and sizes, at least in a small way; to underline, put into bold face, produce subscripts and superscripts, etc. Many programs automatically number paragraphs; some have extensive 'outlining' capabilities, enabling the user to switch from level to level, viewing first headings, then subheadings and then individual paragraph contents. A spelling checker not only catches errors but also suggests suitable corrections; this is all but essential in today's programs. Several programs offer a full on-line thesaurus around which the user can browse. There is also a slow but discernible trend towards programs that check elements of grammar and style.

Providing all the complex features of today's word processing requirements is no easy task, and the different programs choose very different ergonomic approaches. Some are designed for casual users; others offer power at the expense of complexity, and are only really suitable for regular users. Some are oriented towards direct commands which become second nature to the regular user; others prefer a menu-based approach. Some work with individual pages, others treat documents as seamless wholes until the printing stage. Some are closely integrated with other types of program in a general-purpose 'suite'; others are more stand-alone in their orientation.

Many early word processing programs, evolved from the text editors, used to manipulate files of program code. With these there was a tendency towards a two-step approach. First, the editor program would enable the user to correct and arrange the contents of the document; second, a formatter program would be used to lay it out correctly, according to margin, tabulation and other criteria chosen by the user. This approach, though economical in its demands on the processor, could cause difficulties from a user viewpoint, since the user didn't see what the final layout would look like until just before (or, all too often, after) the document was printed out.

Today editor-formatters are out of favour, and the predominant approach is the rival *WYSIWYG*, or 'what you see is what you get'. Editing and formatting are done at the same stage, and the emphasis is on making the screen display reflect as closely as possible the appearance of the printed document.

Throughout the late 1970s and early 1980s the most popular word processing program was Wordstar, a relatively cumbersome but powerful WYSIWYG program. In recent years Wordstar and its updates have lost ground, and the new market leaders in the full-feature word processor market include Word Perfect, Multimate, Microsoft Word, and IBM's Displaywrite. Many budget programs are also available, of varying quality, with lower price tags but more restricted capabilities.

Desktop Publishing

Word processors up until the mid-1980s were oriented towards the editing and reproduction of relatively plain documents: letters, reports and so on produced in typewriter style, using a single typeface, neatly laid out but with no more sophistication in their reproduction than the occasional underlined heading. This style of word processing was well suited to the daisy-wheel and similar printers that were the mainstay of offices in this period. But with the mid-1980s came the large-scale advent of laser printers, which were capable (as the daisy-wheels were not) of mixing different type-styles and type sizes on the same page, and of integrating text and graphics as well. The market leader, Hewlett-Packard's Laserjet has now evolved into a whole range of laser printers offering a variety of printing speeds, founts and resolution (that is image quality).

Though this mix of output was available earlier, to some extent, with dot-matrix draft printers, the output from these was inevitably 'dotty' in appearance, and even at its best rarely surpassed NLQ or 'near letter quality'. Laser printers produced output that was up to passable lithographic print standards, and more than adequate for run-of-the-mill letters, press announcements, newsletters and the like. At the same time, microcomputer graphics programs were reaching new levels of sophistication. Most microcomputers now boasted adequate graphics capabilities, and simple-to-use programs like the Apple Macintosh Paint and Microsoft Draw enabled even non-artists to produce diagrams and simple pictures with the minimum of effort. Graphic artists and designers using these programs were able to design, adapt, and fit to size and specific requirements complex illustrations that were up to the normal commercial standards required for newsletters, press announcements and the like. With the advent of these printers and graphics programs came a demand for software which would enable organisations to produce in-house the kind of newsletter-type material that might earlier have been routed to a professional printing firm. *Desktop publishing* (DTP) was the result.

A desktop publishing program typically takes input from two different sources: text prepared using a word processor, and graphic images prepared using a graphics program, or sometimes input from another source (e.g. a video camera) and perhaps further processed by the computer. It then enables the user to lay out a publication page by page (much like a newspaper) setting margins, arranging text in columns of varying size, incorporating illustrations at any point on the page, and adding headlines, captions and so on.

The exact capabilities of DTP programs naturally vary, but the best are capable of the necessary degree of sophistication in laying out text and graphics to produce newsletters that are up to acceptable commercial standards. At this top end of the market, desktop publishing programs merge almost imperceptibly with professional computer typesetting systems, and indeed several of the better programs produce output files that are suitable for further refinement by professional typesetters. Sometimes these upmarket programs are described not as DTP, but as EP, or *electronic publishing*.

For this type of file transfer to be feasible, it is necessary for standards to be developed, and widely followed. DTP has developed the concept of *page description languages*, or PDLs: sophisticated sets of printer control instructions, which are incorporated in the program's output file. A PDL-compatible output file can then be used to run any printer which is equipped to handle the language. (This capability is generally only available today on the more expensive laser printers.) The most popular PDLs today are Adobe's Postscript, and DDL or 'document description language'.

So many DTP program packages are currently being launched that it is difficult to list market leaders. The early front-runner, now with a substantial user base, was Aldus's Pagemaker package, orginally designed for the Apple Macintosh but subsequently also made available on other micros. On the IBM PC the Ventura package from Xerox is one of the most powerful available.

A word of warning should be sounded over DTP. Using a DTP package involves skills of graphic layout that many users will not have. The software provides no help with the design, so a lot of time can be wasted producing rather poor results. Many users will be better off using one of the more sophisticated word processing packages such as Microsoft Word, which supports proportionally spaced founts, layout control and simple graphics.

Facsimile

Facsimile (usually referred to by the abbreviation 'fax') is a method by which a copy of an image on paper is transmitted and reproduced electronically at a remote site, using the telephone network as the connection mechanism. Facsimile was invented in 1842, but widespread commercial services were not available until the 1920s in America, and considerably later elsewhere. Until recently fax was seen as a rather specialist service with a limited market: for example, for transmitting weather maps, or newspapers. The recent re-emergence of fax is due in part to a perception that reprographics-related products and services are a significant component of the electronic office, also (and more obviously) to a significant price reduction in the technology employed.

All fax equipment operates in a similar manner. The page to be transmitted is scanned on a fine grid pattern, and at each point the shade is recorded, transmitted, and reproduced at the remote location. The shade description (grey intensity) can be transmitted either as an analogue signal or as a numeric value in binary form. The image on the document may be text or data, but the fax equipment makes no attempt to 'read' individual characters. Each character will instead be conveyed as a large number of different grid readings. Fax was initially an expensive method of sending textual messages, used primarily where graphics needed to be transmitted (for example, for sending engineering drawings) or where a special image had to be reproduced (for example, for signature verification). It became particularly widely used in Japan, due to the difficulties of transmitting ideographic messages by other methods, and by 1986 over one million fax machines were in use in Japan. Now fax is highly cost-competitive, and many organisations have adopted it as a basic means of communication.

Fax equipment differs in its scanning density, copy quality and transmission speed, and is generally constructed to meet one of the standards of the Consultative Committee for International Telephone and Telegraph (CCITT), the PTTs' international standards committee. There is inevitably some trade-off between scanning density (and thus copy quality) and transmission speed — the higher the density, the more time is needed for the scan — but these measurements are also affected by the transmission speed and by the type of equipment.

The CCITT has formulated three standards for fax equipment:

Group I machines which transmit an A4-sized page in analogue form in 4–6 minutes;

Group II machines which transmit an A4 page in 2–3 minutes;

Group III machines which operate digitally and transmit an A4 page in less than a minute.

The current boom in fax in North America was sparked off by the appearance of cheap Group II equipment, but Group III equipment is now effectively the norm.

The CCITT standards ensure that users can operate with other users who may use equipment from different manufacturers. It is also possible to use sending and receiving machines from different groups, though the transmission speed will inevitably be that of the slower machine.

Fax services were initially made available via public machines. For example, British Telecom made available at major post offices their Bureau Fax service within major cities in the UK, and the Intelpost service to North America, Europe and the Far East. This was a cumbersome procedure, since the sender had to deliver the document to the nearest centre, and alert the receiver to recover it from his or her nearest centre. Today the trend is towards private ownership of fax machines, and most large and many smaller businesses have their own facility. Each fax machine is allotted a number, and for the user the system operates very similarly to the telex network.

We are likely to see the same trend with fax machines as we have seen with word processors. When laser printers become the norm on personal computers, then the addition of a simple scanner and some additional electronics will turn the pc into a fax machine, and eliminate the need for a separate piece of equipment. In fact, cheap 'fax cards' are already available for pcs, and it is likely that in a few years personal fax machines will be widely used.

Reprographics

Another basic item of office equipment, the copier, has also benefited from the incorporation of processing capability. The reprographic process in which an image is placed on an electrostatic drum and then transferred to paper many times is steadily being superseded (in the major office market, though it is still used in cheaper machines) by laser technology.

With the advent of the laser, the earlier distinction between printers, which produce a single original of a document, and photocopiers, which reproduce copies of an existing document, has largely disappeared. Laser machines use broadly the same technology to do both, and indeed some larger machines perform both these functions.

In laser systems, a laser under computer control 'paints' the image to be reproduced on the printing drum. The image, which might include text, data or graphics, is presented to the printer in digital electronic form, typically from a host computer system, though most of these printer/copiers do have a communications capability which enables them to accept material sent over a network. As the image is sent in digital form, it is possible for it to be processed before reproduction — for example, to be reduced or rotated, the type fount to be changed at any point, material from several sources to be merged onto a single page, or standard forms or layouts stored in the machine's memory to be overlaid at will. Facilities such as these provide a considerable improvement in operational flexibility over conventional copiers, and a consequent increase in throughput.

The laser system creating the image works to an extremely high degree of accuracy. The exact degree varies from machine to machine, but it is generally sufficient to produce output of typewriter quality or better. These machines are admirably quiet when compared with conventional dot-matrix or daisy-wheel printers, and they are relatively fast in operation, especially when compared with earlier generation printers rather than with photocopiers.

Daisy-wheel printers provide good quality, but at a relatively slow speed, typically from 45 to 60 cps (characters per second), and less on very cheap machines. Big laser printing systems can operate at speeds of 45 pages per minute or more, though the speed is reduced when a series of originals is required, rather than many copies from the same original, and when graphics as well as (or instead of) text is being reproduced.

Teletex

Teletex is a service offered by the PTTs, enabling electronic transmission between Teletex-compatible terminals on a memory-to-memory basis. It was perceived by the PTTs as a way of retaining and developing the telex market, and moving into electronic mail services. Among its several advantages over telex is its ability to handle both upper and lower case characters.

The document to be transmitted is prepared locally at the word processor, and then transferred to the Teletex part of the terminal, from where it is transmitted to another Teletex terminal at speeds of up to 240 characters per second over the public network. Use of word processors as the originating device means that messages can be created, edited and stored, using all the features of the word processor prior to transmission.

The Teletex system also interfaces to the existing worldwide telex network, making it possible to exchange messages between the two systems (though at telex standard). Among the countries operating this service are West Germany, Sweden and the UK, where British Telecom began their Teletex service in 1982.

Teletex has been slower to catch on than was originally anticipated, in an era when telex itself has been slow to die, in spite of its manifold shortcomings. Though it has some specialist uses, its slow speed of transmission limits appeal to large organisations and those generating very many messages.

Part V

OFFICE AUTOMATION

In this part we shall be looking specifically at the effect of information technology on the office environment, and especially at the automation of the office. The term office automation means different things to different people, from distributed data processing to word processing, from local area networks to management work-stations, from microcomputers to complex computer systems. It has also been given a number of other labels such as the Electronic Office, the Paperless Office, and the Office of the Future.

12

What is an Office?

Data Processing and the Office

To put this discussion into perspective, it is worth recalling that the first commercial data processing computer was called LEO, Lyons Electronic Office. The objective of these early dp applications was to increase the productivity of the office. Thus the first stage of office automation began more than twenty-five years ago. There is much academic discussion about the meaning of the term automation and how it differs from mechanisation, which we will review in the following pages. But these early office applications all had similar characteristics: they all involved a high volume of transactions (to justify the high costs of latter-day computers), which were concerned with well-defined problems (highly structured in computer jargon). These kinds of problems were mainly in the accounting and administrative functions of the organisation. One can look at the development of dp applications in terms of volume and structure, as shown by Figure 12.1.

Traditional dp applications began with those having the characteristics of the top left-hand corner of Figure 12.1, that is, those with high volume and structure. Once these applications were mastered it was possible to develop software which was more complex and could automate less structured procedures (1). These would be systems where the users drive the software down their own chosen paths (i.e. the user is providing the structure). However, it was still necessary for the volume of transactions to be high to justify the cost of developing this software. A manufacturing information system would be an example of this type of system.

The second movement (2) was a result of the falling cost of hardware, which allowed low volume applications to be developed, as the processing

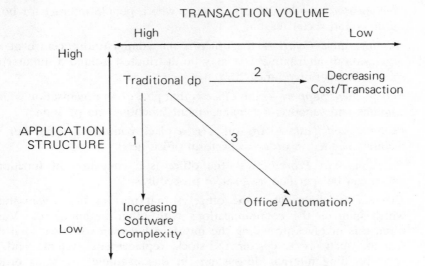

Figure 12.1 *Development in dp Applications*

cost per transaction fell. This cut hard into the puritan dp ethic, where idleness was considered a mortal sin and the thought of computer equipment sitting idle for most of the day was not easily accepted. Such systems are characterised by the multitude of small business systems which automate functions traditionally tackled by dp (e.g. financial accounting) for smaller and smaller organisational units.

This leaves only the bottom right-hand corner of Figure 12.1 undeveloped (3). It is a space which has only now become possible to think about occupying. This is because the hardware is now sufficiently cost-effective for low-volume applications to be economic, but the problem of efficient production of complex software is still unresolved. We would argue that the second stage of office automation, which is the subject of this section, belongs fairly and squarely in this segment of Figure 12.1.

Aspects of the Office

Before we can discuss the practicalities of automating an office, it is necessary to have some idea of what an office is. It is an interesting exercise to ask this question of a room full of managers because of the variety of answers that will be given. We list below some different aspects of an office; the order is in no way significant.

Location — the office is a physical place separate from the home, where people go to work.

Meeting Place — the office is a place where people interact for both business and social reasons.

Administrative Centre — the office is the administrative centre of an organisation; alternatively, it may be distributed around a number of small administrative units.

Management Support — the office is that part of an organisation which contains and supports the management functions and personnel.

Facilities and Tasks — the office is a place containing a number of facilities needed in order to perform office tasks.

Functions and Procedures — the office is a collection of functions which can be specified as a set of procedures.

External Relationships — the office is that part of the organisation which handles the communications with other organisations. Very often this involves providing the interface between some external dp system, such as a customer's stock replacement system, and a corresponding internal dp system, in this example the sales order processing system.

System Interfaces — the office provides the interfaces between a number of information systems. This mainly involves collecting data to be put into dp systems, much of which has usually been generated by other dp systems.

From this list it is obvious that the office can fulfil a number of different functions at the same time, dependent upon the type of organisation being considered. There are essentially three different types of office: the clerical office, the administrative office and the management or professional office.

A *clerical office* exists where an organisation deals mainly with paper and information; in such an organisation the office becomes the shop floor, effectively. It is not a servicing part of the organisation: its product *is* the organisation's product. Typical examples of organisations with large clerical offices are insurance companies and banks. In these, much of the clerical work is routine: the clerical workers are broadly comparable with blue-collar workers in manufacturing organisations.

Administrative offices are usually found in a manufacturing or service organisation, where the office performs an administrative support and control function, making sure that operations run smoothly. The function of this office is not an end in itself, but provides a service to the rest of the organisation.

In contrast, the *management/professional office* is set up to support a number of skilled managers or professionals, often termed 'knowledge workers'. This could be a typical professional firm like accountants or solicitors; or alternatively, it might be the group headquarters of a multidivisional company. In some instances it might also be called a secretarial office for it will be mainly staffed by secretaries.

Each of these types of office has a different way of working and requires a different type of solution if automation is to progress further.

Information Flows

Another way of looking at the office is in terms of the information flows within an organisation. In Figure 12.2 we depict some of the different personnel, the information that flows between them, and the functions they perform within an organisation. At the bottom level data are captured, classified and stored. This information is filtered and structured by the middle managers and supervisors before being passed to senior management. Senior management will set or modify strategy, and contribute to the formulation of plans and budgets. The information is then passed back down to the middle managers to administer the agreed plans and control operations. Again this gives us a different insight into

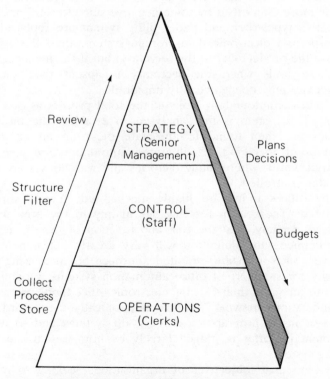

Figure 12.2 *Office Functions and Information Flows*

the office and shows its workings from a different angle. All of these perspectives are important if we are to be successful in 'automating the office'.

Automation versus Mechanisation

There is much academic debate about the difference between mechanisation and automation. This may in practice be purely a semantic argument; however, the case is clearly stated in Michael Zisman's article in the *Sloan Management Review* (4, 1978). He applies Richard Nolan's stage hypothesis of EDP growth to office automation. Zisman argues that at the mechanisation stage the office is viewed in terms of the discrete tasks that are carried out within it, such as typing, filing, message handling, calculating, etc. Each of these tasks can be mechanised by the provision of a suitable tool; for example, word-processor, data storage and retrieval systems, electronic mail, calculator, etc. There is a direct parallel with the mechanising of industrial tasks; each task is viewed in isolation and a solution is found for increasing local productivity. However the local gain may be more than offset by some negative side effects. For example, if a secretary's typewriter and paper filing system are replaced by a word processor and electronic data storage system, then this will hopefully increase the productivity of the secretary; but if the manager is unable to use these tools when the secretary is absent then the manager's productivity may be significantly impaired.

In contrast, automation looks at the total process as one interrelated system. The system is first analysed to establish the basic functions; methods are then found to automate these on an integrated basis. Examples of this kind of integrated automation are common in the industrial world, where many factories and warehouses are now largely computer controlled.

Many offices today are highly mechanised; few, if any, are fully automated. The reason for this lies mainly in the area we have just discussed: namely, that the role and function of the office may not be easily defined, and definition will vary greatly between organisations. However, such a systems-oriented approach has increasingly become a necessity for suppliers of office automation systems. Organisations now expect to integrate their existing electronic office tools, primarily through communications networks to link electronically their word processors, filing systems, reprographics systems, dp systems and so on, and new equipment on offer is judged largely by how well it can fit into the existing system.

The immediate objectives of organisations seeking to integrate and develop their automated office systems may be general and rather

imprecise — such as improving the effectiveness of large-scale administrative functions, and of co-ordination between decentralised units (for
example, in both public and private bureaucracies). Alternatively, they
may be procedures at higher structural levels within the organisation,
such as integrated order processing or manufacturing control.

The present state of office automation still lays emphasis on the
provision of technical building blocks aimed at supporting individual,
personal activities, such as word processing, electronic mail, and
spreadsheet-type analysis. These tools appeal to the 'knowledge workers',
and support specific tasks that they perform; yet from an organisational
viewpoint the need may be to install systems addressing not these local
functions, but global functions.

The Nature of Office Work

This leads us to identify a third dimension to the tasks undertaken by the
occupants of the office, building on our simple structure illustrated earlier
in Figure 12.2. Some degree of structure in the task is retained, whilst our
original concept of volume is better expressed by the type of activity
performed in the task. Following the familiar ideas of Anthony (*Planning
and Control Systems*, Harvard University Press, 1965), these may be
characterised as Operational Control, Management Control and Strategic
Planning — closely corresponding to our previous classification by
volume. Our third characterisation is to identify the degree of
interdependency in the task being performed. Three broad classes can be
identified: tasks *independent* of interaction with any other; those requiring
some *pooled* action by several people; and those occurring in a situation
in which they have to be performed in a strict *sequence*. These three
characteristics of office tasks are illustrated in Figure 12.3. The third
characteristic of task interdependence plays an important role in the
achievement of successful automation of the office.

Thus, the clerical functions that are directly affected by existing dp
systems usually have certain qualities. For example, they are in general
uni-functional; that is, the clerk performs only a single function, such as
order entry. Where the clerical workers have a multi-functional role, then
the different functions are usually performed in batches in sequence. This
contrasts with the general nature of office work, which involves a number
of independent functions, probably happening concurrently. For example,
an office worker could be preparing some document and be interrupted
by a request for information which involved information retrieval from a
filing system. This could involve several documents being available to
work on at one time, with the worker switching between them as
necessary. This is very much in contrast to the normal dp approach of one
thing at a time.

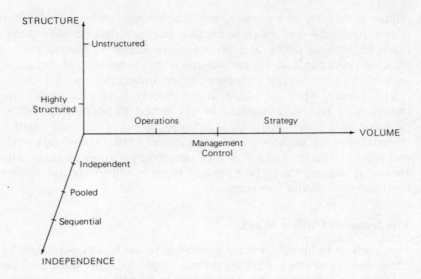

Figure 12.3 *Characteristics of Office Tasks*

One attempt to measure the different tasks undertaken in the office is shown in Figure 12.4. This represents an analysis of the time spent by secretaries and managers at one of IBM's research labs. The proportion of typing is disproportionately higher than in a normal office due to the number of research papers. However, even in this instance it is clear that using a word processor is unlikely to show any dramatic productivity gains. It will be necessary to provide systems which improve the productivity of a number of these activities before significant overall gains will ensue. Thus systems attempting significantly to impact global office productivity will have to support a number of different functions simultaneously, in an integrated manner.

In general, office workers themselves decide on the sequence of their work. Activities are usually event driven so that an incoming document or message initiates a procedure. There may be a number of conflicting events that cause the office worker to schedule and structure his work. This contrasts with the normal dp approach where the system is 'in charge' and dictates the structure to be followed.

Certain procedures will be explicit and laid down, but many situations will be handled informally, often by precedent — for example, 'Ask Fred what he did last time it happened.' The informal networks within an office are vital for its well-being, since they represent much of the context of an organisation. It is not that such informal networks cannot be formalised, it is more the scale of them (probably exponentially proportioned to the number of people in the organisation), and their

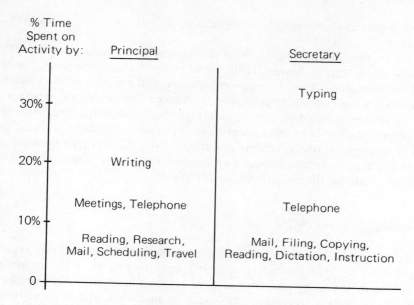

Figure 12.4 *Breakdown of Time Spent on Various Office Activities*

dynamic nature (they are constantly being modified).

Another factor affecting office work is that for many organisations a significant amount of the data processed come from outside the organisation. This means that the organisation will have very little control over the format and content of the data. Human beings are particularly skilful at taking unstructured data and interpreting them. They are using not only their innate mental skills, but also their whole education, training and experience. There may be no theoretical reason why computers can't be made to perform this task equally well, but there are some good reasons why this is unlikely to happen in the near future.

Why Automate?

Having examined the complex nature of the office, one may at first wonder whether it is even worth attempting to automate this complex organism. A large body of opinion would support the view that the status quo has much to recommend it. Is it really sensible to spend a vast amount of time, money and energy on replacing a system that currently functions acceptably, the net effect of which will be to reduce the demand for labour even more? Leaving aside for a moment the employment question which we consider in detail in Chapter 17, there are some very strong pressures driving the movement along towards increased automation.

First, the business climate is becoming ever more hostile. The competition grows fiercer both from home-based companies, multinationals and also from overseas companies. But, being a trading nation, we have no option but to compete. Regulations grow stricter, whether it be in the areas of employment, safety guarantee or marketing. And the market-place becomes increasingly sophisticated, particularly with the use of computers to collect, analyse and model data. All this puts pressure on management to increase their own productivity, to be more effective in an environment that is growing in complexity.

Productivity in the Office

One of the major factors in staying competitive is to achieve greater output while proportionately reducing operating costs — by improving working methods, by investing in more efficient machinery for employees to use, or even by replacing employees by machines. All of these things have been done in manufacturing industry over the past fifty years; but they have been done to a much lesser extent in the office.

	Output per Worker	Output per Production Worker	Output per Knowledge Worker
All Industry	3.6%	16.9%	−6.6%
Goods Sector	10.8%	20.0%	−6.9%
Information Sector	1.7%	9.9%	−2.6%

Figure 12.5 *Changes in Productivity: 1986 compared to the average of the 1970s*

In manufacturing, the ratio of capital investment to labour costs is typically high; in the office, it is very much lower. In part, this appears to be due to an uncertainty whether capital investment in the office does actually pay off in terms of an increased productivity ratio. For example, a study in the USA by Stephen Roach of Morgan Stanley suggests that the productivity of 'knowledge workers' (that is, managers, professionals, clerks, administrators etc.) has actually *fallen* since the 1970s, as Figure 12.5 shows. In the mainframe computer boom of the late 1960s and 1970s, very substantial sums of money were spent on computer systems. But the number of staff actually employed changed very little: some clerical staff were lost, but technical dp staff were employed in their places. Whether overall output increased sufficiently to justify the cost of the equipment is generally very difficult to judge, though some organisations undoubtedly managed to enlarge their businesses considerably without increasing their white-collar workforce.

Today, though, the balance is undoubtedly swinging in favour of technology. Staff costs are increasing steadily whereas the cost of hardware is falling dramatically. An office long on labour and short on technology is expensive and inefficient by today's standards.

In many organisations, office costs now exceed half of the total overheads, a proportion which has steadily increased. Surveys suggest that, on average, roughly 10 per cent of revenue is spent by manufacturing companies on office costs, though this might range from 3 per cent to 4 per cent for process industries such as oil companies, to as much as 14–15 per cent for fabrication manufacturing companies with large sales and service operations. In the case of organisations where the office is the shop floor, such as insurance companies and financial institutions, the average overhead appears to be around 15 per cent and can easily exceed 20 per cent.

Further productivity increases in the manufacturing side of an organisation can be difficult to come by, so the office is an obvious candidate for attention. In a period of slow economic growth, the focus has to be on reducing costs, and as the office represents such a sizeable proportion of these, it has to be an opportune time for office automation to be extended.

What to Automate

The next question is, what is one trying to achieve by automation? This goes back to our previous discussion on automation *versus* mechanisation. A mechanical copy of the current system is unlikely to be effective. Similarly automating individual activities will show short-term gains, but may not help towards an overall solution.

If the objective is to reduce office costs, then it is obvious where the major part of this lies, namely the cost of managers, their salaries and the enormous infra-structure needed to support them. Other costs are usually a fraction of this, though one must qualify this when talking about a clerical office. Thus a major objective must be to increase the effectiveness of a manager.

One of the major functions of management is decision taking, and office automation must improve the quality of the decisions. However, this is more easily said than done, for the quality of decision making is a very difficult thing to measure. Indeed, the process of taking decisions is one that is very imperfectly understood, and is one on which there are several conflicting views. We have to rely heavily on the subjective view of managers as to whether this type of technology helps them to do their job better. The measurable achievement of improved decision-support systems may become apparent only after some considerable time has elapsed, when it becomes possible to see that the whole organisation is functioning more efficiently as a result of office automation. Even so, productivity is a subjective measure, as it all depends on who you are and what you are measuring.

Managers require support in four main areas: communications; storage and retrieval of information; management of information (avoidance of 'information overload'); and provision of analytical tools.

Many of the existing forms of message-sending are cumbersome. There is nothing particularly straightforward about the process of dictating a letter to a secretary, waiting for it to be typed, proof-reading it, and returning it to the secretary for sending through the post or a manual internal mail service. Manually dialling the telephone number of someone who is frequently away from his or her desk (or asking a secretary to do this) is also a frustrating and unreliable process.

New forms of information technology have a clear role to play here. Electronic mail, word processing, automated telephone dialling, paging systems, telephone answering systems: each one improves the process. But if these methods are to be used regularly, they need to fit easily into the infrastructure of the manager/secretarial support system.

Word processing and electronic mail improve the process only peripherally if the manager still relies upon a secretary to perform the necessary keyboarding. There has been much debate about whether managers will, or even should, use keyboards themselves. Today the answer is slowly becoming apparent. They will, so long as they perceive it as being to their benefit timewise and so long as it is seen as a task which corresponds with their status. Dealing directly with a personal computer, and typing in short instructions or messages, can be a managerial task; inputting a long report or memo, or even correcting one already in the system, is typically still seen as a secretarial function. It is significant that today the word 'typing' is out of fashion. Managers may put their fingers on the keys in just the same way as typists do (albeit more clumsily, much of the time), but they don't type; *they* have 'keyboarding skills'!

Storage and retrieval of information is an increasingly important task in today's office. Information collected in many different forms, from many different sources, needs to be filed away in a structure that enables its easy retrieval when required. Some of the technical problems associated with file structuring are discussed in the next chapter.

Another aspect of the information issue is the need for easy access to external sources of information: for example, financial data such as the IMF (International Monetary Fund) database, or any of the wide number of on-line databases now available.

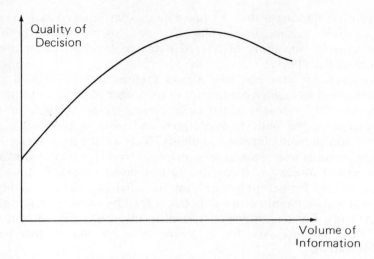

Figure 12.6 *Information Overload*

Automated solutions to these issues involve the linking of communications and filing facilities, so that — for instance — all electronic mail is automatically filed, perhaps in date order. Diary maintenance, too, is often automated today: the computer stores structured information about the manager's schedule, and it can be automatically interrogated (perhaps in conjunction with several other electronic diaries) in order to find suitable dates for a meeting.

The problem of *information overload* is summed up by Figure 12.6. The quality of a decision initially improves as the amount of relevant information available increases from zero; but at some point it reaches a maximum, and from then onwards the effect of extra information is actually detrimental. With too much information available, the individual's ability to sift out the relevant data, assimilate it and use it as a basis for making decisions, rapidly begins to fall under the burden. Passive retrieval systems can add to information overload simply by making it too easy to obtain too much information. Today's managers need active retrieval systems that are capable of automatically scanning incoming information according to preset criteria and presenting to the manager's attention only what needs to be presented.

Two methods of information reduction can be used. The first is a modelling method, whereby the data are scanned for patterns, and then the exceptions and trends that the modelling makes apparent (not the raw data) are presented for attention. The second is a filtering method: information filtering has long been done by people, but today they can be aided by machines which can, for example, scan documents for keywords which suggest that they may be of particular interest. One difficulty with information filtering is that the raw data used as input to each stage may subsequently become inaccessible if it fails to pass through the net. Consequently, the users of filtered data are entirely reliant upon the quality of the filtering.

Consider, for example, how a sales forecast may be arrived at. The salesmen and women give estimates of their next year's sales to their area manager. The manager may revise these, taking account of his/her knowledge of the individual salesmen and women, their sales performance and previous forecasting ability. This area sales forecast is then passed upwards to a regional sales manager who repeats the process, and the regional forecast is forwarded to a national manager who also has scope to use his/her judgement on its reliability. The resulting final forecast will be based on raw data but shaped by many different people's judgements. For an automated system to take on a task such as this, it will first be necessary for it to be able to mirror this level of sophistication.

Finally, the manager needs a set of *analytical tools* to be used in manipulating and investigating the information. Modelling a process, for example, means that various different assumptions can be incorporated, various decisions tested, and their outcomes assessed. Sensitivity analysis and the 'what if' process make decision-making a less trial-and-error operation: the trials are made, and the errors hopefully discovered, *before* the decision is put into operation.

The first tool for managerial analysis was the electronic spreadsheet: a simulation on computer of the rows and columns of data which managers use in, for example, budgeting, cash-flow forecasting, sales forecasting and similar operations. The first widely used spreadsheet, Visicalc, has now been superseded by a host of more powerful second generation products, of which the long-standing market leader is Lotus 1–2–3, an integrated product which also includes some word processing and graphic capabilities. The spreadsheet is the supreme general-purpose tool, but a whole host of more special-purpose aids to managerial decision-taking have also been developed.

Obviously a manager has to perform many other functions to these basic four, but help in these areas alone could contribute to an enormous improvement in management productivity, as well as to an improvement in the quality of management. There are two important qualifications about the way these facilities must be provided. First, it is all but essential that the different functions be integrated. Once information is held within the system, it should be capable of being used by any program, any resource, without need for re-entering or for elaborate translation routines. And second, the system must be easy to use. In the next chapter we discuss these two points more fully.

The latest breakthrough in integrated information management systems is 'New Wave' from Hewlett-Packard. This is a software front end, utilising the PC standard 'windows' software to provide a consistent user interface both to PC applications and to those elsewhere on the network. Its breakthrough capabilities are twofold. First, it maintains 'hot' links between applications. For example, data from Lotus 1–2–3 can be used to produce a graph, then both data and document are processed by desktop publishing software. Changes to the Lotus spreadsheet automatically generate changes to the graph and the final document. Second, it incorporates 'agents': expert systems which can be 'trained' by the user to repeat commonly performed complex tasks at a single command.

There is a considerable difference in the way different levels of management utilise information: senior management spend more time on planning activities, while junior management would be mainly engaged in control activities. To do this, senior management are more likely to make use of external information which would tend to be unstructured, while junior management are more likely to use structured internal information. To perform their control functions, junior management would make use of detailed internal information, whereas senior management would rely on summarised information. This is obviously an oversimplification, but it highlights the different requirements of any integrated information processing system.

Having looked at some of the requirements for the electronic office, we will now turn our attention to the way that many organisations are progressing along the path.

Towards the Electronic Office

The starting point for many offices is word processing. This is a natural entry point for two reasons. One, it is an area in which productivity gains can easily be seen and measured; and two, it deals with the task of putting information into electronic form, and thus introducing it into the automated system.

Most large typing pools have by now been mechanised or automated, and the productivity gains have often been dramatic. The size of the gain depends upon the type of work. Long documents needing several revisions may show gains of 5 to 1, and similar gains can be achieved where documents consist largely or even entirely of standard paragraphs put together in different combinations. In typing short, one-off letters the improvement in productivity is much smaller, though here there is at least a quality improvement: no errors, no Tippex!

The transition from copy or audio typing to word processing has changed the relationship between document originators, keyboard operators and supervisors. There are far fewer natural breaks with word processing, and this leads to the danger of expecting too much continuous effort. Typists who can theoretically operate at 60 words per minute cannot be expected to keep up this rate for minute after minute, let alone hour after hour.

Today, though, it is questionable whether word processing centres are the real way forward, or just a transitional stage, much as the dp punch room proved to be. Remote word processing is as unsatisfactory to many document originators as remote data processing proved to be to data originators. It is a major chore for the operators to check on ambiguities or possible errors in dictation, for example; all too often they simply guess, and guess wrong. It is difficult for individuals to ensure that their particular preferences in layout and presentation are adhered to. And for the wp operators, too, the battery-hen atmosphere and the lack of contact with other staff can make it difficult to achieve any job satisfaction.

Now that it is relatively simple to transmit documents electronically, there is a growing trend for word processors to be dispersed throughout an organisation, just as personal computers have been. The continuing fall in the cost of the technology, and the much lower importance placed on intensive use of this resource, enhances the trend. Five years ago, individual secretaries could hope for an electronic typewriter at best; the word processors were confined to the pool, or provided as a communal resource, a system which makes many people shy about learning to use new technology. Today the word processor is cheap enough for it to be possible to put one on every secretary's desk.

Electronic Mail

In the mechanised office, the word processor is seen as a tool for the production of a defined end-product: a letter on paper. The automated office takes a different approach. Why use paper at all; why not keep all but a small minority of information in electronic form throughout?

The 'paperless office' is a concept that has been bandied about for a good fifteen years, and many people protest that it was a misguided concept: it hasn't happened, and won't happen. But slowly and quietly it *has* happened, at least to a measurable extent and one which can be expected to grow still more over the next decade or so.

Once upon a time, all messages which could not be conveyed in face-to-face conversation were transmitted on paper. Then came the telephone and the telex, and, with their widespread acceptance, a tendency for letters to be used only for semi-formal communications, where a subsequent record was required to be kept. Now we have electronic mail — a facility for both formal and informal messages to be sent over long distances, even to individuals who are not readily available at the end of a telephone.

As the electronic mail system becomes more widespread, as more and more organisations and parts of organisations are linked together by special-purpose or general-purpose networks, and as more and more people have electronic 'mailboxes', so electronic mail comes to be seen by an increasing number of people as a first-resort method of communication. Many individuals now start their working day by checking on the contents of their computer mailbox; only afterwards do they turn to the pile of paper the postman has delivered.

The mailbox is a facility for sending quick messages, not formal, carefully written letters. There is no scope for fancy layout or the electronic equivalent of embossed notepaper; instead, there is a definite trend towards shortened, cryptic notes. 'HOW R U', 'C U TONITE', 'PLIZ SEND ME NEW SYS DOC MAN': this 'terminalese' is common among users of computer terminals, particularly among researchers and journalists whose communications are governed by a very tight budget.

Electronic mail seems today to be used largely for these short messages and for their opposite: very long communications, which can be sent down the wires at off-peak periods. Many journalists today send their copy to their newspaper or magazine offices by this method. There is no need for them to take the time to print out a hard copy and carry it to the post office; no risk of the letter getting lost in the post, no hefty parcel charges to pay. (Others 'cheat' with a half-measure method: they send their documents on floppy discs through the post.)

The term 'electronic mail' embraces many other methods and services, including (in some definitions) fax and telex. We discussed some of the permutations in Chapters 10 and 11. The great advantage of all these methods is that the data arrive at their destination in a form in which not only can they readily be read and assimilated (and printed out on paper, if required), but they can also very easily be stored electronically for subsequent retrieval.

To an organisation which is moving away from rooms full of paper files, and towards compact electronic databanks held (for example) on magnetic or optical discs, it is the paper communication that is a nuisance; the electronic communication is positively welcomed.

Word processing, on-line databanks, at least a small measure of electronic mail, personal computer work-stations as support devices for managers — many organisations now use all these tools of the information age. The question now is, where to next? This must depend to a very large extent on the suppliers and the strategies they adopt. We discuss them in the next chapter.

13

The Electronic Office

Having explored the nature of the office, we can now look at the various strategies that the suppliers are adopting. Why is it that so many different types of organisations are trying to enter the office automation market? One reason is the technological convergence that we have already discussed. Industries which traditionally were in different markets, such as computing, communications, and office products, now find that they are developing products that overlap the traditional market boundaries.

All the suppliers believe that the Electronic Office Systems (EOS) market will expand at a rapid pace. This conclusion is usually arrived at by assuming that organisations will increase their capital investment per office worker, as we discussed in the previous chapter. However, each industry has its own reasons — the dp industry is beginning to mature, with growth rates dropping to those of more traditional industries. They have a great need to find new or expanding markets in order to maintain revenue and growth, as their raw materials (i.e. the electronic components) are falling in cost every year by about 20 per cent. Both the computer and semiconductor industries are thus hoping that EOS are going to be voracious consumers of their products.

The communications companies are in a different position, particularly with the growing wind of deregulation that is sweeping through the world. New aggressive companies are entering the market and the communications giants are finding that the previously quiet, protected havens are being disturbed by unruly competitors from other industries. The office products industry, on the other hand, is fighting for its very life and unless it makes the change to a total system supplier, it is likely to be relegated to the role of component supplier.

Widely Different Strategies

The electronic office is neither entirely distant today, nor absolutely here. There are still very real limits to the types of equipment that can communicate with each other, and to the ways in which they can communicate. We are not yet in a situation where data-flow from device to device is always simple and straightforward. Though it is possible today to discern approaches which different suppliers are taking, and to outline the types of system which they hope will be the outcome, it is important to appreciate that electronic offices, functioning perfectly in every respect, are still in the future. Distributed data processing is here; the local area network is here; but many of the important links that will be needed before the electronic office is a commonplace reality are still being forged today. Indeed, several false starts, especially in the USA, in terms of overambitious claims for the capabilities and benefits of office automation, have led to its becoming almost a derogatory phrase in many management circles. Today the reference is increasingly to 'integrated information management' as the desired end.

The very wide range of strategies adopted by suppliers of electronic office equipment inevitably reflect the traditional businesses of the companies concerned: computer vendors, mini, micro or mainframe; office products suppliers; or telecommunications equipment companies. The major variations in approach are as follows:

Distributed Data Processing   a linked network of PCs, mini- and microcomputers

Local Area Network   a standard communications 'ring main' into which can be plugged work-stations and many other devices

Computerised PABX   computer controlled telephone exchange which can handle any type of different digitised signals

Integrated Computer Systems totally automated dp systems which replace the office

DDP Approach

Many traditional computing companies approach office automation as a natural development of distributed data processing. New applications will, according to this philosophy, be grafted on to the existing 'star' type configuration of computers and terminals linked in a hierarchical network. For example, in a very large organisation a large mainframe computer can provide the most appropriate core for a central database, storing all the structured corporate data. Individual applications might more appropriately be processed in minicomputers dedicated to a particular use (e.g. sales order processing, or financial accounting). Clusters or intelligent terminals or personal computers would be grouped round one or more co-ordinating minicomputers, and would provide work-stations for individually oriented applications such as word processing, financial planning, electronic mail, and diary and calendar maintenance. In a smaller organisation all the co-ordination and centralised data maintenance might be carried out by a single mini- or mainframe computer, or a cluster of linked minis.

This is very much a systems approach, and a natural extension of the type of dp organisation that has grown up in medium-sized and larger organisations with a long history of dp experience. The key characteristic is its hierarchical nature, with clearly delineated lines of responsibility; the data processing department acts as a co-ordinating force, ensuring that all equipment and applications are run on compatible and consistent lines, and are interrelated as far as is technically possible. But it will only reach its full realisation when manufacturers have reached a stage at which large and small computers genuinely *do* use the same operating systems, the same data structures, and when their applications present a common front to the user. This is by no means absolutely the case today.

Local Area Network Approach

The looser, less hierarchical local area network approach is very popular at the moment. One of its strongest original advocates was the Xerox Corporation, but LANs are now offered by a very wide assortment of suppliers, from telecommunications authorities to major computer manufacturers. Its technical characteristics were described in Chapter 10.

In the LAN approach, the emphasis shifts away from the central controlling computer, and *towards* the concept of linkages. The vital element is the network itself, which might be thought of as a kind of electronic 'ring main', or information highway, which runs around the building being co-ordinated. Work-stations (broadly autonomous micro-computers and similar devices) are then plugged into the network and provide the primary computing resources to their individual users, while being supported by the network's wider resources. In its fullest realisation, these resources would typically include a file storage system, on which all the work-stations can store documents of common interest, and from which those documents can be retrieved; a flexible communications gateway, allowing stations on the local network to communicate also with the wider public network; and various printers and other specialist input and output devices: perhaps a video camera interface, a document reader, a telex interface, and so on.

Much progress has been made on developing a set of standards that will allow a wide variety of different devices to communicate freely on this type of network. The ISO/OSI model (International Standards Organisation Open Systems Interconnection model) deals with the myriad complexities by separating them out into a series of physical and conceptual layers, and standards are being developed to describe the necessary protocols at each layer. However, to fully specify such standards, and then to develop a wide range of equipment which complies with them, is a very long and slow process.

If the example of dp systems is anything to go by, customers initially like single supplier solutions, so that at first they will install a network containing only equipment supplied by, say, IBM or DEC. Once they feel confident about the network's operation they will then experiment with devices from other manufacturers that conform to the same communications standards but provide improved facilities in other respects. Finally, maturity will be reached when a full range of plug-compatible devices becomes available, and the choice of each network component is made on the basis of the individual merits of the competing devices.

Computerised Telephone Exchange Approach

This approach has been adopted by manufacturers of telecommunications equipment on the philosophy that the heart of the office lies in vocal communications, and on the basis of the actuality that many offices already possess a very extensive network of telephone extensions, which makes a natural focus for extension into a comprehensive data network.

As we outlined in Chapter 10, great strides have already been taken, particularly in PABXs, towards the provision of intelligent telecommunications facilities: for example, exchanges that incorporate sophisticated telephone-answering and message-switching facilities, as well as semi-automated dialling. With the switch in telecommunications to a digital network, the way is opened for this network to act as the arteries of the electronic office. One building block of this approach has been the introduction of integrated telephone/personal computer devices, such as ICL's One Per Desk, which act as multipurpose personal terminals giving access to every part of the system.

The advantage of an approach based on the telephone exchange is that it builds on the major existing means of office communication, i.e. voice, and so provides a natural evolutionary path. There need be no dramatic change, but rather the gradual introduction of new facilities which can coexist with the less powerful older devices during the transition period.

Integrated Computer System Approach (via Electronic Data Interchange: EDI)

This approach seeks to make the office virtually redundant, or at least the clerical part of it, by integrating office functions with the overall automated running of a manufacturing, warehousing or similar organisation. It is best illustrated by two examples.

First, there is the motor vehicle spare parts system run by both UNIPART and Ford (illustrated as Figure 13.1). Each dealer who uses the system has a touch-tone phone (commonly used in the US as a simple computer terminal, each key emits a different tone which is normally used to indicate the dialling code). To place an order for spare parts, the dealer dials the appropriate computer which communicates with the user (the dealer) via a voice response system. So the computer welcomes the dealer with an appropriate greeting and asks for an identification code to be entered; this will be confirmed by the computer system by replying with the dealer's name. Stock items, numbers and quantities are then entered by the dealer, with the computer confirming vocally the type of part requested, then checking the stock file for availability. The voice response can come either from pre-recorded messages or from a synthesised voice which has far greater potential range of vocabulary. Once the order has been received it can be processed automatically. Picking lists are generated for an automatic warehouse; accounts are automatically produced and in theory the funds transfer could be

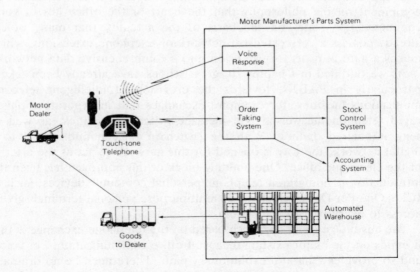

Figure 13.1 *Motor Spares System*

automatically initiated. Not all of this system is yet working, but potentially it does have a major impact on a number of hitherto separate office functions.

The second example is in the food retailing business. Consider what normally happens when an order is placed. A supermarket stock control system would identify items to be ordered and produce the necessary paper work. This would probably be checked manually, then put into envelopes; the order would be dispatched through the print room, then to the post office and on to the food manufacturer. Here, the mail would be opened and sent to the relevant input point to the order processing system which, if appropriate, would generate an acknowledgement. This process would continue with documents travelling backwards and forwards between the supermarket and the food manufacturer until the goods were delivered and payment made. The information flows in this process are illustrated in Figures 13.2a and 13.2b.

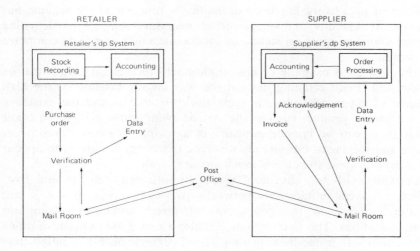

Figure 13.2a *Food Retailer/Supplier System*

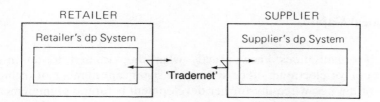

Figure 13.2b *Food Retailer/Supplier System, Electronic Ordering and Invoicing*

In the UK, the Retail Consortium, a group of major supermarkets (Boots, Fine Fare, Woolworth, Tesco and Makro) and food manufacturers (Birds Eye, United Biscuit, Reckitt & Colman, Pedigree Petfoods), introduced a pilot scheme to automate this process, and a number of other large organisations have now followed suit. The Retail Consortium's scheme is centred around the Article Numbering System, the bar-code series of black and white stripes that is now displayed on virtually all packaged food and associated items. Using the Article Numbering System and bar-code readers to feed information on items sold directly into the computer system, it is possible for sales and purchases to be linked together automatically. Thus when Tesco's stock of frozen peas runs low, its computer identifies this and automatically initiates an order for new supplies from the Birds Eye computer.

In theory no paperwork need be exchanged at all in this type of system, as all communications are electronic and automatic. In practice supermarket chains do still have offices staffed by human beings! But the volume of paperwork has been dramatically reduced as the scheme has proved its viability. Obviously it is necessary for all participating organisations to agree on standards for the messages sent from computer to computer.

This is a good example of how traditional office clerical work can be automated. Food retailing has led the way largely because of the high volume of expensive-to-handle paperwork previously, and the existence of a common product coding: the Article Numbering System. In other fields there can be greater difficulty in agreeing standards for product codes and messages, but already this type of system is starting to appear on a general (and sometimes much smaller) scale.

Certainly with the advent of more sophisticated, reliable and cost-effective telecommunications networks, we can expect to see a still greater increase in the proportion of direct computer-to-computer communications. This latter situation is also a very good example of office automation systems addressing a high-level strategic problem, rather than specific, personal tasks.

Technical Gaps

Even if organisations knew exactly what they wanted to do in the application of electronic office systems, a significant number of technical pieces of the jigsaw require further development before total implementation is common. The following paragraphs describe some of the more significant problem areas.

Document Input

One of the transitional problems of EOS is the interface to the printed word. Most organisations have large archival files of printed paper, and before an electronic system can fulfil every function all of this information needs to be captured by the system. This problem will gradually diminish over time, but at the moment it presents a very real obstacle in many organisations.

There are two ways in which a document may be displayed on a video screen. The computer may interpret and then display it character by character, or it may view it as an entire digital image, a pattern of black and white dots, or of coloured areas. Though the two can look very similar, there is a vital difference. With a digital image, the computer has no knowledge of its contents. It is solely a 'picture', and it is not possible for individual words or figures to be retrieved and manipulated, except in purely visual ways. If digital images are subsequently to be retrieved, then it is necessary for additional reference information to be entered with them.

Digital images can be captured and displayed in a variety of ways; perhaps most commonly, via a video camera. If the information on a document is to be captured intelligently, the corresponding device is an *optical character reader* (OCR). This scans a document, identifying individual characters, and then interprets the information in the same way as if it had been typed in, character by character. OCR devices have been developed to a considerable degree of sophistication, but this process is still complex and consumes a great deal of time and processing power. All but the most complex OCRs can read only specially prepared documents — a category into which, alas, many archival files do not fall.

Voice Input

The most natural means for people to communicate is by talking, and commentators have been predicting for many years that eventually the keyboard will be superseded by the advent of terminals that can directly process voice input.

Voice input is a reality today: computers do have the capability to recognise human speech, and to store it in character form. But this capability is still very restricted. Many systems have to be 'trained' to recognise every word and phrase in a limited vocabulary, spoken by specific voices only. Most can identify only disconnected speech, and have great difficulty in interpreting the kind of continuous speech that we habitually use.

Voice input systems have developed a niche market: they are a practical alternative in areas where operators are unable to use keyboards (perhaps because their hands are fully occupied on some other task), the background noise is low, and the input vocabulary is relatively small and predetermined. But the original predictions that this input method would expand out of the niche market to become the normal input method, now seem to have been rather overoptimistic. The great difficulties in devising a system that can cope with words and phrases with similar sounds and different meanings (e.g. 'grey tape' and 'great ape'), with extraneous background noise and with unusual voice pitches or accents have not yet been overcome.

A computer that can understand, or even recognise, speech with the same facility that another human being can will certainly not be with us this century, and probably not until well into the next. However, the motivation to produce such systems is likely to remain high because of their universal appeal (e.g. for automatic language translation), and because they will be enormous consumers of computer memory and processing capability.

Data Storage

There is an enormous requirement for the storage of all types of information in machine-readable form, and quantitative data represents only a small part of this requirement. Textual data require greater storage capacity, as do graphical and recorded voice data, and visual data require even greater capacity. Even a single screen image may comprise hundreds of thousands of bits of information.

We have already discussed secondary storage technologies (see Chapter 3), of which the most important today is the magnetic disc. Though considerable advances have been made in magnetic disc technology, this medium still suffers from relatively limited capacity and from relatively poor reliability. The electronic office will require the capability to keep very high volumes of data on-line, with a rapid access time and total reliability. Today it looks as though optical media offer the best prospects of this, though it remains possible that advances in semiconductor technology, or in some other technology (e.g. holography), may provide a viable alternative within the next few years.

Another aspect of storage is in many respects more problematical: the system by which information is indexed and retrieved. As volumes of data stored are increased many times over, so this becomes an extremely difficult problem. The standard technique is to define a number of *keywords* for a document which is to be indexed. For a letter this could be the date, person, organisation, and a few keywords reflecting the general content. The point about this kind of technique is that when a document is stored, judgements must be made about how it will need to be retrieved in future.

Alternatively, a full text retrieval system requires no prior decisions to be made when a document is stored, but searches all the text for relevant or matching words at the time of retrieval. This obviously places a considerably greater strain on the hardware during the retrieval process. A number of software methods have been developed, including ICL's Content Addressable File Store (CAFS), where much of the work is done by special hardware rather than software. Many of these systems are using indexing techniques in order to cut down the access time.

In typical retrieval systems, the user specifies a set of keywords and the system then responds with the number of documents referenced. The search may then be narrowed down before the documents themselves are actually scanned.

Reliability

A major consideration with the design of an electronic office is its vulnerability to failure. Present offices are vulnerable to power failures, but even during these a basic level of operation can usually be maintained. Failures with an electronic office could mean the work was actually lost, destroyed or 'corrupted' (spoilt), and that the entire office comes to a standstill. If the computer breaks down, no one may be able to process any words, retrieve any documents, transmit any mail or whatever — designing a lot of redundancy into the system could appear extravagant, but in emergency it may be a vital safeguard.

For example, this was brought home to us in the summer of 1981 when the London Business School was struck by lightning. No physical damage was done to the building, but every interface card in our Apple network was disabled, as were a large number of terminals. One of the authors can testify to the frustration of having a morning's work sitting in front of him in an Apple microcomputer, but with no way of saving it. Reliability can be designed into systems by ensuring that they 'fail soft'. In other words if a failure occurs, nothing is lost or corrupted, except maybe the current operation. When the system is restarted then work can continue at the point where it was interrupted.

14

The Challenge of System Development

Even if all the technical gaps discussed in the previous chapter were filled, it is still debatable whether we are yet capable of developing the software for more than a minority of fully automated office systems. Another difficulty is apparent from the many surveys, in both the UK and the USA, which indicate that very few companies have yet developed coherent strategies towards office automation. Several still see the best strategy to be to keep as many options open as possible.

Indeed, many organisations have difficulty in keeping up with the requirements of developing new dp systems, without any of the problems that office automation may bring. To a significant extent this has meant that the strategies are being dictated by suppliers and that potential user organisations are waiting until the shape of competitive products becomes more distinct. As we have already seen, in the electronic office information processing is seldom structured, repetitious, well-defined, or even remotely similar to the characteristics of a good dp application. That makes the traditional dp development process particularly unsuited; but perhaps it is worth while first of all to review this process.

Traditional DP Approach

The first step in the development of a system is to define the objective(s) of the system. This may not be easy if the system is needed to serve a number of different purposes, as they may be conflicting. Unless the objectives are clearly stated, there may be subsequent confusion about the performance of the system and about how to evaluate it. Next a clear statement of the problem can be made in terms of 'what it should do', rather than 'how it should be done'. Having defined the problem, then all of the possible alternative solutions should be identified and evaluated. It may be that none of the solutions is fully acceptable, in which case it may be necessary to go back and modify the statement of the problem. These stages have very often been overlooked in the past as no alternatives were allowed; for example, 'everything will be done on the main UNIVAC computer' may be the only choice given!

Having decided on 'what', the focus can now move to 'how'. A system specification is drawn up which defines the inputs, outputs, database and processing steps. At this stage the emphasis traditionally has been on trying to nail the specification as firmly to the ground as possible (a proverbial analogy would be carving it in tablets of stone). Once specified, a system can be implemented in various ways, traditionally by programming in COBOL or Assembler. The system is then tested and when working to the satisfaction of the dp department, it will be passed to the user for acceptance (at which point the tablets of stone often become important!). Systems of any complexity are not liable to be error-free when delivered, and a period of live usage will be necessary to make it sufficiently robust.

Having developed a working system it must then be installed. This may involve conversions from other systems, parallel running to ensure accuracy, phased implementation, etc. Users must be trained and

---

1. Set Objectives:
    reconcile conflicting needs;
    statement of 'what'.

2. System Selection:
    identify alternatives;
    evaluation and choice.

3. System Design:
    statement of 'how';
    data entry, database, reports.

4. Implementation:
    programming, testing, acceptance;
    documentation and training;
    installation and parallel running.

5. Evaluation:
    systems audit and review;
    maintenance and update;
    replacement.

Figure 14.1 *System Development Cycle*

documentation provided at various levels. Some evaluation must be made as to whether the system meets its specified performance criteria and as to the success of the development process. This will be an ongoing process as the system needs to be maintained and adapted. At some stage in the life of a system it will be necessary to replace it and this will restart the system development life cycle. These stages in systems development are summarised in Figure 14.1 — or alternatively Figure 14.2.

Uncritical acceptance
Wild enthusiasm
Dejected disillusionment
Total confusion
Search for the guilty
Punishment of the innocent
Promotion of non-participants

Figure 14.2 *Phases in System Development*

Limitation of Traditional Approach

There are three major principles involved in the traditional dp approach to systems development, namely:

people know what they want, and this is capable of being precisely specified;

it is possible to divide office operations up into discrete groups, each of which involves sufficient individual operations to justify the cost of writing a program to automate it;

once a system is specified, only minor changes are likely to occur to it.

Unfortunately none of these applies with any degree of accuracy to the electronic office. It certainly does not seem practicable to specify all the procedures that make up the function of an office. Even less is it possible to classify them all into neat, self-contained groups, with tidy interfaces to each other. The typical office is a dynamic environment, constantly adapting itself to new conditions, and this conflicts with the static nature of dp systems and tools. The potential number of different types of transaction in an office environment is infinite and many of these may occur infrequently, or even once only.

However, the case should not be overstated. The work of the typical office *does* involve a great many routine tasks, which those who handle them automatically tend to divide into certain basic categories. In an insurance office, for example, it is not difficult for the rawest of clerks to tell the difference between new business, renewals and claims, even if he or she ends up with a left-over pile of work which has to be classified as 'miscellaneous'.

In the era of centralised dp departments, the traditional approach concentrated on mechanising the routine operations and leaving the miscellaneous for manual exception handling. In contrast, the electronic office has to find a way of automating *every* operation, of fitting every exception into an overall system.

Precisely programmed dp applications provide a structure within which the user can operate; and this in itself is admirable and necessary, so long as the structure is sufficiently flexible to accommodate at least most cases. The basic applications are main roads down which the user can travel. But if the user is to live in his motor car and never step out of it, then he or she also needs side roads, even tiny tracks. It is necessary to give users the capability to define their own paths, or to deviate from the prescribed paths as they find necessary: to provide their own structure.

This is no small demand, and it is made in an era in which it is increasingly being perceived that the traditional approach to dp development no longer functions satisfactorily, even for the most precisely definable, unchanging applications. New systems are not implemented on time, do not meet user needs, or are over budget; even the simplest of modifications to existing systems appears to take months, and complex changes are not attempted; dp staff are increasingly tied up in maintenance of present systems, with fewer and fewer resources being available for new system developments; in many organisations the backlog of applications (identified but not implemented) accounts for several years of development time, and continues to grow.

Clearly not all of these points apply to all organisations, but enough do apply for these caricatures to strike chords in many organisations. And indeed it is very understandable that when a system reaches mammoth proportions, and users expect every part of it to interconnect satisfactorily with every other part, then the problem soon attains an intolerable level of complexity.

Systems scientists have already pointed to some tentative solutions. Total interconnectivity is simply impracticable, so it is necessary to limit connectivity, to reduce the number of potential paths down which users can travel. Doing everything centrally imposes an unacceptable administrative overload, therefore it is necessary to decentralise some applications, though in ways which are carefully defined so that file consistency is maintained, and anarchy avoided. Telling the computer *how* to do everything is impossible; the current trend, as we saw in Chapter 4, is towards non-procedural programming techniques which merely tell the computer *what* to do, and leave it to figure out the rest for itself. Writing a custom program for every small application is not practicable; therefore it is necessary to use more general, off-the-peg tools to handle the smaller scale tasks.

General-purpose Tools

The personal computer, delivered as it is, straight from the box, is merely a lump of hardware. Connecting it to a mainframe computer and making it act as a terminal is only half a solution; as we have seen, it does not address the problem of work that is not centralisable, and does not need to be centralised. Managers and professionals have neither the time nor the expertise to program their own specific applications. Instead, they need general-purpose tools that give them a framework within which they can develop their own working methods.

Personal computer software development has concentrated largely on providing just these. Many software houses *do* market programming languages, but many, many end-users never write a line of source code. Instead, they use general-purpose application packages — spreadsheets, word processors, filing programs, and all-in-one packages — which they can twist to fit their own requirements with the minimum of effort.

The spreadsheet is perhaps the most fundamental of managerial/professional tools, as the word processor is the fundamental secretarial tool. Millions of copies of the most popular spreadsheet packages — Visicalc, Lotus 1–2–3, Multiplan, and an army of imitators — have been sold. They are used for millions of different specific purposes.

At its simplest, the spreadsheet simulates a blank spread of paper, divided up into rows and columns, which are typically labelled with numbers and letters (A1, B1 and so on) and can generally be given more descriptive names as well, such as 'January, February' or 'Projected Sales Product A', or 'Sales Subtotal'. The total sheet is usually much larger than can be displayed on a typical 80-column by 25-line video screen; the screen acts as a window on to a small area (or sometimes several areas at once) of the total sheet that is held in memory.

Into each cell of the sheet can be inserted text, numbers, or formulae which determine how the numbers are to be manipulated (e.g. $G3 = G1 + G2$, though they can be much more complex than this!). Absolute or relative relationships between various rows and columns can be specified, so that it is easy to — for instance — indicate that sales are to be made to grow at 10 per cent per year or month in either a simple or a compound manner, or that the unit price must be multiplied by the sales volume to produce the total sales value.

The really clever part of the system is that the effect of changing any number on the sheet can quickly and easily be reflected throughout the sheet — so that, for instance, it is only a few seconds' work to compare the effect of estimating the growth in sales at 10 per cent, 15 per cent or 20 per cent. This enables a whole range of interactive sensitivity analyses to be undertaken.

Today's generation of spreadsheets responds to a wide variety of commands that effectively add up to a non-procedural programming system. Most have sophisticated commands for controlling the screen window on to the spreadsheet contents, locking some columns and scanning through others, changing the size of rows and columns, inserting or deleting rows or columns, sorting the sheet according to the contents of one or more row or column, and so on. As well as handling simple (and complex) algebraic formulae, they contain inbuilt formulae for calculating compound interest rates, rates of return, net present value, the number of days elapsed from any specified calendar date, and a host of other features. Spreadsheets can be saved, retrieved, and merged with each other; formula outlines can be saved, and different sets of figures entered into them. In the hands of a practised user, this simple tool can become anything from a double-entry accounting system to a stock control system to a budgeting system, and many, many other things as well.

Today's spreadsheets are not stand-alone tools; they are carefully integrated into wider suites of managerial aids. One basic enhancement, for example, is to enable the data on the spreadsheet to be transferred to a word processor, so that they can be incorporated into (for example) a professionally laid-out financial report. Another is to integrate graphics capability, so that the same data can automatically be displayed (and printed out on a suitable printer or plotter) in any of a variety of line or bar graph formats. These three capabilities — the spreadsheet with additional word processing and graphics capability — were put together to create Lotus 1–2–3, a massively successful integrated software program which has since spawned many imitators.

Many managers use 1–2–3, or a similar program, as the basic tool on their personal computer: the program they call up automatically, whose commands they know inside out, and whose capabilities they stretch to the limit in order to enable it to do absolutely everything that they might wish to do on a computer. Others turn full-featured word processors to the same purpose. Some of the better programs can sort data alphabetically, can link files in simple record structures, and have quite comprehensive arithmetical features, making them excellent general-purpose tools for the less numerate manager or professional. Others still use 'cardbox'-type filing programs (Cardbox is one of the better known) or database programs designed to run on personal computers. An increasing number use integrated suites of programs. Word Perfect's Executive package, for instance, comprises a fairly simple word processor, a spreadsheet, a telephone directory-type filing program, a calculator, a diary, a disc file maintenance program and several other oddments — all using similar commands and available in seconds from one unified main menu.

Another very common component of integrated sets of programs is a communications program, which enables the user to exchange files with other computers in a local area network or a mainframe-terminal configuration.

Compared to the astronomical cost of purpose-written software developed on a huge centralised system, these general-purpose packages are astonishingly cheap. Even the fullest featured programs rarely cost more than £500 today, and intense competition has pushed down the prices of mass-market software so far that many perfectly adequate spreadsheets and word processors cost £100 or even less. For this minimal price, users often find that they have access to features that their organisation's cumbersome mainframe system simply cannot provide.

One of the most important parts of this type of system — designed for use not by dp professionals but by run-of-the-mill managers, professionals, secretaries and other non-expert users — is the interface between the system and the user. This is often referred to as the *man–machine interface*.

User-friendly Systems

This overworked label is much favoured by suppliers to describe their particular software. The characteristics of these systems would hardly qualify them for the label of friendship in human terms, so we must view this as a relative statement which compares these offerings to the standards set by their predecessors.

The complexity of a system depends on its functionality. The more functions that can be performed, then the more complex the interface necessarily has to be. (It is relatively simple to design 'user-friendly' systems that don't do anything.) But careful planning can make a very powerful system easy to use: for example, basic facilities that every user will need can be made easily accessible, while other, advanced features are tucked away, and need come to the notice only of expert users.

There is also much confusion between 'ease of use' and 'ease of learning'. Electronic office systems need to be sufficiently simple and straightforward that the vast majority of general office staff can handle them; without necessarily making every conceivable task effortless, they must avoid being unduly cumbersome to operate. But it would be naïve to believe that someone could effectively use a multifunction workstation with no training at all, and impracticable to make this a predominant design requirement.

   Many professionals are used to training; years of education and training lie behind the acquisition of their professional skills. The evidence to date is that they are prepared to undertake a reasonable amount of training to use the tools of the electronic office, so long as they are convinced of the benefits to be achieved. But many managers in the UK have learned most or all of their skills 'on the job': the concept of in-service training is relatively alien to them, and they cavil at being asked to take time they can ill afford from their managerial duties in order to learn how to operate a new gadget. Systems for these managers must be quick and easy to learn, or they will not be used at all. But there is a trade-off between the level of knowledge required of the user and the degree of functionality delivered by the system: those who put little or nothing into learning about their tools can expect to get little or nothing out of them. This is illustrated in Figure 14.3, which also indicates where there may be room for improvement in system teaching methods, to ensure that those with minimal time and effort to spare get as much as possible from their systems.

   Users should have to refer to manuals as little as possible, and preferably only in exceptional circumstances. Even the most conscientious user cannot be expected to plough through hundreds of pages of turgid information before starting to use a system; essential information can, and should, be provided on-screen rather than in a manual that is easily lost or ignored.

   The system should contain a hierarchy of information about its operation, so that only the information that is actually necessary is presented at any time. At any point the user should be able to request a list of functions that are available, and should be able to obtain on-screen

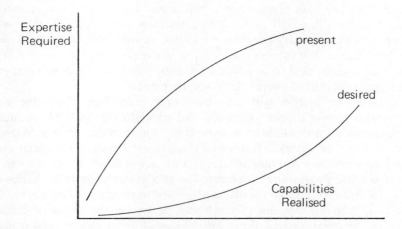

Figure 14.3 *Systems Development*

as much help as is necessary to enable him or her to use those capabilities correctly.

There should be a consistent syntax, so that the user knows the rules of any dialogue with the system. (For instance, it might always be necessary to press Return after replying to a query, or never necessary; but not a random combination of the two.) A list of valid vocabulary should be available at each point in the dialogue.

The dialogue with the user should have at least two levels: novice mode, and expert mode. (Some programs provide three, four or even more user levels.) In the novice mode the dialogue will be verbose, with sufficient explanation to instruct a newcomer what to do at every stage. The regular user will find that this verbosity is intrusive; it takes up time, and may fill an unacceptably large area of the screen. He or she needs the facility to reduce it to a minimum, giving quick, direct commands rather than working through a long series of nested menus, or entering a number of items at one time, thus skipping over a series of questions.

There should be a facility to put the system into reverse, to allow the user to back out of transactions: to say, 'Oops, I didn't really mean that', and be given a second chance to make a choice. The system should check before performing drastic actions, particularly when these may lead to irretrievable loss of data (for example, exiting from a piece of work without saving it on disc, or deleting one or more disc files). The system must also be tolerant of errors such as invalid choices, pointing out that the command given cannot be executed, and requesting a new choice. All this may seem self-evident, but to programmers it is not so: the traditional approach in dp was for the system to rap users over the knuckles and effectively say, 'As a punishment for not following my instructions to the letter, I have just destroyed your morning's work!'

All these are basic requirements before any system can be described as 'user-friendly'. It is sad to have to relate that until recently they were ignored in many, many program packages, as well as in specially written program suites. But intense competition in the packaged program market has done a great deal to improve standards, and now the most successful packages generally do meet these requirements.

No complex system will ever be totally error-free. Even the most exhaustive testing cannot anticipate and try out every possible sequence of commands a user might give, everything a user might attempt to do, or end up doing by mistake. But a well-programmed system will make every possible allowance for human error, and as much allowance as can be made for the programmer's error, too. If a system regularly 'backs up' files, for instance, automatically saving work in progress to disc every few minutes, then a minimum of work will be lost in the event of disaster striking. In every system there are highways and byways: well-trodden channels down which the user moves quickly with no fear of obstruction, and seldom-trodden paths which are rather more vulnerable to nasty surprises or obstacles. In a good system, if a tree falls on a byway it falls in front of the user, allowing steps to be retraced and another path taken, rather than falling on top of the user, causing total immobility.

One great advantage of mass-market packages is that they have so many thousands of users that in the course of months and years they *are* exhaustively tested. Good professional software houses take note of 'bugs' that are reported by end-users, and make every effort to eradicate them in subsequent releases of the program. This basic level of thoughtful programming is a fundamental requirement of user-friendliness, but a good program will offer more, too. For example, many programs contain some facility for users to define their own procedures; sometimes called a 'macro' facility, this effectively allows users to specify sequences of commands that they use regularly, and substitute for them a single, overall new command. For example, the word processor on which this book has been written allows us to create a special command for 'change the default directory to the "THISISIT" directory, and display a list of all the working files in that directory': a sequence that would normally require ten or eleven key presses, but can then be performed with one.

Even harder to evaluate is that indefinable quality of grace which makes some programs more pleasant to use than others, simply because the key sequences seem to come naturally to the fingers — random guesses when the user is too lazy to check the 'help' pages generally turn out to be right and not wrong, and the programmer seems to have the knack of anticipating what the user will want to do and making it as easy as possible to take the right steps and as difficult as possible to take the wrong ones. *Real* user-friendly programs are ones that regular users enjoy using, whereas user-unfriendly programs have users fuming regularly from start to finish of a work session!

Good programming — that is, thoughtful but rigorous programming — does much to overcome the basic fact that the system is incapable of conversing with us in natural language. Indeed, some innovative programs do make a brave attempt to do just that; and when this is generally possible, systems will truly be user-friendly! Until that time it is necessary to design systems that behave in a predictable manner, that can be learned and used without too much difficulty. This constrained and alien world will hardly be friendly, but at least it may become familiar.

Friendly Operating Environments

A major recent trend has been towards the provision, not only of friendly programs, but also of friendly operating environments within which application programs function.

Typical 'last generation' operating systems were designed primarily for expert users, even on personal computers. When a personal computer was switched on, for example, the operating system would typically come up with a terse prompt like 'A>' and wait for the user to give specific (generally cryptic) instructions before going any further.

Today's operating environments appreciate that end-users need to be encouraged and guided. The trend now is towards graphics environments which display attractively the potential options on screen, and make it easy and simple for the user to select one of them. The windows/icons/mouse/pull-down menus (WIMP) approach, pioneered by Xerox and popularised by Apple's Lisa and Macintosh micros, has been widely adopted — for example by Digital Research in their Gem operating environment, by Microsoft with their Windows environment and by Presentation Manager in IBM's OS/2. On systems like these, the initial screen shows a selection of 'icons', little labelled pictures that illustrate the options available: programs that can be called up, files available on disc, housekeeping options, and so on. A mouse (a device that moves around the desktop, thus moving a small pointer on the screen) is used to point to, and then select (by pressing a button), an icon. With a single button press, an application program can (for example) be called up and a file selected for working on.

'Windows' are a concept devised to enable the user to alternate between several programs on the same personal computer, and to see them operating on screen simultaneously. Each 'window' is effectively a section of the screen, with a clear border drawn around it, within which a program functions. Mouse-operated devices allow windows to be resized, opened and closed, and moved in front of and behind each other, thus allowing the user to make the most flexible use possible of the screen space.

Gem and Windows both create operating environments which enable applications programs running within them to use the same facilities. All Gem programs, for example, can appear on the initial icon screen; all of them use the same mouse commands and the same windowing techniques; all of them have the same type of 'pop down' menus: selecting a keyword displayed at the top of the screen automatically causes a menu to be superimposed on the screen contents; the same mouse movements are always used to select menu choices; the same sequences are used to exit from the program each time, and so on.

These environments are (by current standards) user-friendly in themselves, in that they are simple and straightforward to operate. But beyond this, they make it easy for the user to learn new application programs, simply because each new program works in much the same way as other programs which the user may already be familiar with. Learn one program running under Gem, and it is a quick and simple business to master other Gem programs, too.

Another trend is to make these environments responsive to user requirements: the computer 'remembers' what kind of an introductory screen the user requires, which disc drive is to be used as the default choice, and so on; it remembers what colours the user likes the screen to appear in; it will remember familiar 'macro' sequences of commands for starting up often-used programs and files; it also remembers about the printers used, communications facilities and so on, so that to use any one of the system resources is a quick and simple matter. Novices and experienced users alike are enabled to get more out of their systems, more quickly and easily — which is surely the real meaning of 'user-friendliness'.

Expert Systems

This search to equip our current computerised systems with a 'human window' is likely to prove totally misguided. We are currently building systems which function internally in a totally different way to the human brain. This is because of the vastly different technical characteristics of the 'pieces of hardware'.

The brain is capable of storing a vast amount of information (maybe 10,000,000,000 bits); it can retrieve virtually any chunk of this within a couple of seconds, yet its ability to 'process' information is slight. Short-term memory can hold only about 7 items, maximum processing speed is about 20 discriminations per second and internal information transfer rates can only be described as pathetic (30 bits per second). In comparison, a modern day computer can process millions of instructions in a second (even hundreds of millions). It can store millions of items in its short-term memory and transfer data internally at astonishing speeds. A decent sized dp system can even store about the same amount of information as the brain, but its ability to retrieve information is very clumsy and wooden.

Donald Michie, Professor of Machine Intelligence at Edinburgh University, believes that trying to equip our current type of system with a human face is a bit like giving the inhabitants of Dover a powerful telescope so that they can see the Eiffel Tower. Apparently sound in principle, it overlooks the small matter of the earth's curvature. Michie and a number of academics in the US and elsewhere have been trying to build systems (and succeeding) which in some way mirror the human thought process. *Expert systems*, as they are known, are moulded on the conceptual framework of a human expert in a particular field. These systems, which are specific to a particular application, have the ability to learn from an expert, codify this knowledge, and then store it in a database. The other part of the system is known as the 'inference engine', which allows the system to make inferences from the codified data and thus hold a dialogue with a non-expert. What gives this type of system a 'human face' is that it can explain its decisions by expounding its reasoning; the user can even give the system new information to see if it affects things. This is in total contrast to a black-box system whose answers are given on a 'take it or leave it' basis.

Expert systems for commercial use have been available for several years, but their take-up has been relatively slow, and though the early ones have proved successful and relatively long-lived, only a trickle of new ones have joined them in the market-place. Among the established systems are DEC's system (and other similar ones) to help engineers diagnose faults in computer hardware. This system builds on the experience gained by engineers, so that when a new type of fault is discovered, or a new way of detecting an old problem, the information can be made available to all users of the system. It is an active, rather than a passive, system in that all the information contained in the database is retrieved at the appropriate time, and the engineer is not presented with reams of irrelevant information. Another well-known system, Prospector, helps geologists to analyse rock samples in the search for oil and other minerals; and others are used in medical diagnosis, for example, and to give advice on pension planning and other financial matters.

A newer trend has been the development of *expert system builders*, products somewhere between application programs and non-procedural programming languages, which guide the user through the task of setting up an expert system for himself/herself. The package provides a basic data structure (typically a simple tree-structure, but adaptable within limits to enable it to meet the requirements of the individual system being designed) and an inference engine. The user feeds data and rules on how to use this data into the framework provided, so as to generate an individual expert system. Products such as this (e.g. Intelligent Environments' Crystal, and Expertech's Xi) may become as common-place in tomorrow's office as are spreadsheets in today's, to be seen as fundamental computer tools, a vital building block in the task of helping the office worker to automate as much as possible of his or her work. The business of devising and implementing expert systems — either using builder packages or from scratch using suitable programming languages — is sometimes described today as *knowledge engineering*.

Prototyping

One approach being adopted by several organisations in order to tackle the system development problem is the prototyping of new systems. This is being done both in an attempt to remove some of the existing problems, and to adapt to the changing nature of the systems to be developed. Prototyping is a first attempt at a system design (subsequently it may be enhanced) which is both quick and cheap.

There are several important characteristics of such an approach. First, the prototype system is an operational system — it meets some (limited) real user needs. It can therefore be evaluated against these needs. Second, it provides a mechanism to test out assumptions — both those of the user and the designer — before they are 'cast in stone'. Third, it is developed quickly — the timescale is one of days or weeks, not months or years — so that the user need hasn't significantly changed. Fourth, its development is relatively cheap — using specific development tools, rather than traditional high level languages. Fifth, the prototype system may well turn out to be the final system — alternatively, a more efficient use of resources may suggest a more professional coding. Finally, in concept the prototyping system is an iterative process — the evaluation after each step suggests a next step — abandon the system, finalise the system, or develop a further specific function.

Apart from these generic characteristics of the prototyping approach, there are three major reasons cited by users for its adoption. First, as a way of *clarifying user needs* — as we have discussed previously, the traditional system development process assumes that the user knows what he wants, and can write it down. We have already pointed out that this is a problem with dp systems, and is clearly going to be even more so in the development of electronic office systems. Thus systems development has to acknowledge that users may well be unable to specify exactly what they want. Rapid development of a prototype system may well help to clarify these needs, if only in a negative way. In some organisations this has perhaps been taken to its logical conclusion by providing tools which enable users to develop (or modify) systems for themselves. Such an approach may well, in practice, encourage users to change their minds!

The second reason is as a procedure by which the *validity of a particular system design* can be verified. For example, this can be especially useful in applications where there is a high degree of interface necessary between several systems — prototypes can be designed to evaluate alternative interface designs. A further example is in situations in which particular performance characteristics are critical, such as response times in real-time systems. Again, a prototype system can provide a means by which the performance of alternative system designs can be examined. In comparison with the point made in the previous paragraph, the points in this paragraph deal with the internal design of a system, as compared with the external design described previously.

However, the third reason cited by users is that with which we began this discussion of prototype systems — namely, an effective process for the *successful creation of a final system*. It is this iterative process which lies at the heart of the prototyping approach to system development. Essentially it can be envisaged as a way of breaking down a potentially large development problem into a number of smaller entities, each of which fulfils some need in its own right, and can be individually evaluated. It presupposes that the interface standards can be specified. Although the development of the final system may appear sub-optimal as compared with a single, global development process, this presupposes that a global approach is feasible at the outset, not just with hindsight. However, the overriding advantage of the prototyping approach is its flexibility to modify, or even abandon the overall development strategy. Furthermore, the user receives some supporting system which he can use on a much earlier timescale. This gives him confidence about the success of the overall project, and tends to make him its advocate, rather than detractor.

One thing to remember is that prototyping requires different software tools to enable the designers to create systems rapidly and cheaply. Most of these we have reviewed already. database management systems, application development systems, expert systems, and so on. Not only does it require different software tools, it also requires different skills on the part of the system designers and users. The designer requires the skills of a business, rather than systems analyst. The development procedures too are different from those described earlier in this chapter. As explained earlier, the significant characteristic is the iterative nature of prototyping.

Pragmatic User Strategies

Whilst there are many theories and concepts as to the appropriate next steps in the development of office automation in organisations, these are often perceived by practising managers as being an ideal, but unattainable situation. So it would appear useful to review what pragmatic steps may be taken by an organisation wishing to take the next steps. Five major steps may be identified, based on concepts typically applied to strategic choices facing an organisation.

Critical Success Factors

Critical success factors are a familiar concept to those involved in formulating strategic business policy — they are those few key areas of the organisation which ultimately *must* be got right if it is to be successful. For most organisations critical success factors are few (typically in single figures), and are already identified and generally accepted within the organisation. It is important to appreciate that these factors are in the context of the purposes of the organisation as a whole, not of the dp or information systems department. This step should identify the areas in which efforts should be concentrated, ensuring that the goals of office automation are supporting the overall goals of the organisation.

Needs and Requirements

Having identified the critical success factors for the organisation (or the part of it under consideration), the next step is to examine how improved information support systems could meet specific needs and requirements. Generally, this is accomplished most easily by consideration of the specific needs of the managers concerned. The particular needs of managers that might be addressed have already been discussed in detail in Chapter 12 — namely, communications, storage and retrieval of information, information overload, and analytic tools. The balance between these needs and the specific systems will obviously be determined by the characteristics of the organisation. However, what we must not lose sight of at this stage is the overall critical factor being addressed — specific tools for managers are a means, not an end. Formal procedures have been implemented in some organisations to help identify these needs. Typically these are based around the concept of *Information Resource Management*, and involve current and prospective information flow and requirement surveys, in the form of questionnaires, activity diaries, personal interviews, statistical analysis of file and task activity rates, and so on. Often a useful by-product of such activity is some more coherent view of the current status of automation in the organisation's procedures.

Future Goals

Trying to predict the future, especially in a situation where technology is changing rapidly, is clearly risky. Too often the process is focused closely on the changes in the technology, rather than on the overall system that may be required. Projections are probably best made in the form of scenarios describing how a particular portfolio of technologies might be applied to meet a specific need. These scenarios would include a consideration of the context and environment in which the desired system was to function, both in terms of organisation structure as well as human factors. The aim would be to examine the characteristics of the technologies required for the system to be a success, perhaps the two most important characteristics being price and performance.

These scenarios also have to consider how the functioning of the organisation may change if the systems envisaged in the scenario are indeed successful, and also if they are not. Some examples of such scenarios can readily be seen; for example, the clearing banks may well have as a future goal a system in which personal customers can initiate (and complete) a whole range of transactions from their own homes, perhaps using some viewdata system. Customers could examine balances, initiate and modify standing orders, order foreign currency, order cheque-books and (eventually) make payments. Such a system is technically feasible now, and may well be cost-effective in the not too distant future. But its implementation would clearly have a major impact on the bank's organisational structure, yet meet the needs for reducing operating costs, providing a better service to customers, and improving competitiveness.

Thus, so far in this procedure, critical factors in the success of the organisations — and specifically of a target group of managers and/or processes — have been identified; for these factors specific needs and requirements have been itemised; and, finally, some alternative future goals have been examined, typically in the form of future scenarios. So, how do we progress from the current situation to meet these specified needs? How do we achieve the chosen scenarios?

Building on What You've Got

Most organisations have now taken at least tentative steps towards office automation: usually by mechanising particular office tasks, particularly word processing. As we have discussed earlier, however, the entire development of commercial data processing (from the mid-50s at least until the end of the 1970s) involved the automation of more and more office functions. This led many organisations into a situation where they had a number of data and word processing systems which were operating quite independently of each other.

Many organisations have difficulty in imposing common standards on their existing dp activities, let alone in adding new activities to the roster. For these, the next immediate step is normally to bridge the gap between existing systems — for example, by creating local area networks, and by setting up common files and file protocols.

Building on what is already in place can save in terms of design and development effort, and usually appears as the lowest risk alternative, since the steps involved are typically small ones. It may be possible to implement new systems without making major changes to existing systems, and building on their strength. Even where existing hardware is approaching obsolescence and requires replacement, there is typically a large investment in data capture, program development and staff training in existing systems, and organisations naturally wish to minimise changes that will involve repeating this work. However, there is also the danger that this piecemeal approach may confine developments in areas which are inappropriate. It is important that the previous step of examining future goals should remove any blinkers imposed by existing systems. Many of the products, especially software, that have recently come on to the office automation market are particularly targeted at filling in some of these gaps in existing systems.

As we have described above, a natural strategy for the suppliers of electronic office systems is to build upon their existing market strengths. Thus the computer companies sell ddp, enabling the customers to build networks linking the parts of their present dp systems. Now many of the computer companies are trying to integrate new applications, particularly telecommunications, with their existing dp offerings. Similarly, the telecommunications companies are building voice and text messaging systems into their PABXs, and office products suppliers offer local networks of their word processors, reprographic systems, file stores and so on.

Developing Alternative Plans

In our earlier discussion of system development, and in particular our discussion of some of the problems that users encounter in the use of computer-based systems, we employed the analogy of a highway system: if you stray on to unused by-ways, you may encounter some surprises. In our earlier analogy, we suggested that in complex systems users would inevitably venture down such by-ways sooner or later, and that a characteristic of a good system is that it enables the user to extricate himself safely from such a situation.

As the final stage in our development of a practical plan for the successful implementation of electronic office systems, we would suggest that the user organisation attempt to chart out both the highways and the by-ways facing the organisation in its attempts to adopt such systems. The danger is that the new systems will be seen only in terms of the broad highways opened up by them. The implementing organisation should endeavour to make sure that there are no nasty surprises lurking down the by-ways.

The challenge is to create plans which map out these alternative routes and their consequences, and minimise the nasty surprises. There are several rules of thumb which might be followed: progress should be in the form of short steps, building on established systems. Each new step should be seen as justifiable in itself in the facilities it provides. Unless vitally necessary in terms of the critical factors, the organisation should not be involved in leading edge technology — established, well-understood technologies should be used. It will be important to establish organisation-wide standards where appropriate — especially in communications and user interfaces. Systems should be developed only with full management support in the user departments, and so on — the usual criteria for successful systems development apply. However, perhaps more than present computer-based systems, the new electronic office systems will have greater potential impact on organisational structure and the role of the people who make up the organisation. Thus creation of user standards, support, documentation, education and training is as important as the design details for each system, but an overall concept of the goals of the business and the place of electronic office systems in supporting their achievement is critical. This is the objective of the steps set out in the previous paragraphs.

Conclusions on OA

In conclusion, one might consider the comments of P. A. Strassman who once worked in the Xerox Palo Alto Research Center (PARC). He observed that the office of the future is a label which hides more than it reveals. It is certainly not explicable solely as a technical phenomenon but is better understood as the beginning of structural changes in the job relationships amongst 'knowledge workers'. We can observe some very strong pressures working to make it a reality. Organisations certainly have an increasing problem in the operation of their offices. They would like to be able to substitute capital for labour, thus reducing their overhead costs and increasing their effectiveness. However, in general, they have no clear idea how they are going to do this, but rather are relying on suppliers to provide systems that have the desired effect.

The suppliers believe that if they can just get the bandwagon rolling, it could mushroom into the world's biggest industry. Unfortunately there are still a number of technical gaps which they are doing their best to paper over by designing systems which fit the available technology rather than suiting the user. Even when technology closes these gaps it is still not at all certain that we have the skills to build the software systems necessary.

It is an area that nobody can afford to ignore but at the same time everyone is very wary about making the wrong move. The danger of technological *cul-de-sacs* is very real and the memories of similar disasters with dp systems are fresh in the minds of both users and suppliers. One things seems certain: one day in the not-too-distant future IT is going to happen, and when it does those left out will really be in the cold.

Part VI

THE IMPACT ON SOCIETY

The preceding chapters of the book have mainly concentrated on the technological, business and marketing aspects of IT. What differentiates IT from previous major advances in technology (e.g. electricity, railways, telephone, television and nuclear power) is that while the technology is still in its infancy, we can foresee some of the effects it may have on our society. We do have options for the future, but these need to be brought to the wider attention of the public. All too often this is done by the media in such a way as to induce fear (through ignorance), or amazement at technology's magical powers. We need to realise that we have options for the future, and to appreciate that now is the time to consider them, before too many doors have been closed.

In Part VI we will be looking at three major issues and their impact on individuals, organisations and society as a whole. First, we look at the related and interlinked questions of privacy, data protection and security. Next we consider possible changes in the nature of work, and in particular its implications for training and education. Third, we look at the potential impact of IT on aggregate employment and the creation of wealth and we contrast the approaches taken by different national governments in their policies towards IT.

15

Privacy, Data Protection and Security

Privacy

Privacy has always been a central political issue. It is possibly one of the major distinctions between the Western democracies and the Communist bloc. It reflects the relative importance of the individual within society, as compared to the state. In Western society one's privacy as a person is considered as a basic human right, and typically is extended to encompass your own private space: 'An Englishman's home is his castle.' However, the privacy of one's living space will depend greatly on the wealth of the individual. Living in a small flat in a high-rise block scarcely affords the same privacy as living on a 5,000-acre estate.

Another aspect of privacy is the status of personal information. To whom does such information belong? To the individual (to whom it relates), to the state (as custodian of society's rights), or to the public at large (through the media)? In this respect the influence of wealth may have the reverse effect. Information regarding the personal conduct of the wealthy and famous is of far greater interest to the newspapers than that about the poorer members of society.

It has always been a difficult matter to set a balance between the public's right to know, and the individual's right to privacy. The piecemeal development of English law has provided remedies to the worst abuses in the laws of trespass and libel. This question became far more vital, however — and the existing laws were seen to be less than adequate — with the development of computerised information sources.

Civilised societies have always kept records about their members for administrative purposes. Electoral rolls, medical records, police records, and dozens more have been in existence for centuries. These records have always been open to abuse, but the abuse has generally been kept within limits by two factors: the professional discipline imposed locally by those responsible for collecting the information, and, possibly more importantly, the sheer inefficiencies of the filing system used. With the advent of computerised files, these controls have ceased to be sufficient, and the result has been the introduction of a major new piece of legislation, the Data Protection Act.

Computerised Name-linked Files

It is interesting to consider how many computerised files may contain information about you personally. For example, you probably feature on some or all of an employer's personnel and payroll files, the customer records of public utilities (gas, water, electricity), local authority files for collecting rates and local taxes, and — in the UK — government files maintained by the Department of Health and Social Security (DHSS) and the Inland Revenue. UK car owners are recorded at the DVLC (Driver Vehicle Licensing Centre) at Swansea. If you have ever been the subject of a police investigation in Britain (or, quite likely, even if you have not) a record on you will be kept on the Police National Computer (PNC) at Hendon, which presently holds files on over 22 million people, more than half the adult population of the country. Your bank will have you on file; as will the companies which administer your credit cards, and, most likely, one or more credit checking agencies. A credit card company may have passed your name on to a direct mail agency, or the direct mail agency itself may have picked up your name from the Electoral Roll or from one of the many other readily available sources of selected names and addresses. It is estimated that the number of computerised personal records held by government departments in the UK is now over one billion, and there are perhaps many more times as many private files maintained by commercial organisations. Many of these files will contain nothing more than a bare record of your name and address, but others may contain potentially sensitive factual information about your finances, your state of health, your personal relationships and other intimate subjects, while others still may contain not only facts, but also speculation about your political and religious beliefs, any criminal or antisocial activity you may have engaged in, your creditworthiness, and so on. Often you will not know what information is on file, or even that a file on you exists. Perhaps the information in some of the files on you is inaccurate, or even damaging.

It has always been a matter of concern to thoughtful people that such information may be held without their knowledge or consent. Today it is a much greater problem. Increasingly, the computers on which information is held are being linked together, so that it is technically possible for information originally gathered for one purpose, and held on one computer, to be transferred to other files which are being maintained for quite different purposes. For example, the hub of the British government's information on private individuals is the DHSS's computer network. Every person in the country with a National Insurance number has a file on what is now called the Departmental Central Index. The aim is to link this index with the computers of the Inland Revenue, the Department of Employment and various other government departments, so that by the year 2000 Britain will have a central computer network holding the name and insurance number, current address, date of birth, sex, and basic details of finances and family relationships for virtually every person in the country. Though the data on this network will theoretically be confidential, it will be available not only to DHSS officials, but to a wide variety of other interested parties, including the police and the security forces. Because of the very nature of computer technology, it is always a possibility not only that other legitimate users may gain access to this (and other similar sources of) information without your knowledge, but also that illegitimate users may obtain remote access to your files, and discover their contents, to your detriment.

Even on a relatively innocent level, the sharing of data can lead to annoyance or inconvenience. For example, many people object when names and addresses held on the Electoral Roll are sold to direct mailing companies, or when the membership records of a club or society are passed on to other bodies without consultation. It is exasperating to be deluged with unwanted 'junk mail', all too easily produced by combining a computerised mailing list with a word processing capability; it is worse than exasperating when somebody with a legitimate reason to keep his or her address or telephone number private finds that it is being made freely available to all sorts of casual enquirers. A number of cases in which this has happened have come to light, and many more have doubtless remained undiscovered. In Britain the information held on the PNC, for example, is theoretically confidential to the police: but it is difficult to maintain complete confidentiality with a system which now provides more than 700 terminals, spread across the UK's 51 police forces. When thousands of policemen have instant access to the records, it is only too easy for others to find out what is on record, too, by asking (or, if necessary, bribing) a friendly policeman.

Journalist Duncan Campbell gave a graphic illustration of this in 1987 in his much-publicised 'Secret Society' television series, when he was filmed paying a police informer a remarkably small sum for confidential information of this sort; and when he surprised many members of the public by showing them how much sensitive information about them he could quite legitimately obtain from computerised public sources.

For official purposes, there are many very real benefits to be gained from networking databanks together, and providing cross-access. It is to the advantage of legitimate taxpayers, for example, if tax-dodgers can be brought to book and made to pay their share; it is to the advantage of virtually everyone if dangerous criminals can be caught as quickly as possible. Investigations into the police's handling of the Yorkshire Ripper murder enquiry provided a graphic example of the difficulties the police face in attempting to deal manually with vast quantities of disordered information: the police had received several tip-offs from concerned acquaintances of the Ripper, and had interviewed the murderer himself on several occasions, but because of their information overload they had failed to draw the proper conclusions from the information actually available to them. If the information had been recorded and processed by computer they might have identified the murderer much sooner, and saved one or more lives as a result.

But the price to be paid for this desirable ability to trace the life-patterns of criminals is a wholly undesirable ability to invade the privacy of those who are not criminal. Another, perhaps more disturbing example was provided by the West German police's attempt to fight the Baader-Meinhoff terrorist movement. In Germany, at this date, nearly all libraries had a computerised lending service, and from the library computers it was possible to identify the names and addresses of all those who had taken out books on 'revolutionary' subjects: texts by Marx and Trotsky, etc. Even those who fully sympathise with the need to use whatever methods are necessary to catch terrorists cannot fail to be concerned at the implications of this capability, put perhaps into the hands of a repressive government anxious to identify and control its innocent opponents.

Years of debate and pioneering legislation in several Western countries, have helped to clarify the issues involved, and to suggest some potential solutions to them. It is apparent that the time for guidelines to be developed is when computerised databanks are being built up and linked together, and not when working practices are already firmly established and much less open to alteration.

Two types of legislation are possible. First is the provision of a capability for concerned individuals to see what information is actually being kept on them, to correct it if it proves to be accurate, and perhaps to control the uses to which it can be put: for instance, by registering the fact that they do not wish their name and address to be forwarded to direct mail organisations. Second are legal guidelines that actually determine the ways in which databanks can be linked together, and define the types of linkage and data application which are *not* acceptable.

Of these two methods, the first has been much more widely enshrined in legislation to date. Sweden led the way with legislation on data protection, and the Council of Europe (of which the UK is a member) produced the Strasbourg Convention on Data Privacy, which all member states agreed to ratify. This move committed the UK to introduce legislation on the subject, though this was not actually done until comparatively late, with the passing of the Data Protection Act in July 1984.

The UK's Data Protection Act

The UK's Data Protection Act came into force in two phases. In the first phase, a Data Protection Register was drawn up, listing the files that were being kept on computer in the UK; in the second phase, individuals were given the right to inspect entries affecting them personally.

Phase one of the Act affected data users: that is, persons and organisations maintaining files of data about individuals on computer systems. (Manually maintained files are not covered by the Act.) Data users were required to register with the Data Protection Registrar, indicating what files they maintained. Though the scope of the Act was extremely wide, there were various exceptions: for example, for very small files, and for files concerned with national security. However, the range of data users covered stretched from major government departments down to small businesses, and even to clubs and societies that maintained lists of members' names and addresses in a computer file, and to self-employed people who might, for example, keep a file of customers or contacts for mailing purposes.

There was an initial registration period, and it subsequently became a criminal offence (from May 1986) for any organisation to hold this type of data on a computer system without registering with the Data Protection Registrar.

The difficulty of this system is that it has required the active co-operation not only of large businesses and government departments, but also of many smaller individuals and organisations, many of whom have perhaps quite genuinely believed their own records to be so trivial in scope as to be of no public interest. The Registrar estimated in 1986 that at least 300,000 individuals and organisations were affected by these provisions, and should in theory have registered. In practice, only around 50,000 registrations were made, so by far the majority of those affected did *not* meet the provisions of the Act. Assiduous following-up by the Registrar and his staff will have improved the proportion of those registering, and it can be assumed that the largest and most influential databanks are virtually all listed in the register, but even so there is a very real chance that not all the records that affect people personally are indicated in the register.

After November 1987 the Data Register was opened to the public, and it became possible for interested parties to consult it and ask to see their personal records. This is by no means an easy task. The list of data users is indexed only in alphabetical order, and there is no attempt to cross-reference all the files kept on individuals. It is only really possible to find out whether an organisation keeps a file on you personally if you already have reason to suspect that this is the case. And even when a record has been located and consulted, your powers to have it altered or removed are extremely circumscribed.

The Data Protection Registrar has made little if any attempt to employ his criminal powers of persuasion, and it is not yet clear whether the provisions of the Act will have any great effect upon the inexorable spread of databanks. However, many commentators do believe that the legislation has had the positive effects of ensuring that the information held on individuals is limited largely to factual information, that potentially libellous opinions or suspicions are not recorded, and that proper efforts are made to update records (and, for instance, to remove data on criminal convictions from the records after the proper number of years has elapsed). More cynically, it may be felt that the Act has simply delayed the time when highly sensitive medical records and the like will be transferred to computer, and thus be subjected to its provisions.

Trans-border Data Flow

This impressive-sounding phrase refers to the passing of computerised information over national borders in electronic form. In an era in which information has a (often very high) value of its own, this is an extremely sensitive subject.

Several countries, including Sweden and Holland, now have legislation which prohibits organisations from transmitting personal data to countries which do not have adequate data protection legislation in place. This has proved a source of inconvenience particularly to multinational companies, and has provided a spur to slow-acting Western countries to fall into line over the data protection issue. Some commentators have speculated that this could eventually give rise to *data havens*, unregulated countries where unscrupulous operators would be allowed to store data without restrictions. Thus a credit reference agency might operate on an off-shore basis, though there has been some debate about the practicability of this. Another ironic side-effect is that the Third World countries have realised the potential of such legislation as a means of controlling the multinationals, and so the multinationals may press for more countries to adopt data protection measures.

Data protection for individuals apart, the flow of technical and scientific information has been the subject of much debate, and of considerable action, particularly by the USA. It has always been difficult to restrict the spread of technical information, but it is particularly so in an era when a computer user in Moscow, say, could easily call up a computer in the USA, and access an on-line technical database. Efforts have been made to ensure that information on new developments, particularly when these have defence or security implications (as does so much new technology), is carefully controlled. At times this has led to extraordinary situations, for example when companies in the UK and elsewhere have transmitted information to associates in the US, and then found themselves unable to retrieve it themselves because of the tightness of the regulations!

Data today are a worldwide commodity, and the ownership of data is an international issue. There has been increasing concern in Europe and the Far East about the tendency of American companies to dominate the international database business, and thus to provide, and on occasion filter, technical, financial and other information to the rest of the world. A number of databases have been set up, in Europe and elsewhere, with government backing in order to try and ensure that the US does not attain a total monopoly position, and that other countries retain their interest in (and their control over) the information business.

Data Security

In many organisations information has become a major resource. The computer provides the organisation's nervous system; without it, often, literally no part of the organisation can function successfully. This fact has not been lost on terrorists: in Italy, for instance, urban guerillas discovered years ago that blowing up a computer centre causes far more chaos within an organisation than kidnapping the chief executive! It is a basic necessity for any organisation to ensure that its computer system is operated in a secure and fail-safe way, and that it will be possible to recover as quickly and smoothly as possible from either accidental or deliberate physical damage.

Just as vital is security of the information within the system. Company computer systems contain vital and often highly sensitive information about staff, customers and pricing policies, about research and development projects, and about future plans and projections. It is necessary to take security precautions to ensure that only authorised staff will be able to gain access to confidential information, and that the unauthorised can neither inspect nor (far worse) alter information, either for personal gain, or through grievance and a desire to cause disruption.

Even more stringent precautions need to be taken when information is transmitted via the telecommunications network. And it is necessary to take particular care to anticipate the potential opportunities for the computer criminal to get to work, and to ensure that computer fraud is identified and countered rapidly.

Computer Crime

The scale of computer-based crime is a much debated point. Many organisations hesitate to think about it, for fear of what they might find. Certainly the scale of crimes reported is fairly impressive, and most commentators are agreed that many sizeable frauds are *not* reported, because financial and other institutions are reluctant to own up publicly to the shortcomings in their security systems, and prefer to deal privately with the perpetrators.

The simplest — and almost certainly the most common — form of crime is straightforward, electronic theft. The criminals use methods, simple or not so simple, to divert funds that are being transferred electronically to benefit themselves or their associates. Sometimes this is done internally: employees of a company (not infrequently, the programmers themselves) take advantage of their knowledge of the computer system to exploit loopholes in its internal security. Sometimes it is done externally by 'hackers' who find unauthorised ways of accessing the system remotely. There is, for example, a very sizeable volume of credit card fraud.

Simple methods of fraud typically involve the setting-up of 'dummy' accounts: phantom suppliers, to whom large sums are paid for goods that do not exist, or phantom employees, who appear only on the computerised payroll but still collect a handsome salary each month. The famous Equity Funding Scandal, which involved the creation of phoney insurance policies that were sold to reinsurers, was a variation of this simple method. Even today, some poorly run companies have computer systems that are vulnerable to this blatant form of computer theft. But other criminals are more subtle. Some have profited to the tune of thousands or even millions, for example, simply by creaming off odd pennies from accounts in credit, and diverting them to dummy accounts that they control themselves.

Huge 'glamour' crimes are not infrequently uncovered simply because the criminals are too greedy, and the scale of the crime makes discovery inevitable even when proper checks are not in place. Many, many other computer criminals probably go on making a modest profit year after year, without ever being caught. Yet other criminals profit indirectly, through indulging in electronic espionage. Obtaining confidential company information electronically, they either act on it themselves (for example, by speculating in the company's shares) or sell it to other interested parties — for example, so that a rival can learn what bids have been made for contracts under discussion, and consistently produce narrow overbids. A further type of fraud consists of unauthorised usage of an electronic service. In the days of time-sharing computer bureaux, who charged a high price to users for a slice of processing time, this used to be a more serious problem than it is now that processing power is cheap. Today, however, high prices are often charged by information services (on-line databases and the like) and it is they who probably lose substantial sums through the ingenuity of unauthorised users who manage to bypass their password and billing systems.

Computer Vandals

Sometimes, as a form of blackmail, threats are made to wreak havoc with a company's data files. In other cases, programmers with a grudge against their employers — resulting perhaps from refused promotion or a dismissal — have programmed a delayed-action 'bug' into a system. In yet others, 'hackers' (a term applied to all compulsive, unauthorised dabblers in systems, not all of whom have criminal intent) damage files for political or social reasons. Also in the language of computer vandalism, the programmer's 'bug' may show up only in certain circumstances (but still may do immense damage) or it may spread as the occasionally accidental, but more often deliberately induced, 'virus' that can spread throughout a linked system or become the 'logic bomb', which does just what its name suggests.

Even the most innocent, unwitting bug can immobilise a computer system for seconds, hours or even days, perhaps flashing a message on every terminal screen in the process. There was a well-known programming bug in early Commodore Amiga personal computers, for instance, which would 'crash' the program being run, and reset the computer. Some systems have quite a variety of silly, humorous or rude messages which programmers with a strange sense of humour have left among their labyrinth of programs. More damaging bugs and bombs may not only destroy a single program run but also erase data files, or scramble directories so that files, though intact on disc, can no longer be accessed. Sometimes the device is activated by a certain password or entry code — which may be entered remotely, through a communications link; other 'bombs' are wired to explode when an employee's password is deleted, as would happen when the employee leaves the company; and others are set in action at pre-set dates or times.

It is extremely difficult for systems designers to anticipate and avoid the danger of this type of disruptive activity. It is also extremely difficult to catch the perpetrators, since a well-programmed bug or bomb will destroy all trace of its own operation; even so, in recent years several cases of computer sabotage of this kind have been brought to court. In March 1985 the Los Angeles Water and Power Department had its computer files frozen by a logic bomb, and in 1986 a complex two-phase device in a Heathrow Airport freight firm's terminal system 'locked' every terminal in the computer network. Sometimes (as in these instances) checks on disgruntled past employees, and scraps of evidence such as the time the device was triggered, can bring to light how and why such actions were taken.

The White Collar Criminal

From research into cases that have been unearthed, a fairly clear picture has been built up of the typical computer criminal. Donn Parker of Stanford University has studied many cases and concluded that the offender will be young, highly motivated, bright, and usually an employee (past or present) of the defrauded or sabotaged organisation.

Many organisations are unwilling to prosecute the guilty parties when they are uncovered, partly to avoid adverse publicity, and partly because court proceedings are a minefield. As with all complex fraud cases, it is difficult to explain to a jury exactly what was done, to convince them that all that happened was planned, and to bring home to them the seriousness of the losses incurred. Even when criminals are convicted, the penalties are often modest when compared to those handed out to more traditional robbers.

For many hackers the introduction of evermore complex security precautions simply presents a greater challenge to be met and overcome; their motivation in trying to 'beat the system' is even greater. There is also the belief, among criminals and the public at large, that defrauding large organisations is quite acceptable so long as the perpetrator is not caught. Only a change in the law — classing computer fraudsters with traditional criminals, and imposing much heavier penalties for this difficult-to-detect type of crime — can lead to a change in this social attitude to white collar crime. Even so, it may be that the computer criminal will always have a Robin Hood image in the public eye.

The problem of computer crime has undoubtedly been increased by the much greater availability of personal computers, and the wider use of telecommunications, networking, terminals and other remote access facilities. Many more young people have the necessary expertise today to turn into hackers, and the equipment needed to gain access to even the largest and most powerful systems is now well within the reach of hobbyist teenagers. Moreover, the problem is compounded by a certain ignorance, and often naïvety, amongst senior management. A company's computer systems are often viewed only in technical terms, and the technical staff are forced to make many decisions which, in view of their wider implications, logically should be more widely participated in. The pressure on technical staff can mean that anti-fraud measures are viewed with hostility, as they can slow down the development process.

In order to build secure computer systems the programmer has to think like an auditor. Unfortunately, however, there are few greater contrasts in mental approach than between the volatility of the innovative programmer, and the steady caution of the auditor! Systems are obviously most vulnerable to the programmers who create them, and one essential control is a separation of responsibility between development and operations. It is common today (though by no means routine) for external security auditors to be called in to review system set-up and advise whether additional precautions are necessary. In the long run, only a realisation by senior management of the critical business role of corporate data and information processing systems will lead to the recognition of computer crime as the very serious threat that it undoubtedly is today.

Data Protection

With the advent of networks, it is essential that proper data protection standards should be employed on all files containing sensitive information. The use of password protection systems has always been standard on mainframe systems, but today many personal computer packages, too, offer this type of basic security precaution.

Password protection should not be thought of, however, as the only (or even the best) method of protection. There is always the difficulty that employees are liable to forget unusual passwords, and that it is easy for unauthorised personnel to guess at memorable ones! A quick run through likely options has brought many hackers back-door access into supposedly secure systems.

Encryption and file protection software is an increasingly large market, and many products now offer far greater levels of sophistication. Among the file protection software now available is IBM's RACF, or Resource Access Control Facility. IBM have also developed a Data Encryption Standard, or DES, for the sending of scrambled data through telecommunications systems, but because of the defence applications of this it is not currently widely available outside the USA. British Telecom have also developed an encryption system, centred around the B-crypt microchip.

Work, Skills, Education and Training

16

The Nature of Work

The whole history of civilised man has been a constant struggle to improve productivity, to move away from subsistence living where every second of every day had to be purposefully employed simply to stay alive. Gradually we have had to work less hard for the things we need and want. But suddenly in this last part of the twentieth century we find that we can now harness technology to such an extent that we apparently have labour surplus to our requirements. This leap in productivity is not likely to be short-lived, as that most productive of all technologies, the microchip, has only just started to be deployed on a wide scale. In the next chapter we will discuss the wider issues of aggregate employment; but first we will look at the nature of work and speculate on what changes IT may bring to it.

More than anything, work today symbolises a place to go which is separate from the home. This separation of work and home occurred with the industrial revolution. The new manufacturing industries required large labour forces that worked together in specialised factory buildings. These industries soon built up large offices where white collar workers were required to assemble every day. With limited communication facilities, it was considered only practical to run an office under a single roof.

Separating the work and the home has served to emphasise that work occupies the major part of our waking lives. We probably spend about the same amount of time either working (and travelling), or awake and not working. Of our non-work time maybe half is spent doing necessary things in life — washing, dressing, cooking, eating, shopping, etc. This

leaves us with maybe one quarter of our time to spend at our own
discretion. It is not surprising then that work is the largest single thing we
relate to. We relate to people through our jobs; when asked, 'What do
you do?' we reply that we are engineers, mechanics, postmen or
undertakers. This describes the major part of our lives and the fact that
we like gardening or squash or Beethoven is of secondary interest. An
alarmed reaction is hardly surprising then if we are suddenly confronted
with the possibility of totally altering the balance of our lives. If we only
worked for half as long as our disposable leisure time then the question
'What do you do?' has a different meaning.

Whether we need to work to have meaningful lives is a difficult
question to answer. B   it would seem logical to argue that members of a
society will feel more   alued if they are needed by society, and that in
turn will lead to more social behaviour. However, the question becomes
more focused when we consider whether society has the obligation to
provide that work in the form of employment. Nobody is disputing the
right of anybody to work, what is being disputed is the obligation of the
state to provide jobs for everyone. The responsibility for work is thus
transferred from the state to the individual — a concept well recognised
in the USA and currently being emphasised by the present UK
Government.

Employment is in practice discouraged through a series of legislative
and fiscal measures. There are labour taxes, employers' insurance
contributions, health and safety regulations, pension rights, employment
protection, and a host of other measures. All of these are excellent and
commendable in their own right but they exert a negative influence on the
willingness of organisations to employ people. The net effect of this may
be to change organisations from operating in an environment in which
they directly employ people to perform tasks, to one in which they enter
into contractual arrangements for the provision of services. Thus many
people would become self-employed, and could potentially work for a
number of organisations. This does not mean everyone working in
cottage industries, but it might well require the establishment of
community work centres where individuals culd share the cost of facilities
such as telex, electronic mail, photocopying, computer work-stations etc.

The Wired Society

Developments in the equipment that may now be attached to the
telephone network mean that not all office functions need to be retained
under one roof. Thus the office may be distributed into smaller local units
without an intolerable reduction in the communication capability between
these units. These local units may actually be people's homes. It has long
been fairly common for regional sales representatives to be based at their

own home, with only occasional visits to a regional office. This is now a realistic alternative for a wider range of occupations. With the generally increasing cost of transport, the economics of using a terminal and a telephone link from home, rather than travelling daily to an office, are becoming more and more favourable. It may mean that extended sessions using a terminal are best left to the off-peak charging hours, but this emphasises the fact that working at home means scheduling one's own time. Microcomputers, capable of handling simple business applications, are now so cheap that it is perfectly feasible for virtually all self-employed individuals to acquire one. Prices for the Amstrad PC–1512, the cheapest of the IBM PC clones, which can run most contemporary personal computer software, start at just £399.

A user of an Amstrad, or any similar budget machine, gains the ability to use a spreadsheet package like Lotus 1–2–3 or Multiplan, to set up models, analyse data, and store both models and data on disc. A whole range of word processing software is available, making it possible to prepare anything from a short memo to a lengthy novel. Simple accounting packages make it possible to maintain self-employed or small business accounts on the computer. Work can be transferred easily to and from other computers that are IBM-compatible, and files can be conveyed electronically, or sent through the post in floppy disc form. A computer like this can access electronic databases remotely, via the telephone line, or be used to call up the company's main dp files. It can store relevant data on disc, in very little space: a single box of floppy discs can hold as much information as that contained in a large filing cabinet full of paper; and compact disc technology will undoubtedly reduce the space requirements still further. These, and a host of other facilities, could mean that many 'knowledge workers' would actually be better off working from home.

However, the concept of the home-based society, communicating primarily in electronic form, would seem a little unrealistic. In his book *The Wired Society* James Martin considers the telecommunications networks to be tomorrow's highways. Instead of people travelling so that they can communicate face to face (to work, to do shopping, to obtain services) all their communications could be electronic, and any physical goods could be brought to people rather than vice versa. But Martin is only exploring the possibilities; in practice this idea needs to be tempered with a little realism. Not everybody finds their home a desirable place to spend a majority of their time. Many people prefer both the ambience and the company at their regular workplace, and are willing to endure the cost and inconvenience of commuting long distances in order to enjoy it. On top of this, the pressure on many family relationships would be intolerable. Most relationships need the external influences of separate experiences that going to work offers.

What would seem more likely is that an increasing number of people will work partially from home. Most of these will be knowledge workers of some sort, with a high standard of education and motivation. But for the rest of the workforce, having a separate and gregarious workplace will continue to be essential.

The Balance of Skills

Many organisations have already found that IT has changed the range and scope of skills needed in their workforce. In pre-computer days an organisation would have a continuum of clerical skills, from apprentices, juniors and trainees to senior clerks and supervisors. Today there tends to be a polarisation, between those who design applications and program them, and those who merely use them.

For many users of IT, in the office, the factory and elsewhere, the technology is a de-skilling force. They become mere button pushers, with a totally mechanical knowledge of the system. There's no need to do any more than input data to the system; the computer does everything else automatically. At this mechanical level, speed, accuracy, stamina, and the ability to follow rules are all desirable, while creative and inquisitive skills may be a positive hazard.

Contrast this with the programmers, technicians and other professionals who have a conceptual understanding of the system and what it does, and are able to use it, rather than be used by it. These workers must be able to conceptualise, to make inferences, to be creative. They need enquiring minds. These kinds of skills are usually acquired at school and through higher education, not through company training of any sort.

Skills at Risk

In the days when electronic components were discrete and not highly integrated, either faulty equipment had to be returned to a repair centre, or an engineer had to be sent to diagnose the fault and repair it, if possible, on site. Maintenance engineers needed a high level of training in electronics, and an intimate knowledge of the equipment with which they dealt. This type of repair engineering was a highly skilled manual job.

Nowadays, most of this complex electronic circuitry has been reduced to a few chips and connecting wires on a small number of circuit boards. The actual complexity of the circuitry has generally increased, in that there are far more transistors, resistors and other components; but large-scale integration means that the number of discrete components has fallen dramatically. Today very few boards are repaired on site; and then, only those with the most obvious faults — connecting wires adrift, and so on. More usually, the board is replaced and the faulty one taken back to a repair centre, where automatic test equipment is used to diagnose the problem. An increasing tendency is for the equipment user to carry out the necessary maintenance himself or herself. In-built diagnostic routines can pinpoint the fault, and swapping circuit boards is a relatively simple task which can be done by almost anyone who can handle a screwdriver. The faulty board can then be returned to the supplier, say by courier. There is a still more advanced trend, too, towards 'fault-tolerant' computers and other equipment that can repair itself, diagnosing faults automatically and bypassing damaged circuitry.

None of this augurs well for the future of electronics maintenance staff. This may be a natural consequence of change, but it is also a de-skilling process: a skilled manual job of the recent past is being squeezed out of existence. The big question is, what happens to such people whose jobs disappear as the result of this kind of process? Do they succeed in adapting their redundant skills, so as to fill new roles, or in acquiring new skills?

Middle-grade clerical workers, too, are at risk. Such workers generally have a good 'mechanical' knowledge of the part of the clerical system with which they interact. Older workers may have worked in several different departments, and thus have acquired a wide range of experience. What value will these skills, this experience, be if the clerical functions of the organisations are automated? And if they are no longer seen to be of real value, will the loss of such experience prove to be a significant deficiency in the automated system?

In an automated office, low-grade skills are necessary for the staff who feed data into the system and generally follow the procedures laid down by the system. High-grade skills are necessary for those who must comprehend the concept of the system and its functions: for supervision, control, maintenance and development. But the middle-grade skills have often become unnecessary, and the only option open to these workers, other than redundancy, is to work at the less skilled levels.

One of the great illusions of IT is that there is a glamour and sophistication attached to working with leading-edge technology. Workers are often led to believe that their jobs will become more demanding and interesting; unions negotiate higher skill payments for those learning to use new technology, and so on. While this is the great promise that the technology holds out to us, too often the reverse has turned out to be true. For example, at first sight word processing can seem quite exciting to a typist. It requires learning new skills; and, environmentally, the word processor may be a more pleasant (and certainly more impressive) piece of equipment than the typewriter it replaces. However, word processors are typically acquired not to improve the typist's job satisfaction, but to increase his or her productivity. The word processor does make it easier, and quicker, to correct mistakes, to revise text, to go on to the next page, and to lay out letters acceptably. But the thought, care and time required in a manual system to produce high-quality work is no longer necessary — thus eliminating any natural breaks. Word processor operators can find themselves in a production-line regime where the only breaks are the scheduled ones.

Skills in Demand

In the short term at least, there has proved to be a high demand for 'production line' clerical workers capable of operating the new forms of electronic office equipment. These individuals need keyboard skills, and must be able to follow rules and procedures that are often complex. It is the very nature of technological advance, though, that jobs are lost at the expense of capital, and even where there have been no redundancies through the introduction of higher technology, there is often loss of jobs through natural wastage. More insidiously still, companies which are expanding their operations, and would in other circumstances have taken on more staff, no longer need to do so because of the improved productivity of existing staff. Moreover, increasingly data are being entered automatically to the system — for example, through electronic ordering, financial transactions, funds transfer and so on. This removes the need for data entry staff, and in the long run must act to diminish the prospects for those whose main skill is in keyboarding.

The skills in shorter supply — on the other hand — and more certain long-term demand, are those of the knowledge worker: that is, someone technically literate with strong conceptual skills. Such a person has only to know that the possibility of some action exists, to find out how to do it. Though it is not necessary to be highly numerate, a logical mind is essential, so a course in philosophy could be an excellent training!

The demand for skills in designing and developing IT will increase for the foreseeable future. In applying the technology in products, it is necessary to be familiar with both the hardware and the software so that the appropriate balance can be struck. Our current training schemes tend to separate these two areas. In contrast, applying IT to a process places a strong demand on systems thinking. At present hardware and software are often totally separate developments.

The computer industry often talks of chronic shortages of staff, but no longer of major shortages of programmers except in specialist areas. What does continue is a high demand for systems designers, systems analysts, and business analysts — the people who translate the business problem into a computer solution.

A great weakness in the UK labour force has been a lack of well-trained managers, and particularly ones who are technically literate. Technology has always had an 'oily rag' image in the UK, which has discouraged generations of potential managers from learning about it. By the time they realise that they need this knowledge it is often too late to acquire it, and technical decisions, even those with far-reaching consequences, have to be left to technical experts. In contrast, many American, Japanese and European managers have a strong technical grasp of the processes and products relevant to their organisations. The training for many American managers is a first degree in engineering followed by an MBA, and it is noteworthy that the largest class of first degrees of entrants into the London MBA programme is in engineering.

In spite of this demand for knowledge workers and managers, it seems clear that the overall effect of information technology has been, and will continue to be, a reduction in the number of jobs available. The structural employment that is the result is likely to remain a serious problem for the foreseeable future.

Education and Training

Though the British Government has made some attempts in recent years to develop a policy towards IT, it has been lamentably piecemeal and inadequate, and this is nowhere more obvious than in the areas of education and training. Instead of a coherent plan based on a careful projection of the level of each type of skill required, the projects that have been initiated tend to come across as fire-fighting exercises designed to quieten down criticism.

Though most British schools now possess at least one computer, this is totally inadequate to enable children to obtain regular hands-on experience of computing. Teacher training in the use of information technology has been inadequate too, and in many schools there appears to be no clear policy covering the use of the equipment and the future trend in technology studies. Computer studies and similar topics are still minority subjects, all too often provided as 'fillers' for less academic children, and rarely selected by the high fliers. Far fewer students take public examinations in computing than in history or geography, and provision for the study of technology in the currently proposed national curriculum is lamentable.

We discussed education as an application for IT in Chapter 8. It is unclear what skills we are trying to teach children, and it is of great concern that there should be little sense of urgency in the Government, or in the various educational establishments, of the need to formulate or discuss policy in this area. Our belief is that microcomputers should become an everyday resource in both junior and senior schools. All children should be given basic training in using them. Where budgets are strictly limited it makes sense to concentrate on the provision of large quantities (hundreds, not twos or threes) of relatively cheap and simple micros, rather than tiny quantities of more sophisticated machines. Care should be taken, too, to ensure that the general practices and procedures in school computing mirror normal commercial practice, and do not run counter to it. For instance, there is clearly a place for 'educational' computer languages (e.g. Pascal and Comal), but it is necessary, too, for young people to grow up with an appreciation of the kind of *commercial* computer programming that is performed in the outside world.

In British universities considerable sums are spent on research into computing and on providing computing as a service, but the number of computer science degree places is still very small, and in spite of Government indications that the field is considered to be of vital importance, little has been done to improve the proportion of students. Indeed, since technical courses are often disproportionately expensive in terms of resources required per student, they tend to be among the first candidates for axeing when cutbacks are demanded. Nor does academic training in computer science have a high reputation among commercial organisations. A degree in computer science is not regarded as a prestige qualification, or a particularly desirable one; often organisations indicate that they prefer to take on graduates with more general qualifications. This might have been an understandable situation in the early days of computer science courses, when educational institutions were still experimenting and trying to devise suitable courses; but now that the subject is well matured, it adds up to a serious indictment of the state of education in information technology.

As we shall argue in the next chapter, an educated labour force exploits technology, while an uneducated labour force is exploited by it. The UK's labour force is one of the least well educated in the developed world, and its performance (in terms, for example, of the proportion of young people continuing on to higher education) continues to lag behind that of its industrial rivals. It is amazing that the UK is now the only industrialised country in which higher education is not available as of right to all those qualified to receive it.

The British Government's initiatives in terms of technology colleges, TVEI (Technical and Vocational Education Initiative) training and the like are to be welcomed, but their scale is not sufficient to significantly improve the situation. All too often training is carried out on a token scale, giving young people a 'taster' of technology but not educating them to a sufficiently high level to equip them to become the knowledge engineers of the future.

All young people today need to acquire a basic level of familiarity with high technology; but only a minority have the aptitude or the inclination to go on to become tomorrow's knowledge engineers. Only by special provision of additional resources can such capabilities be encouraged and developed. The talents of the gifted can to some extent be encouraged through school computer clubs or access to the resources of local technical colleges. Past experience with computer clubs has not always been positive, however: all too often they degenerate into a forum for game-playing.

The craze for personal computing in the early 1980s seems now to have done more educational harm than good. In the perception of many people, the home computer was reduced to the conceptual level of the Rubik cube, or any other faddish toy. Now that the bubble has burst, some young people see computing as yesterday's 'thing' — an unfashionable pastime which they would not be seen dead indulging in. Time and careful encouragement will be needed before the home/educational computer is restored to its proper place, not as a gimmick but as an essential, indeed basic, educational tool.

Using computers can encourage children in the pursuit of numeracy. Maths can seem a very dull and irrelevant subject when taught solely through textbook examples. Computers bring numbers to life. For example, colour graphs, histograms, pie charts, simulations and animations can illustrate mathematical relationships and operations. Teaching teenagers to use spreadsheets and graphing tools can provide them with useful experience in non-procedural programming, and a practical insight into the nature of mathematical model building. In higher education it is necessary to concentrate more on system skills, problem analysis and logical reasoning. In addition, more attention needs to be paid to communication skills such as graphic arts, data presentation, report writing, interviewing and negotiating.

But quite apart from the skills needed to apply IT, there is a bigger reorientation needed in our view of education itself, and our perspective on its role in society. In the past it has been reasonable to think of jobs as being for life. Educational processes have been concentrated in one massive shot during childhood and adolescence, and the hope that this will be sufficient to set people on a life-long course has generally been justified. It is now being realised that part of the inflexibility of most European workforces is due to this concept being reinforced by our schooling, both by the content and by the length of time invested.

If we are now moving into an era when many people can expect to have a number of different jobs or careers, then it is necessary to take a different attitude to education. It must become a process that continues throughout our lives, both formally and informally. Instead of being educated full-time until the age of 16, 18, 21, 23 or whatever, young people should be encouraged to obtain some work experience before continuing into higher education. University professors in the UK have often observed that degree courses were more effective in the days of National Service, when students had a slightly wider perspective than that of the average school leaver.

Continuing education and vocational training will have to become the norm if we are going to cope with the fast-changing world that IT brings. In the USA there is a much greater tradition in this field, due partly to placing the responsibility for employment (and thus for obtaining skills that are in demand, and keeping them up to date) with the individual. In Japan this process is handled by the larger companies. In guaranteeing 'employment for life', the company is able to retrain its labour force as necessary, without generating fear or resistance.

17

Employment, Economic Activity and Government Policy

A Historical Perspective

Economic Activity

Many commentators have suggested that the impact of semiconductors, chips, and the other building blocks of information technology will lead to such fundamental and far-reaching changes in the fabric of our society that it may be thought of as being akin to a second industrial revolution. The first industrial revolution applied machines to amplify the power of our muscles, the second will apply IT to amplify the power of our minds. In this chapter we examine some of the consequences of this possible second industrial revolution, particularly in its impact on employment and overall economic activity.

In the first industrial revolution, the machinery of the great Victorian innovators and entrepreneurs was used to increase the power and effectiveness of muscular and manipulative skills by several orders of magnitude. In the first half of the nineteenth century, total industrial production doubled roughly every twenty years. During that period it was what we would now regard as the basic heavy industries (e.g. coal and iron production) which were providing this expansion, the major consumer products being largely those of the textile industry. In general, a worker's total income went in satisfying his and his family's needs for food, clothing and shelter.

However, the end of the century saw the beginnings of the consumer-goods industries which have dominated the economic development of the twentieth century — radio, telephone, domestic electrical equipment and, above all, the motor car. The historical development of the automobile industry is the only one to match even closely the explosive growth rates of the semiconductor industry. For the years from the turn of the century through to the end of the First World War, the American automobile industry roughly doubled its production every two years. Most other consumer industries increased their output eightfold or tenfold in the first few years of their existence, but then settled down to a more leisurely rate of growth. It is perhaps worth repeating that the present semiconductor industry has doubled its output rather more than every other year for the past twenty-five years, and looks set to continue at this rate for the next five years at least. Such a continuous high rate of growth is unprecedented and unique.

Employment and Productivity

Using the new machines not only increased production dramatically, it also made the population much better off. Referring to Figure 17.1 it can be seen that over the years 1851 to 1911 real income per head in the UK rose by roughly 80 per cent, and over the years 1911 to 1961 by roughly 100 per cent. At the same time there were consequential changes in the pattern of employment — between 1851 and 1911, employment in agriculture fell by 22 per cent, whilst in manufacturing it rose by 99 per cent, at a time when total employment itself rose by 96 per cent. Thus the increased use of machinery resulted in a rapid increase in manufactured output which not only absorbed all of the considerable increase in the working population, but also led to a significant exodus of workers out of agriculture into manufacturing. Not only was there an increase in output per head in manufacturing industry, there was also an enormous increase in agricultural productivity — fewer and fewer agricultural workers were feeding more and more manufacturing workers.

Looking now at the period from 1911 to 1961, there was a much smaller growth in total working population (31 per cent), but much bigger shifts in employment patterns. During this period, the number of employees in agriculture fell by a further 41 per cent and the numbers in manufacturing fell by 0.7 per cent, while those in services (including finance and commerce) rose by 88 per cent. By 1961, only 4 per cent of the UK labour force was employed in agriculture, compared with 49 per cent in industrial and 47 per cent in non-industrial employment (excluding agriculture). Again, there were dramatic increases in productivity during this period — fewer and fewer agricultural workers were feeding more and more workers in the other sectors, and a relatively small increase in the number of industrial workers could produce the goods demanded by the vastly increased number of workers providing services to the

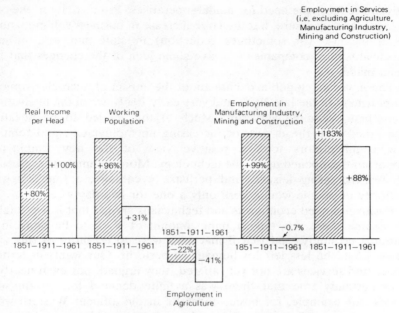

Figure 17.1 *UK Changes in Employment and Output*

community. Over the years a smaller and smaller proportion of the average worker's total income has been required to provide the basic needs of food, clothing and shelter, and an ever increasing proportion is available for discretionary spending on other goods and services. Such a shift in employment patterns — reduced employment in agriculture, a small increase in industrial employment, and a much larger increase in service employment — was common to all industrialised countries during this period.

The Impact on Employment

During the 1970s and early 1980s, nearly all industrialised countries experienced a significant degree of structural unemployment, seen as a shift out of manufacturing employment. Some of this shift was undoubtedly been the result of developments in technology.

The application of microelectronics in the factory has undeniably led to immense productivity gains. Microelectronically controlled products typically have far fewer discrete components than their mechanical predecessors, and they require much less assembly. Much of the work of manufacture is itself automated by electronically controlled systems, and this too reduces the need for human operatives. Productivity in the office is less easy to measure, but the large increase in business volume, and the small increase (or sometimes reduction) in staff numbers, in many financial service companies can give some idea of the changes that have been made.

There was much public debate about the impact of microelectronics on employment in the late 1970s and very early 1980s, when the likely effects were first becoming apparent. Much of this tended to be negatively concerned with the danger of increasing unemployment, and relatively few commentators took a positive view of the new employment opportunities opened up by the technology. More common was a scenario of ever-increasing leisure, and perhaps, eventually, a time when the majority of people would work only a one- or two-day week.

Positive-minded economists and technicians argued that it was a fallacy to assume there was only a finite amount of work to be done in the national economy, and that if machines were to do more of this work, there would be less left for humans to perform. Our wants in terms of goods and services are not yet satiated, they argued, nor even nearly so. It is certainly true that there was a finite demand for certain staple goods: for example, for basic foodstuffs in the affluent Western world. But there were many manufactured goods and services of which many households would purchase more, if they were easily available and the price were right. For example, one-television households might purchase second or subsequent sets. New products, too, would appear: electronic calculators, video cassette recorders and video cameras were often cited as examples.

Office automation was seen as a particular problem, likely to lead to considerable unemployment, either temporarily or permanently. Some commentators suggested that by the end of the century the total UK production of goods could be manufactured by only 10 per cent of the labour force.

Examination of previous changes in employment patterns suggests that rarely, if ever, has mass long-term unemployment occurred as a direct consequence of technical change. Indeed, rather the opposite would seem to be the case. Relative technical competence would appear to be strongly associated with real differences in living standards between countries. The evidence available suggests that the employment effects are relatively small and of short duration when domestic firms take the lead in technical innovation. In this situation overall growth in the economy is stimulated through the multiplier effects of increased output. However, the employment effects are likely to be substantial and long-lasting when foreign competitors adopt new technologies faster than domestic producers and, through lower relative costs and/or improved products, dominate both domestic and third-party markets. The major national concern in the UK should be with competitive price pressure from technologically superior foreign competitors. This potential threat emphasises the critical role of the educational level of the workforce in furthering technical understanding and creative positive attitudes to technical change, as well as in leading the way towards the production of better products.

Patterns of Employment

To a great extent these possible developments in employment patterns are a continuation of the long-running trend in employment patterns already mentioned. The long-run decline in agricultural employment and the increase in output and in productivity have now been going on since the middle of the nineteenth century, yet the world's farmers are feeding more people at a higher standard. As the productivity of the agricultural worker has increased, so has his level of skills, to the extent that now the average American farmer possesses a first college degree.

Similarly, there is evidence to support the contention that the countries who have adopted new technology first are those where the standard of education of the labour force is highest. To repeat, an educated labour force exploits technology; an uneducated labour force is exploited by it. Given the experience in agriculture over the past century, suggestions that the proportion of the labour force employed in manufacturing may fall to 10 per cent before the year 2000, and yet produce a vastly higher output, do not appear to be unreasonable. In some ways at least, this prospect can be welcomed.

The argument of some commentators in favour of this trend is that the workers displaced from manufacturing can be redeployed in the service sector, including commerce and financial services, and central and local government. This raises two particular points for discussion in the UK context.

First is the suggestion that the UK already has too great a proportion of its labour force engaged in essentially non-productive activities, and particularly in local and central government, both in the sense that the proportion is higher than that for our major competitors, and in the sense that it would be beneficial to reduce it. Figure 17.2 shows the proportion of the labour force employed in the agricultural, industrial and non-industrial sectors (excluding agriculture) for the UK and for our major competitors. It does not seem to be immediately obvious from this that the proportion employed in the non-industrial sector in the UK is significantly out of line. Further, it is also not immediately clear how, or why, reducing this proportion would be of benefit.

Throughout the postwar period, up to the early eighties, British

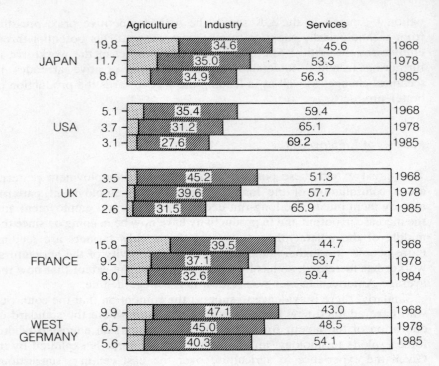

Figure 17.2 *Percentage Employees by Category, 1968, 1978 and 1984/5*

governments spent immense amounts of public money in an attempt to try to maintain employment in manufacturing industry. At best, this endeavour only delayed the inevitable time when outdated industries were forced to modernise, face up to competitive pressures, streamline their operations and shed a substantial proportion of their workforce. Though a case can be made for stimulating new endeavours in the manufacturing sector, there is no evidence that the existing UK manufacturing sector is short of labour (except in certain skills). There is much more evidence of unsatisfied demand for public services: a better health service, better pupil/teacher ratios in schools, a more effective police force, and so on.

One of the major boom sectors of the UK economy in recent years has been in private provision of social services. The demand for private education has never been higher. The cutting of private beds in National Health Service hospitals did not sound the death knell for private medicine in the UK; on the contrary, it ushered in a new era of purpose-built private hospitals. There is a very real demand for services of better quality than those the state currently provides free; and there are plenty of statistics that show how far British standards of health and social care have fallen behind those of other major industrialised countries.

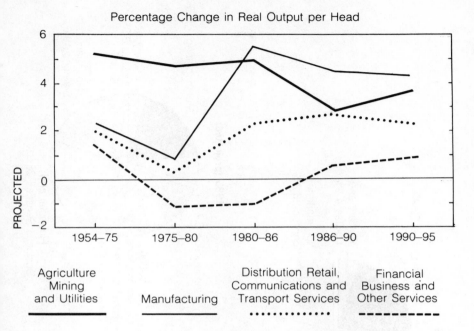

Figure 17.3 *UK Productivity Growth, 1954–86 and Projected*

The second, and more fundamental, point related to the switch of employment in the UK to the service sector is the disastrous productivity record of the UK economy in the 1970s and the significant improvement in the 1980s, with the UK then enjoying a faster rate of growth in productivity than that of other Western European countries. As Figure 17.3 shows, this productivity growth was mainly in manufacturing industry, not services; whereas, as Figure 17.4 shows, the distribution of employment is moving ever more strongly towards the service sector. One of the challenges is to improve productivity in the service industries.

Another problem is our apparent inability to innovate to the point of successful market exploitation. As we have discussed, added value in the semiconductor revolution is found to be highest at the point of application to the final consumer — both private and corporate — and it is therefore a particular problem if the UK fails to carry its technical innovations through to a significant presence in the information processing industry.

At one point the British Government showed itself to be aware of the necessity to foster this sector by creating INMOS, a semiconductor manufacturing company, and NEXOS, an office systems company, as

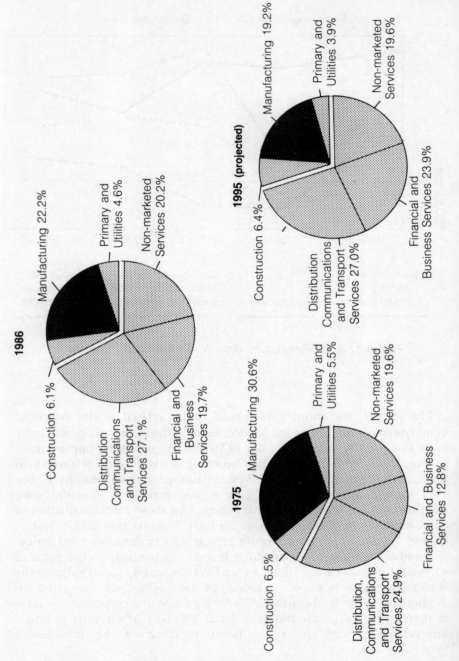

Figure 17.4 *UK Distribution of Employment by Industry, 1975, 1986 and 1995 (projected)*

subsidiaries of the National Enterprise Board. While INMOS was set up with the tangible and immediate objective of producing chips, it was never clear what role NEXOS was designed to play. NEXOS was subsequently dismembered, and though INMOS has established a reasonably substantial presence in the semiconductor field, its finances and its future ownership still pose large question marks.

In our view one of the most telling criticisms of recent UK governments is that they have no coherent policy addressing the impact and role of information technology in general, and in the innovatory process in particular. Therefore we will devote the remainder of this chapter to examining the process of innovation, particularly in information technology, and compare the situation with regard to the Government's policy in the UK towards information technology with that in other industrialised countries, especially Japan.

Aggregate Economic Impact

Balance of Trade

If we examine the recent performance of some of the major sectors of the UK electronics industry in a worldwide context, we find it fairly uninspiring. Some statistics are shown in Figures 17.5 and 17.6.

Product Classification (SITC code)	← UK Share (%) → Imports		Exports		World Market Value (US$ millions)	
	1980	1984	1980	1984	1980	1984
Calculating machines (7512)	8.1	6.3	2.9	1.0	1,837,648	1,636,267
Digital computers (7522)	13.7	7.6	14.9	2.5	1,868,894	3,215,643
Digital central processors (7523)	14.1	21.7	7.8	18.0	2,060,946	4,435,095
Colour televisions (7611)	4.9	7.5	5.0	3.2	3,263,731	4,191,541
Electronic microcircuits (7764)	6.1	7.3	3.8	4.4	6,971,718	15,011,039

Source: UN International Trade Statistics Yearbook.

Figure 17.5 *UK Share of World Trade in Electronic and Related Equipment, and the Value of the World Market*

	Electronic Products 1979 1984	Automatic Data Processing Machines 1979 1984	Consumer Electronics 1979 1984	Telecom- munications 1979 1984
Japan	11.59 31.77	0.01 4.37	6.13 13.58	2.82 6.20
USA	2.84 −8.23	4.52 5.38	−3.10 −8.33	−0.36 −4.18
UK	−0.79 −2.96	−0.40 −1.32	−0.67 −1.03	0.54 0.05
West Germany	0.40 −0.68	−0.50 −0.72	0.16 −0.40	0.95 0.73

Source: GATT International Trade, 1984/5.

Figure 17.6 *Trade Balance in Electronic Products (in percentage terms), 1979 and 1984*

The British share of computer imports has fallen, reflecting the persistent presence of domestic manufacturers in the home market, but its share of exports has dropped dramatically from the peak of 1980 when domestic manufacturers of home computers made a significant impression. In central processors and electronic microcircuits the performance has been a little better, reflecting the investment of foreign microelectronics firms in British manufacturing plants. Scotland's 'silicon glen' now has the largest concentration of chip manufacturing facilities in Europe, and these are able to fulfil the (still relatively low) domestic demand as well as contributing to export performance.

British performance in telecommunications has been moderate. System X has not been the worldwide success that was once hoped, and has not succeeded in regaining lost export markets on a large scale. At present the really big market for telecommunications equipment is in the less developed rather than the industrial countries of the world. This is because the industrialised countries already have a large, complex telecommunications network which they can update only slowly over a fairly long timescale. Several less developed countries, however, are going from a basic system in one or two major cities to a nationwide satellite or microwave-based digital system almost overnight.

British Economic Performance

The impression that this review gives is that the UK has failed to adopt new technology as rapidly as its major trading competitors, both in the production process and in the final product itself. Obviously there are notable specific exceptions that can be cited to this broad generalisation, but at the aggregate macro level it holds true. Thus the UK has lost out in two ways. First, the machines and the processes used in the production process are not as technically advanced as those of its competitors, with the result that far more men are employed to produce the same goods; and second, the goods that are produced are technically inferior to those of the competition. And in many markets, particularly the high value-added final consumer markets, there is simply no significant domestic UK producer on a world scale.

The market for these technically advanced products is therefore satisfied by increasing imports, whilst exports suffer. The UK's balance of trade in manufactured goods continues to decline, and once the North Sea oil runs out this will again become a major problem. Thus British manufacturing productivity suffers by not producing high value-added goods, and by using inefficient methods of production for the goods that it does produce. The problem is compounded by the predilection of many UK manufacturers for badge engineering — that is, the practice of buying in goods and relabelling them with a different manufacturer's name. Not only does this practice provide the foreign manufacturer with access to a UK distribution network and marketing name, which it would have been extremely difficult for him to achieve otherwise, but it can mean that the UK manufacturer makes it much more difficult for himself ever to get back into local production of the product concerned. This is because each pound of sales revenue from the UK provides a percentage (typically around 10 per cent) to support the R & D activity of the foreign manufacturer; as the foreign manufacturer is likely to be already technically ahead of his UK counterpart, this means that the UK manufacturer is helping to perpetuate the situation. Although this analysis is perhaps exaggerated and somewhat simplistic, it does convey significant features of the macro-economy over recent years. Examples can be readily found. How many video cassette recorders sold this year were produced by British firms (excluding UK packaging and badge-engineering activity)? The same question could apply to electronically controlled washing machines, sewing machines and telephone answering machines.

The two deficiencies of the UK response to technological advance compound each other. The labour shed by the introduction of more efficient productive processes cannot be employed in new high value-added industries, where the value of its product is larger, as these are the selfsame industries that we have failed to develop. It is the high technology end of the consumer market that continues to expand. As a trading nation, the UK has to improve on its capability to produce high technology goods and services, and to automate production processes, otherwise the British will have fewer and fewer products and services to trade in exchange for those they do not choose to produce for themselves.

Opinions on the impact of information technology in general, and the cheap, pervasive intelligence of microprocessors in particular, have ranged from the wildly optimistic to the equally wildly pessimistic. The optimists have suggested that they would usher in a new age of prosperity, in which robots would produce an infinite range of wonderful new goods; products and services would be personalised; and we would all have ample time to lie on the beach. The pessimists have agreed that the robots would indeed produce the goods, but they emphasise the problem of distribution of income: how to give the unemployed sufficient money to buy the goods produced. Experience over the last ten years, since the beginning of serious debate on these subjects, has served largely to emphasise how extreme both these views are. The adoption of microelectronics, though dramatic in small ways, has proved to be more of an evolutionary process than a revolutionary one, and many people now consider that its general impact on employment levels has been relatively marginal. But this should not distort the realisation that both optimistic and pessimistic views contain a part of the truth. Which of the extremes the future actually approximates most closely to is, to a significant degree, under our collective control.

Impact on Manufacturing Industry

Before exploring the policy options available to the British Government to meet some of these problems, it is perhaps worth examining some overall characteristics of a manufacturing organisation in order fully to understand the place and role of microelectronics and information technology.

The product of a manufacturing firm, as delivered to the final customer, often contains a relatively small value-added share attributable to the actual manufacturing process (i.e. casting, forming, shaping, cutting, joining etc). A rapidly growing share is attributable to packaging the product and getting it into the final consumer's hands: a process which involves distribution, advertising and so on. A large, and also growing, share stems from conceptualising, designing and differentiating the product, relative to its competitors. Further, for a growing number of products, information, support, maintenance and insurance (guarantees) are a significant part of the product definition. Thus, for example, a survey of America durable-goods manufacturers suggested that less than 50 per cent of their employees were engaged in direct production activities, and for many electronics manufacturers the figure is typically less than 20 per cent. As a result, many large manufacturing organisations are in reality as heavily involved in marketing and distribution as in production. The impact of information technology is as much on these non-production activities as on the production processes themselves.

However, this does not mean that the product itself, or the processes employed in its creation, can be ignored or marginalised. All other functions of the organisation derive their strength and purpose from the competitive characteristics of the product, which in turn derive largely from the processes used in its manufacture. What this does imply is that an organisation's investment in buildings and production machinery is no longer the sole critical part of its investment strategy. The large and increasing service and support component — investment in marketing, design, R & D and human resources including know-how, understanding and knowledge — is also critical. Increasingly, the technological component in the design, production, marketing, distribution and support of a product or service is the critical competitive weapon in the hands of the organisation. Many organisations, whose primary business is not of itself technically based, have been discovering nevertheless that the application of appropriate technology is a significant competitive factor in the delivery of their product. This is true, for example, of the travel industry, of much of the financial sector, and of insurance companies. And for some industries, most notably the entertainment industry, information technology is blurring the distinction between products and services. For example, films may be shown in cinemas or broadcast on public or pay-TV (all effectively service operations), or sold or rented video cassettes or discs, a product-based operation.

It is important to appreciate that the two types of technical change (i.e. in the products themselves, and in manufacturing and support processes) are often mutually dependent. Commercial success stems from, and is dependent on, changing products and product design. New products typically lead to the introduction of new production processes; the two are seen as aspects of the same decision. As an explanation of technical change, this is probably much more important than a simple desire to upgrade production techniques.

Surveys have illustrated that many of the individual machines used in the production process are old (that is, ten years old or more) or very old (sometimes a hundred years old, or even more). In an era of slow technical advance, the age of machines was not a significant factor in the competitiveness of an organisation; but today, when the newer machines are far more cost-efficient in operation than their predecessors, to hold on to obsolescent machinery undoubtedly handicaps an organisation. The taxation rules in Japan, which encourage the rapid updating of machinery, have helped to give the country an edge by equipping its factories with more modern, more efficient machinery. In recent years, many firms elsewhere appear to have concentrated their attention more upon organising the flow of production, than on considering the capabilities of individual machines. Studies have shown that in an engineering shop most productivity improvements have come from developments in production scheduling, rather than from improvements

in individual machine performance. Computer-control has its part to play
in efficient scheduling, but even so this process has finite limits, and no
organisation can afford to postpone updating its equipment for too long.

Advances in technology enable us to produce more goods (both
existing and new) and provide more (existing and new) services with
the same input levels. Thus productivity rises. Higher productivity
results in lower unit cost, and therefore either higher profits, lower
relative prices, or both. Consumer and corporate real income rises
(leading to an increase in overall demand, whilst labour demand falls and,
in perfect markets, so do real wages to maintain equilibrium. Insomuch as
the new technology allows new products and services to be provided, this
generates investment, and increased output and employment in the
economy that produces them. Similarly, some existing products, processes
and services will be rendered obsolete, with corresponding reductions in
output and employment in the economy producing them.

What is clearly critical is, first, the speed with which the multiplier
effects on aggregate output work through the economy, so that the labour
displaced by higher productivity (assuming unemployment rises, and
wages do not fall) is re-employed in those industries benefiting from the
increase in aggregate demand; and second, the mix of industries present
in the economy, between those created by the new technology and those
rendered obsolete by it. If the mix tends towards the latter, then
increased demand will simply create wealth in other economies whose
mix tends towards the former. Thus in order to minimise temporary
unemployment we require that the benefits of productivity gains be
passed on as rapidly as possible, and preferably in the form of lower
relative prices. To minimise long-term structural unemployment, and to
have any chance of improving our real wealth, we must develop industries
exploiting new technology products, processes and services.

Innovation and Growth

The capabilities of microelectronics and information technology enable
superior production machines to be developed but, much more important, enable complex production processes to be modelled and controlled.
In principle this has been possible for many years, but now it is possible
in practice. This focuses our interest on the innovation process as being
the critical factor in technical, and ultimately commercial, success.
Innovation is the process of bringing developments in science and
technology out of the laboratory and into the market-place, as *successful*
products and services, or productive processes. The emphasis on
successful products in this definition is of paramount importance: the
process of invention creates new products (and processes); innovation

further develops them into successful products. This stresses the importance of innovation not only in the creative stage of a new product, but also in the making and marketing stages. The UK has an enviable reputation in invention — the creation of advances in science and technology — but an even more unenviable one in innovation.

In one sense the problems of the UK economy described above might be seen as part of a national economic life cycle: underdevelopment, followed by a period of very rapid growth, then a slow-down into maturity, and finally stagnation in old age. Historical examination of ancient civilisations — Chinese, Persian, Egyptian, Greek, Roman — bears this out in varying degrees. It could be argued that Britain was an underdeveloped country up until the end of the seventeenth century, when industrial development began, followed by the first industrial revolution in the eighteenth and nineteenth centuries. In this period the British economy went through an extremely rapid period of industrial development. But by the second half of the nineteenth century this had

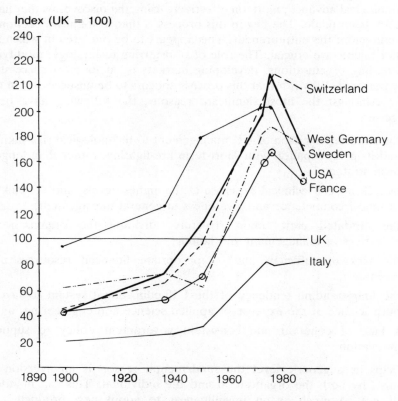

Figure 17.7 *GNP per capita in different countries, 1890–1980*

slowed down, and in the present century the British economy is in its mature phase. One could suggest that it is now entering old age, has become incapable of movement or change, and will be moribund for a century or so, after which it will be an underdeveloped economy once more, and start the cycle again. Some evidence to support this hypothesis is shown in Figure 17.7. Since the end of the first industrial revolution in the UK, other industrialised countries have been slowly overhauling us.

However, we would regard this as a very pessimistic viewpoint, and would hope that there is more than one way for an economy to cope with old age — hence, the importance in our eyes of focusing on innovation as the process by which an economy can remain vital and capable of adapting to a changing world, even in the final stages of its life cycle. By looking at those areas in which innovation is critical, we hope that this book has illustrated that the development and application of microelectronics seems certain to occupy a central role in future economic development.

The emphasis in this area is less on creating new scientific or technological advance; more on effectively using the discoveries that have already been made. The key in this process is that well-known economic phenomenon: the entrepreneur. This appears to be one area in which his or her talents are crucial. The role of transferring technology, modifying or creating organisations, developing markets is, at its most successful, very personal. Why is it that this process appears to be unsuccessful in the UK? Amongst the most significant reasons, the following have been suggested:

the apparent aversion of UK management to technological risk-taking, and its preoccupation with short-term fire-fighting, rather than longer-term strategy;

its lack of real technical expertise at the highest levels, and the lack of technical competence and awareness in general management;

the outdated craft union structure, dividing the organisational objectives of management and labour;

the lack of sufficient and/or appropriate financial resources and incentives;

the long-standing tendency of the UK educational system to favour pure science at the expense of applied science and engineering; and

a lack of coherent and consistent government policy to support innovation.

Perhaps at a generic level the fundamental reason is an aversion to change, by both the organisation and the individual. This can manifest itself not so much as an unwillingness to adopt new products and processes, but more as an unwillingness to give up current products and processes — to unlearn old ways. Products change only when market forces make change inevitable, but by that time it is too late to establish a proper market share. Obsolete technology and outmoded machines are employed because they still have a few more years' physical life in them, when a hard-headed look at the economics of the situation would show the advantage in investing immediately in replacements. Much of the evidence suggests that the UK has a tendency to live more in the past than other countries — reliving past glories, and unwilling to accept new realities.

No one country or company has a monopoly in resistance to change: the phenomenon is all too widespread. As we have mentioned previously, a good example is provided by the major valve manufacturers and their attitude to the new semiconductors in the fifties and sixties. Their response to the advent of the transistor was to try to produce a better and cheaper valve — not because they could not understand the new technology, but because they were unable to change rapidly (and dramatically) enough to embrace it. The established valve manufacturers had too much to lose and forget, whereas newcomers to the industry were in a position to start out with no preconceptions and adapt to the real prevailing conditions.

Research and Development

The engine that drives innovation is R & D, which has three major purposes for an organisation, namely:

to develop existing products and services — if possible to lead the competition;

to improve the range and scope of the organisation's products and services to cover new market opportunities in its main business area; and

to identify and develop new products and services with market potential (possibly unrelated to existing activities), to provide a portfolio of new business opportunities.

This suggests that innovation through successful R & D implies market leadership. Yet many UK companies argue that to follow others into new markets is the best strategy. However, we would suggest that a strategy of following, rather than leading, has several potentially disastrous consequences, especially in such a rapidly changing area as microelectronics. In particular:

the first company to introduce a new product or service may benefit from novelty (gimmick) value;

the second (or later) entrant is likely to have to face the Mark 2 version of the leader's product;

the leader chooses the time and place for the action, while the others may have it chosen for them;

the followers may have to follow a market development strategy dictated by the leader, which is unlikely to be to their best advantage!

A naïve model of technical change, the mechanism of innovation, suggests the following steps:

basic research creates ideas for technical progress;

of these ideas, a proportion encourage applied research, which in turn encourage development projects;

of these projects, a proportion are taken up by the firm into production as new products or processes, which enables new products to be marketed, or existing products produced at lower cost, or some combination of the two.

This simple one-way model would suggest that more expenditure on R & D is a 'good thing', since it would create more ideas for technical progress. But such a model is both oversimplified and distorted; one of the key issues in R & D is to choose the right problems to work on, and, in an industrial context, this requires a better understanding of actual and potential problems in production, marketing, distribution and all of the other areas relevant in delivering a successful product or service to the final customer. This implies a strong feedback loop in our model of technical change, and the integration of the R & D activity with the mainstream production and marketing activities of the organisation. This also has implications as to the nature and number of the skilled human resources needed in this process, and would suggest that in the UK context too many scientists and engineers are engaged at the creation-of-ideas stage, and too few at the make and market, implementation, evaluation and feedback stages.

The Process of Innovation

This discussion of the mechanism of innovation is in general terms. We would suggest that its importance in the area of information technology is critical, given the pervasive nature of IT and its potential influence on products and processes in all organisations. Loss of leadership in IT would appear likely to accelerate the decline of the UK economy into senility — a positive, determined approach to retain a significant design and production capability in information technology products would appear likely to be the best opportunity of giving the UK economy an active and vigorous old age.

The ability to absorb new technology and exploit its potential is based on several important factors, one of the most significant of which is the level of education of the workforce. The level of literacy, numeracy and technical understanding will be a major determinant of their capability to understand change, and people's willingness to accept and actively foster change is strongly influenced by their capability to understand it. If people cannot cope with numbers, follow sequences of instructions, and infer logical conclusions, or interpret and understand diagrams, then technical horizons are limited. But education in these skills, above a certain level, enhances people's ability to absorb and adapt, to change and grow rapidly. Observation suggests that the percentage of people reaching particular levels of academic achievement in the UK is substantially lower than in other industrialised countries.

There are many situations available to illustrate that once a technological breakthrough has been made, a newcomer to the technology can reach an equivalent level of competence faster than the originator. (It takes less time to get to the corresponding level, but the newcomer is unlikely ever to close the gap with the originator.) The educational level of the population has a major influence on the time it takes the newcomer to become competent in the new technology.

Thus, the ability in simple manufacturing technologies, especially textiles, and assembly operations has now spread all over the world. Higher level technologies — such as the ability to make internal combustion engines and simple electrical components, and to undertake fairly complex assembly operations, such as motor cars and electrical appliances — first spread to the most educated of the countries with lower labour costs, Japan, and then to its neighbours, as their skill levels improved and Japan's labour costs rose. Now countries such as Hong Kong, Taiwan, Singapore and Korea also have skilled workforces, and even Japan is surrendering its supremacy in these higher level technologies to the newcomers. The skill levels necessary to exploit other people's technological advances are now spreading to the Philippines, Indonesia, Vietnam, and the remaining countries of South East Asia, as well as to several of the South American countries.

The new competitors' products are not simply inferior imitations either; generally they are at least as good as the originals, and often are significantly better. Technology is being transferred around the world ever more rapidly, encouraged by economics, increasing skill levels and political initiatives. No one country or company has any natural permanent leadership or supremacy in any technology. Supremacy remains with those who provide the leadership in innovation into new products and processes — the number of potential imitators may multiply, but the originator will always have an initial advantage. The Japanese were supremely successful imitators for twenty-five years, but they now recognise that the path to continuing technological dominance lies through innovation, research and development.

From Mechanisation to Automation

Before focusing on the possible impact of information technology on the economic development of the UK and other industrial countries, let us return to review the place of IT in an overall historical view of economic development and industrialisation. As we have remarked earlier, machines magnified the power of muscles, and the microprocessor magnifies the power of the brain. However, this statement is too generalised for us to appreciate the role of IT, and we need a finer understanding of the significant characteristics of the industrialisation process.

The industrialisation process involves several facets: one is the developing of a trading economy, so that advantage can be taken of specialisation in products, services or skills; another is the organising of the production and distribution process, so that, where appropriate, technology can be brought to bear. Throughout history, one of the major factors in furthering economic development has been the application of more and more technology.

This process (the application of technology) can be broken into two major parts — the application of a machine, and the application of some form of control to a machine. A more detailed framework for these categorisations is shown in Figure 17.8, with some examples of each. Thus, the first technologies used people (or animals) as the source of mechanical power, typically harnessed to a wheel. Each major applications area for technology, manufacturing, transportation, communications and so on, developed in this way. The next stage in development was to harness sources of natural mechanical power: the wind and falling water. The problem with these sources of power was that they were uncontrolled — if the wind dropped, or there was a drought, then the machine stopped.

Thus the first industrial revolution really took off with the advent of controllable mechanical power — first the steam engine, then the internal combustion engine, and then the electric motor. In some ways, the latter was of the greatest significance since it enabled the distribution of mechanical power to where it was needed, and the supply of an appropriate amount. The significance of this can be gauged by imagining for a moment that all of the present electric motors in factories, homes, offices, vehicles and so on had to be replaced by an alternative source of

Characteristic	Product Examples	Power	Control
MECHANICAL			
(i) no power	plough, cart	human/animal	human brain
(ii) uncontrolled power	sailing ship watermill windmill	wind water wind	human brain
(iii) controlled power	steam train car	steam engine internal combustion engine	human brain
(iv) semi-automatic control	packing equipment assembly line	electric motor	fixed program (mechanical)/ human brain
AUTOMATION			
(v) individual automatic control	clock steam pump Jacquard loom NC machine tool	clockwork steam engine steam engine electric motor	fixed program (mechanical)
	robot	electric motor	re-programmable
(vi) full automation	automated warehouse automated factory	electric motor electric motor	integrated adaptive (feedback), re-programmable

Figure 17.8 *Mechanisation and Automation*

power, such as a steam engine or internal combustion engine.

The next significant step was the application of some degree of automatic control. Some form of semi-automatic control, with a significant degree of human control is typified by the assembly line. Fully automatic control of a single machine (with no human control, other than turning on the power supply) dates from before the industrial revolution, in the form of the clock. But until about thirty years ago, fully automatic control was confined to individual machines, and complete systems control required some significant degree of human intervention.

However, we are now entering upon the era of true automation — a word first coined in the 1930s by Ford engineers, who could conceive of a fully automatically controlled system (even though they didn't have the means, at the time, to achieve it totally), growing out of the transfer lines that they had recently developed. Automation implies that one (or more) of three additional features are present, namely:

a systems approach — treating an entire process as a whole, rather than mechanising individual tasks;

programmability — the ability for the control instructions in the machines (i.e. software) to be changed, so that a single machine can perform multiple tasks; and

sensory ability — the machine is aware of the environment within which it is operating, its relationship to other machines, and the process it is currently engaged on, so that some form of feedback or learning ability can be implemented.

All of these three features require a high degree of intelligence to be built into whatever is controlling the machines, a degree of intelligence that was generally available only with the electronic computer. However, as we have discussed earlier, at first computers were expensive, unreliable beasts, very unsuited in temperament to this area of application, and in any case our software skills were inadequate at the time. It is only in the past decade or so that the hardware has become cheap enough (the concept of the computer as a component), and our software skills great enough for us to tackle this area. The cheapness and flexibility of the microprocessor is akin to that of the electric motor, delivering the intelligence required at the place where it is needed. It is the availability of cheap microelectronics which will enable true automation ultimately to come about both in the factory and the office. And again it is worth emphasising that the constraint upon this development will be the availability of people competent to use and take advantage of the new technologies.

Let us now return to consider how the economies of different countries are adapting themselves to these changes, and, in particular, how we see the future development of the UK economy.

IT, Economic Development and UK Government Policy

In our previous discussion we examined the importance of innovation in fuelling economic development, and of R & D in driving innovation. In Figure 17.9 we detail some of the significant measures of R & D spending (which is itself notoriously difficult to measure) for the UK and some other major industrialised countries.

This illustrates the continuing importance of defence-related R & D spending in both the UK and the USA. But in America, much of this results in development spin-offs in the civil sector, and is thus not unproductive; in the UK, however, there has been almost no spin-off. The non-defence R & D spending illustrates how Japan and West Germany have overtaken most of the other industrialised countries, particularly because their industrially funded research runs at a relatively high level compared to government-funded research.

In general, this R & D spending has been oriented towards funda-

	Gross Expenditure on R&D (GERD) £bn		GERD as % of GDP		R&D performed in Business Enterprise Sector (BERD) £bn		BERD as % of GERD		% of BERD financed by Industry		Civil R&D as % of GDP	
	1981	1985	1981	1985	1981	1985	1981	1985	1981	1985	1981	1985
USA	39.9	63.1	2.4	2.8	28.1	45.1	70.3	71.5	68.4	67.2	1.8	1.9
Japan[1]	12.8	19.2	2.3	2.6	7.8	12.5	60.7	65.1	97.9	98.0	2.3	2.5[2]
W Germany	7.9	11.3	2.4	2.7	5.4	8.2	69.5	72.2	81.7	82.2	2.4	2.5
France	5.5	8.3	2.0	2.3	3.2	4.9	58.9	59.2	68.2	71.0	1.6	1.8[3]
UK	6.1	8.2	2.4	2.3	3.8	5.1	61.8	65.0	61.3	66.0	1.8	1.7

Source: Annual Review of Government Funded R & D, 1987, HMSO.

Notes: 1. Japanese data are for 1981 & 1984.
2. 1983.
3. 1984.

Figure 17.9 Spending on Research and Development, 1981 and 1985

mental research, except in the case of Japan, where up to the early eighties it tended more towards the development of other people's fundamental research, a situation which is steadily changing. This is illustrated by the fact that the USA earns roughly ten times more from selling technology (in the form of licences, royalties, etc.) than it spends on buying it, while for Japan the reverse is true: it spends about seven times more on buying technology than it earns in selling it. For European countries the ratio of sales to purchases of technology lies in the range from 1.0 to 1.5.

Earlier in this chapter we suggested that the process of innovation is essentially a personal one, and in particular one suited to the entrepreneur. Yet over the past fifteen years or so the country which has innovated most successfully has been Japan, in an environment in which both the entrepreneurial role and innovator drive have to a significant extent been institutionalised into the corporate organisation. There is ample evidence that Japan intends to continue to be successful in such corporate innovation, so we consider it appropriate to review the Japanese experience.

The Japanese Experience

The major driving force in directing Japanese R & D has been MITI, the Ministry of International Trade and Industry. Much of the development in Japanese consumer electronics can be traced back to programmes directed by MITI in the mid-1970s, specifically oriented first to achieving parity, and secondly to overtaking the American design and production leadership in chip technology.

In the USA the driving force behind developments in microelectronics has been (and continues to be) the demands of the defence and space industries. The basic R & D effort in microelectronics has seen application in these areas as its initial market and paymaster, and this has generally been true in Europe too. With the development costs written off against defence budgets, new microelectronic products and production processes become available for commercial exploitation. In the USA the transfer of the technology from defence to civilian purposes was rapid; although some chips were application-dependent, many were not, and neither was the production technology required to make them. This process was fuelled by the economics of chip production (i.e. seeking larger and larger markets), by the sheer size of the American market for new products, and by the great opportunity offered by this technology to entrepreneurs in the late 1960s and early 1970s. In Europe, with very few exceptions, this technology transfer from military to civilian application did not happen, perhaps partly because of the smaller scale of the local market, and partly because of the perceived poor climate for entrepreneurial risk-takers.

In Japan, which completely lacks any defence-oriented R & D, all the R & D in microelectronics was oriented towards the business and consumer market from the outset. The major Japanese electronics companies took the same technological advances in chip design and production processes from the American semiconductor companies, but developed them specifically with consumer applications in mind.

All of the major Japanese electronics companies participated in MITI's projects, so that they all now have access to a high level of basic technological know-how. Some of the results of these efforts are apparent from Figure 17.10, which indicates the extent of the Japanese presence in the semiconductor and mainframe computer markets. That this presence is even stronger in other consumer electronics markets is evident from Figure 17.6.

The World's Top Ten Semiconductor Producers, 1987

1. NEC — Japan	6. Philips-Signetics — Holland
2. Toshiba — Japan	7. Fujitsu — Japan
3. Hitachi — Japan	8. Matsushita — Japan
4. Motorola — USA	9. Intel — USA
5. Texas Instruments — USA	10. Mitsubishi — Japan

The World's Top Ten Companies in the Mainframe Computer Market, 1986

1. IBM — USA	6. Hitachi — Japan
2. Sperry Corp. — USA	7. Honeywell — USA
3. Fujitsu — Japan	8. Burroughs — USA
4. NEC — Japan	9. Groupe Bull — France
5. Control Data Corp. — USA	10. NCR Corp. — USA

Figure 17.10 *Japanese Presence in the Computer and Semiconductor Markets*

The Japanese dominance has been achieved through a number of factors. Fortuitous market circumstances have played their part, but so have the fiscal policies which MITI has encouraged. A reduction in the period over which companies could write off machine tools for taxation purposes, for instance, helped to reduce the average age of machine tools in Japanese factories from over twenty years to around six years by the mid-1980s. Japanese factories are well equipped now with modern tools and equipment, and this enables them to produce large quantities of goods of high and consistent quality.

Japanese predominance came first in areas in which innovation and design skills came second to technical competence and reliability. By the early 1980s the Japanese had established a clear lead over American suppliers in the memory chip market, but even today the Americans predominate in the microprocessor market. The Japanese overwhelmingly dominate the market for many consumer electronic goods — colour televisions, video cassette recorders, camcorders and so on — but their position is much weaker in the computer market, though it is steadily improving.

Japanese consumer electronics companies showed two great strengths in the 1980s. First, they excelled in applying generally available technology to their products; and second, they proved exceptionally good at developing custom logic for their products. This latter capability, and the superior product characteristics derived from it, was a critical factor in achieving market dominance. But this has not come cheaply, and the Japanese effort in R & D has steadily grown to match this success, as we have made apparent.

MITI's research initiative today is of very considerable size, and it is more than matched by the research sums committed by commercial organisations. Over $215 million has been spent by MITI in the 1980s on semiconductor research alone; around $500 million has been committed to a fifth generation computer project. However, the fact that many MITI initiatives are highly publicised should not cause all perspective to be lost: IBM's annual research budget, for example, amounts to several times this figure.

MITI's current projects centre heavily on the so-called fifth generation computers and on the leading edge of technological development, and indicate the steady shift in the Japanese emphasis, away from applying other people's research and towards undertaking their own fundamental research. For example, an eight-year programme, costing around $200 million and running throughout the 1980s, is attempting to develop faster supercomputers. The SIGMA (Software Industrialised Generator and Maintenance Aids) project, a five-year project which began in 1985, centres on software developments required for the fifth generation, and suggests that the time may come when we can no longer assume Western predominance of the computer software market.

Some of the consequences of this Japanese success are illustrated in Figure 17.11, showing for manufacturing industry the changes in productivity, output and employment from 1975 to 1980 for Japan and other industrialised countries. The typical pattern has been a considerable rise in productivity, a smaller rise in output, and a fall in employment — with the UK performing worse than everyone else and the Japanese much better. The fall in manufacturing employment has led to an increase in total unemployment and a switch into service employment, and this at a

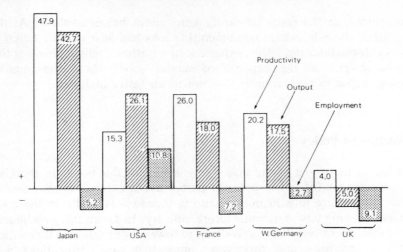

Figure 17.11 *Percentage Change in Productivity, Output and Employment, Manufacturing Industry, 1975–80*

time when the total labour force is rising in most countries. But if we examine the two extreme examples — the UK and Japan — in slightly more detail, a much more significant conclusion emerges. In Figure 17.12 we show the changes in numbers employed in manufacturing and services in Japan and the UK from 1980 to 1985. In the mid-seventies the number employed in manufacturing in Japan actually fell, but by the eighties this trend had been reversed, and Japan saw an increase in manufacturing

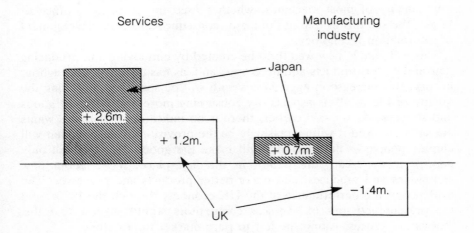

Figure 17.12 *Changes in Numbers Employed, 1980–85*

employment, as the result of earlier innovations began to show. At the same time, the UK, where manufacturing jobs had also steadily fallen in number throughout the 1970s, experienced a further decline. Nor was this Japanese gain at the expense of service jobs, where the number employed rose in both countries — but much faster in Japan.

Government Policy

This brings us to one of the major conclusions of this book. In the UK, the government (of either political party) has spent enormous sums of money preserving jobs in manufacturing industry, typically in the most rapidly declining bits of manufacturing industry. In Japan the government has in total spent less, but this is directed towards encouraging innovation into new products and processes; supporting (and protecting) new industries; and developing the growth industries in the manufacturing sector. As a consequence, we have seen that manufacturing employment fell sharply, but manufacturing output rose even more sharply. The wealth that this generated was spent increasingly on services, most of which are naturally labour-intensive, employing many more people than those displaced. There is evidence that a similar demand for more services exists in the UK too, only here the goods to pay for them haven't been produced.

Our earlier analysis of the structure of industrial and commercial development suggested that we are about to enter into an era of widespread automation, especially in the manufacturing and assembly process; in the processing of transactions of all types; and in the functionality of most machines, whether used in the factory, office or home. We see this as one of the major consequences of the development of information technology.

This will enable new wealth to be created by employing and producing new and better products and processes; and, as has been true throughout history, this increase in aggregate wealth will be spent on improving the quality of life in all its aspects, by consuming more and different goods and services. As we said earlier, there is no indication that man's wants are satiated. And it will increasingly be the provision of services that will employ people — the machines will make the goods. But this will only happen if we create the wealth in the first place, if we adopt new techniques and practices, and make better products and processes. The evidence of the performance of the UK economy through the 1970s, and the present activities of overseas competitors would suggest that this innovatory process cannot be left to pure market forces alone.

European Responses to the Japanese Initiative

The Japanese 'fifth generation' initiative, and the other much publicised Japanese government research initiatives, have not been ignored by the rest of the world. Similar research efforts, on varying scales, have been initiated in the USA and in Western Europe.

The US research effort is being orchestrated by MCC, the Microelectronics and Computer Technology Corporation. In the European Economic Community, fifth generation research has been focused under the ESPRIT Program. ESPRIT stands for European Strategic Programme of Research and Development in Information Technology. From 1984 to 1988 ESPRIT sponsored about 200 different products, with researchers from universities, government departments and computer/electronics manufacturers working together. Among these was the development of INMOS's transputer chip. ESPRIT II is now planned as a follow-up programme.

The UK's own research into fifth generation computing and associated projects was co-ordinated by the Alvey Programme. This was initiated in February 1982 by Kenneth Baker, then Minister for Information Technology, who commissioned a committee headed by John Alvey, senior director of technology at British Telecom, to report on the type of initiative required.

The Alvey Report was published in October 1982, and identified four technical areas in which major advances were required for implementing an AIT (Advanced Information Technology) programme:

1. software engineering
2. man/machine interface
3. intelligent knowledge-based systems (IKBS)
4. VLSI (very large scale integration).

Subsequently the Alvey Programme was started to encourage research in these areas. It had total funds for its first phase (which ended in 1988) of £200 million.

The Alvey Programme was intended to provide a pound of Government funding to match each pound of private research funding on approved projects. It paid the entire cost of university research, in association with SERC (the Science and Engineering Research Council). It was originally funded by three different government departments — the Department of Trade and Industry (DTI), the Department of Education and Science (via SERC), and the Ministry of Defence, thus assuring it of a degree of autonomy.

Alvey's money tends to have been dedicated to research projects carried out by large corporations, rather than by small, entrepreneurial firms. For example, ICL has been involved in no less than 58 separate Alvey/ESPRIT research projects. However, the cross-fertilisation of the initiative is indicated by the fact that it shared this research with 44 industrial partners and 32 universities.

Among Alvey's biggest major projects have been Flagship, a project aimed at developing parallel processing machines running declarative languages, and a £6 million project for developing software to auto-matically design chips with up to 1 million resistors on each, involving Plessey and Racal among other collaborators. Alvey money also helped to fund the Turing Institute (named after the computer pioneer Alan Turing) which was set up in Glasgow in 1984 to carry out research into artificial intelligence.

Late in 1987, the Government began a restructuring of the Alvey project with a view to starting a second phase of research. The original tripartite funding of Alvey (between the DTI, the DES and the MoD) was largely scrapped, and Alvey became effectively a division of the Department of Trade and Industry, headed by a civil servant. This restructuring caused considerable concern at the time, by those who felt that this would lead to a fundamental change in emphasis away from fundamental research, as well as to a downgrading of the entire project. It could also be argued, however, that the UK's weakness is not in fundamental research but in its application, and that Alvey, by emphasising the former at the expense of the latter, has failed adequately to contribute to solving the UK's economic problems. Certainly Alvey, like the MITI project, has concentrated on developments most of which are not yet at the commerical stage, and some of which may prove to be dead-ends in research terms.

The UK Economic Situation

The risk in a situation of rapid technological change is that those countries which fail to innovate successfully will be overtaken by intense, technologically advanced competition from abroad, resulting in loss of markets, unemployment and lower net income than could otherwise be expected. Recovery from such an occurrence is then extremely difficult, since it requires further technical innovation and change, over and above that implemented by competing nations.

To some extent, it can be argued that this has already come about in the UK, as a result of the attitude of government, industry and the unions throughout the 1960s, 1970s and 1980s (and indeed earlier), which centred on the dangers of new technology rather than its potential advantages. Some of the dangers are real: adopting new technology must lead to changes in employment patterns, and may cause transitory high unemployment. But the dangers of not adopting new technology are real, too. It would appear to us that the risks are much lower to the UK economy if we pursue a policy of actively encouraging technical innovation and change, such that UK companies and their employees can reap the benefits of the increased value-added and world markets. Amelioration of the consequences of this policy should be the proper focus of social policy.

The review presented earlier has illustrated how Japan has implemented a national policy of innovation in information technology, and how the benefits have been apparent in terms of improved output and economic performance. The USA, in contrast, largely relies upon market forces to bring about innovation. To a large extent the British Government in the 1980s has pursued a similar policy, but this ignores the fact that the situation is not comparable in the UK. First, the sheer scale of the defence-oriented R & D effort in the USA ensures such a wide spread of activity that some initiatives are bound to bear fruit (though admittedly at a very high cost). Second, the whole economic environment in the USA encourages, supports and rewards entrepreneurial activity in a way not found anywhere else in the world, and certainly not in the UK. Even in America some commentators have expressed concern about the lead the Japanese have achieved in many sectors, and have suggested that a clearer national policy be formed.

Alvey does represent an effort by the British Government to foster the development of leading-edge technology, but it is on a pitiful scale when compared to the amounts that have been poured into BL, British Steel and the like since the war. And Alvey's research orientation does nothing to address the problem that our industrial climate fosters the *status quo*, and does not — in terms of fiscal policy, union attitudes, or management attitudes — encourage the rapid development of innovative new products.

As illustrated in Figure 17.9, the British investment in R & D does not appear particularly deficient in total when compared with other industrial countries, but its global effectiveness does. The proportion of UK R & D going into defence-related projects is high, but unlike the situation in the USA there has been almost no spin-off from this into consumer products in the UK. Generally speaking, the defence R & D in the UK has been a waste of valuable resources on an essentially non-productive activity. As the Japanese electronics companies have illustrated, ultimately R & D has to produce goods and services which people want to buy.

What appears to be lacking even now is a clear global appreciation of the potentially critical nature of information technology: that it is not some particular fad which a short-term expediency-driven policy will hopefully submerge into obscurity. In part it is symptomatic of the general reaction and appreciation of all matters technological in the UK establishment — a great desire not to know. We consider that this is one area where the Government has to lead on a much greater scale. Almost ten years after the serious debate about the impact of microelectronics came to public attention, we still need to formulate a national policy, at the highest level, to address three critical areas:

First, a recognition of the place of innovation in information technology within the wider context of technical change; the formulation of agreed objectives between government and industry, with commensurate purpose, motivation and funding, given that the activities of our competitors mean that reliance on market mechanisms alone will not suffice; that the risks in attempting technological innovation are lower than those of doing nothing.

Second, an awareness of the long-term importance of education — to provide a climate more favourable to an acceptance and understanding of change — and the recognition that education must be a life-long experience, not a relatively short period of formal instruction.

Third, policies to cope with the social consequences; particularly the role of the Government as the protector and guarantor of the rights of the individual and of the quality of society; and the need to cope with the problems of transitional unemployment arising from change, not by protecting present jobs, but by hastening the creation of new ones, and by recognising the specific problems involved.

Conclusions

The conclusions of this book can be summarised as follows:

1. Information technology is pervasive, it is *universal*; potentially it can be applied by all industrialised countries having a sufficient educational and skill level; its potential impact and importance on our future lives is too important for policy to be determined by default.

2. To the extent that the application of information technology affects relative costs, then relative prices in world trade will also be affected; the pervasive nature of information technology means that technical change in general must be the policy objective; change originating from the application of information technology is not separable or different.

3. The direct effects of technical change on domestic output and employment will be such that real income will eventually adjust, through changes in factor prices (including real wages) and industrial structure, such that labour transfers from technically obsolete organisations to those providing more goods and/or services.

4. There will be a period of transitory unemployment as a part of this adjustment process, which does not necessarily lead to cumulative unemployment, but may take a very long time to reach a new equilibrium in times of recession.

5. However, the indirect effects on output and employment could be much worse than the direct effects; serious unemployment and reductions in output (and hence aggregate wealth) may occur in an industrialised economy if an industry is subjected to intense technologically based competition, manifest as superior products or services, or lower prices, or both.

6. Interference in the normal market adjustment processes, by propping up failing organisations, artificially maintaining employment and factor costs, is likely ultimately to prolong unemployment and heighten the risk from external technically advanced competition.

7. There is no particular distinction between the innovation of a technically advanced product, or an advanced process — both tend to occur in parallel, and both generate higher real factor incomes, demand and output.

8. The great risk exposure for the UK economy is the likelihood of being caught unprepared by major technological advances in other industrialised countries, and this really concerns future real incomes; this risk would appear to be much higher than those arising from an attempt to generate technological leadership in domestic industries.

9. The constraint in all industrialised countries would appear to be software in the widest sense. The human capital involvement — directly in the form of knowledge and skills, and indirectly in the form of attitudes to change — will be critical and will take the longest time to create; perhaps it is here that Japan's true advantage lies.

This is the crux of this book. Hopefully you now have an understanding and appreciation of information technology and the immense but pervasive impact that it will have on our personal, corporate and national lives. In our view, information technology provides one of those few critical areas which, as a nation, we have to get right; otherwise our economic and social future is bleak.

Keeping Up to Date

We recognise that in the evolution of Information Technology there will be significant developments in the products available and the applications to which they are put. Therefore we list below various sources of information which we believe will help to make readers aware of these developments.

1. General Business Publications

A number of publications contain regular relevant news-items, including:

> *Business Week* (Information Processing section)
> *The Economist*
> *The Financial Times* (Technology and Management pages; special surveys)
> *The Guardian* (Futures page)

2. Management Journals

Academic management journals occasionally contain articles of interest; those listed below contain relevant material on a more frequent basis:

> *Harvard Business Review*
> *Management Today*
> *MIS Quarterly*

3. Scientific Publications

Publications aimed at the lay scientist contain many articles both about the underlying technologies and specific applications; the best example is:

> *New Scientist*

4. Computer Trade Press

As in any large industry, there is a plethora of publications which chart its happenings. The majority of developments originate in America so that attention to American publications will capture these. Of the many available the most comprehensive is:

Computerworld

In the UK a corresponding review is provided by:

Computing

Certain publications have a different perspective, looking at specific applications, equipment and sustems in greater depth; probably best known is:

Which Computer

5. Personal Computer Magazines

Due to the phenomenal development of, and interest in, personal computing, there is now a wide range of popular magazines covering this area, including titles specialising in games and home computing, education and business applications, and titles focusing on individual brands or types of computer system.

Among the generalist publications, the predominant American one (at times highly technical) is:

Byte

while the two British ones with the best track records are:

Personal Computer World
Practical Computing

6. Newsletters

In America newsletters are becoming one of the major methods by which people are being kept up to date in this area. One that we have found to be particularly useful is:

Microprocessors at Work
      published by   Elsevier International Bulletins,
                     Mayfield House, 256 Banbury Road,
                     Oxford OX2 7DH, England.

7. Finally, in a class of its own, is a bi-monthly American magazine which provides industry-wide application and technology reviews for the technically-literate manager, namely:

Datamation

Glossary

Access Time: the time taken for a secondary storage device to respond to a request for data by the cpu.

Acronym: a word formed from the initial letter or letters of the words in a name or phrase, e.g. Algol from ALGOrithmic Language, Cobol from COmmon Business Orientated Language.

Activity Rate: the proportion of records in a file accessed in a given period.

Actuator: output device that electronically controls a mechanical unit (e.g. water valve).

A/D: Analogue to digital conversions.

Ada: a structured programming language designed for the efficient development of real time systems (named after Ada, Lady Lovelace who first formulated the principles of programming).

Address: a number or label used to identify a particular computer resource, e.g. a location in primary or secondary memory.

AI: *see* Artificial Intelligence.

Algol: a high-level programming language favoured by the European academic community for its structure and formality (ALGOrithmic Language).

Alphanumeric: a contraction of 'alphabetic' and 'numeric'; applies to any coding system that provides for letters, numbers, and special symbols such as punctuation.

Analog(ue): a signal that exactly copies another signal but in a different medium (e.g. sound by electrical voltage). Analogue signals can vary continuously in frequency and amplitude.

Analog(ue) Computer: a computer that operates on data represented in analogue form (i.e. varying continuously). Such a computer will have a specific purpose and not be generally programmable (cf. digital computer).

Analog(ue) Transmission: communication technique whereby signals are sent in an analogue manner, e.g. radio and TV broadcast signals.

Analyst: a person skilled in the definition of problems and the development of systems for their solution, especially systems which may be implemented on a computer; *see also* Systems Analyst.

APL: A Programming Language; a high-level programming language, particularly suited to scientific applications.

Application Language: a programming language designed for a particular application area; often used directly by user, e.g. financial modelling, project planning.

Application Package: a program or set of programs designed for a particular application that can be customised to a limited extent.

Application Software: those programs designed to solve specific user problems and needs (as opposed to system software).

Architecture: *see* System Architecture.

Archive: system for storing (and retrieving) data over a long period of time. Data are usually stored off-line requiring manual intervention for retrieval.

Arithmetic Unit: the part of the central processor that performs arithmetic and logical operations.

Artificial Intelligence (AI): term for the human-like properties of computers, e.g. the ability to understand free-form verbal input, or to make deductions.

ASCII: American Standard Code for Information Interchange. A system for coding individual characters of information using 7 bits. Used very widely on mini- and microcomputers.

Assembler: a symbolic programming language, each one of whose instructions corresponds to one of the instructions in the machine language of a computer.

ATE: *see* Automatic Test Equipment.

ATM: *see* Automatic Teller Machines.

Audit Trail: a means (such as a trail of documents, batch and processing references, log file) for identifying the actions taken in processing input data or in preparing output.

Automatic Teller Machines (ATM): electronic banking terminals for direct use by customers (including cash dispensers).

Automatic Test Equipment (ATE): equipment (usually microprocessor-controlled) capable of automatically diagnosing faults in electronic assemblies.

Automation: consideration and design systems in holistic terms. Does not necessarily imply lack of human intervention.

Back-up: alternative procedures, equipment, or systems used in case of destruction or failure of the original.

Bandwidth: the range, or width, of the frequencies available for transmission on a given channel.

Bar-code reader: a device used to read a bar code by means of reflected light, such as a scanner that reads the universal product code on supermarket products.

Baseband: data communications protocol with relatively limited band width (6 million bps). Unsuited to voice or video signals (cf. Broadband).

Basic: Beginners' All-purpose Symbolic Instruction Code; a programming language, commonly used for interactive problem solving by users who may not be professional programmers. Very common with microcomputers.

Batch Processing: technique in data processing whereby transactions are grouped into batches before processing. Implies significant turn-round time and often centralised processing.

Baud: a unit of signalling speed, in digital communications equivalent to one bit per second (note 300 baud = 30 cps).

BCD: *see* Binary Coded Decimal.

Binary: number system with a radix of 2, involving situations where there is a choice of only two possibilities. Can be represented electronically by means of a switch and thus is the fundamental basis for the stored program computer.

Binary Coded: encoding data in binary/digital form for processing, storage and transmission.

Binary Coded Decimal (BCD): a coding system for numeric data.

Bit: a binary digit (i.e. zero or one); the smallest unit of information that can be represented in binary notation.

Bits per inch (Bpi): measure of the recording density of data on magnetic media (e.g. magnetic tape 1,600 bpi).

Bits per second (Bps): a unit used to measure the speed of transmission in a telecommunications channel.

Bootstrap Loader: a form of loader (program) whose first few instructions are sufficient to bring the rest of itself into the computer's storage from an input device.

Bpi: *see* Bits per inch.

Bps: *see* Bits per second.

Broadband: communications protocol with high band width allowing a number of separate communications bands to coexist, e.g. data, voice, video, etc. (cf. Baseband).

Buffer: a storage device used to compensate for a difference in rate of flow of data or in time of occurrence of events when transmitting data from one device to another.

Bundling: opposite of unbundling; the practice whereby the cost of a computer system may include not only the cpu but also an operating system, peripheral devices, maintenance agreements, etc.

Bus: a passive interconnection system where the devices are connected in parallel, sharing each wire with all other devices on the 'bus'.

Byte: an eight-bit binary number which is used to represent a symbol or character (e.g. 0–9, A–Z, a–z, and special characters) for storage or transmission purposes.

C: a general purpose high-level programming language which became extremely popular among professional programmers in the 1980s.

CASE: Computer Aided Systems/Software Engineering, the development of computer-based tools to aid in the development of applications software.

Cache Memory: special high speed buffer memory between cpu and primary memory.

CAD/CAM: *see* Computer Aided Design/Computer Aided Manufacturing.

CAFS: *see* Content Addressable File Store.

Cambridge Ring: a type of local area network developed in Cambridge in the 1970s.

Cathode Ray Tube (CRT): a visual display device that receives electrical impulses and translates them into the computer.

CCITT: Consultative Committee on International Telephone and Telegraph, a standards-setting body for telecommunications; CCITT No. 7 are the signalling standards to implement ISDN.

CDROM: Compact Disc Read-Only Memory, a form of optical memory with very high capacity.

Ceefax: BBC's Teletext system.

Central Processing Unit (CPU): the 'brain' of the computer; composed of three sections — primary memory unit, arithmetic/logic unit (alu) and control unit.

Centralised: a design alternative whereby computer power is established within a group; includes a common central database that permits authorised users to gain access to information.

Chain: a method of organising record sequence within a file by pointers indicating next and previous records in sequence.

Channel: exclusive high speed communication link between the cpu and peripheral devices.

Character: one of the symbols 0–9, A–Z, a–z, punctuation marks, etc., represented usually by an 8-bit binary number. The most common coding schemes are ASCII and EBCDIC.

Characters per Second (CPS): a measure of the rate of transfer of data.

Chip: a small piece of semiconducting material (usually silicon), on which are manufactured many thousands of circuits.

CIM: *see* Computer Integrated Manufacturing.

Circuit Switching: technique whereby the transmission path through a communications network can be determined by the switching nodes.

Clock Rate: the rate of the internal synchronising clock of a processor determines the speed of processing.

CMOS: Complementary Metal Oxide on Silicon, a form of technology used in chip manufacture.

CNC: *see* Computer Numeric Control.

Co-axial Cable: a cable with central core for the signal and a screening sheath around it, providing very high communications capacity.

Cobol: a high-level programming language developed for universal use in business applications (COmmon Business Orientated Language).

Collator: a mechanical device that collects together sets of information (cards/paper) in some predetermined sequence.

Common Carrier: organisation providing publicly available telecommunications links, usually the national PTT. Alternatively a communications protocol providing a common facility for sending messages.

Compatibility of Hardware: the compatibility between one generation of a manufacturer's computer system and its successor. Also the ability to interconnect equipment from different suppliers (*see* Plug-compatible).

Compatibility of Software: the degree to which programs can be run on different computers without modification.

Compatible: sometimes used on its own to describe a machine compatible with a well-known standard, e.g. with the IBM PC.

Compiler: a translator program for high-level languages such as Fortran or Cobol; translates source program statements into machine executable or object program/code.

Components: the basic element of all electronic devices, either passive, such as resistors, capacitors etc, or active, such as transistors, valves etc.

Computer Aided Design/Computer Aided Manufacturing (CAD/CAM): integrated system co-ordinating design and manufacturing.

Computer Integrated Manufacturing (CIM): a concept in which the computer controls every aspect of a manufacturing process.

Computer Numeric Control (CNC): direct computer control of numerical controlled equipment (*see also* Numerical Control).

Computer Output Microfilm (COM): miniature photographic images of output. Computer output is placed on magnetic tape which serves as the input to a microfilm processor.

Concentrator: a device that systematically allocates communication channels among several terminals.

Connectivity: the ability of different computers and peripherals, perhaps from different manufacturers, to be connected to, and work with, each other.

Content Addressable File Store (CAFS): an intelligent file storage device.

Control Unit: part of the processor responsible for controlling sequences of operations.

Controller: the control unit for a particular peripheral device which may contain considerable processing power and memory.

Conversational Mode: a mode of operation that implies a 'dialogue' between a computer and its user.

CPS: *see* Characters Per Second.

CPU: *see* Central Processing Unit.

Crash: general term indicating any breakdown or malfunction of a computer system.

CRT: *see* Cathode Ray Tube.

Custom Logic: special purpose circuits which act upon information in binary coded form.

Cycle Time: time taken to fetch and return an item from primary memory.

Cylinder: a vertical grouping of each track in the same relative position on each platter of a multi-platter magnetic disc.

Daisy-wheel Printer: slow speed (less than 100 cps) high quality printer where the characters are positioned on a wheel at the end of a circle of protruding stalks (i.e. daisy-like).

DASD: *see* Direct Access Storage Device.

D/A: Digital to analogue conversions.

Data: basic, raw, unprocessed information. Usually bearing direct relationship to facts, events or activities. Data must be encoded before they can be processed by a computer.

Data Dictionary: part of DBMS that contains all the definitions of the data items and their relationships.

Data Havens: countries with a very liberal attitude to data protection.

Data Item: smallest useful unit of information.

Data Processing (DP): the organisation of the processing of business records and information; a generic term for computing in organisations.

Data Protection: concerned with the contents and accessibility of computerised information.

Data Protection Agency (DPA): a British quasi-government agency set up to administer the Data Protection Act.

Data Set: *see* File.

Databank: a structured collection of information usually referring to a specific topic. Fairly static in nature with information being steadily added.

Database: collection of related files usually of a volatile nature.

Database Managament System (DBMS): part of the system software that manages the interface between the filing system and the application program. Also containing a set of utility programs to access the data directly (*see* Query Language, and Report Generator).

DBMS: *see* Database Management System.

DDP: *see* Distributed Data Processing.

Debug: to isolate and remove all errors from a program.

Desktop Publishing (DTP): form of computer application in which text and graphics are combined to produce newspaper-type output.

Digital: representation of data by a numeric value.

Digital Computer: general purpose computer using binary logic (cf. analogue computer).

Digital Logic: special purpose circuits that act upon information in binary coded form.

Digital Transmission: communications technique whereby signals are transmitted in binary form. Thus analogue signals must first be digitalised (A/D) before transmission and then reconverted (D/A).

Direct Access Processing: method of file processing where transactions can be processed in any sequence.

Direct Access Storage Device (DASD): a storage device on which information can be stored and retrieved in a direct, non-sequential manner, such as a disc drive.

Disc Drive: a mechanical device used to record and retrieve data from a magnetic disc. Includes a rotational unit and read/write head.

Disc Operating System (DOS): an operating system including the ability to handle disc drives; a relatively primitive system; *see also* Operating System.

Disc Pack: a stack of magnetic discs.

Diskette: *see* Floppy Disc.

Distributed: a design alternative whereby each business unit has its own computer power although total organisation-wide control exists.

Distributed Data Processing (DDP): organisation of data processing resources in which some capabilities are brought closer to the place where the data originate and/or processing is required.

Distributed System: equipment configuration characterised by geographically dispersed computers linked together in a communication network; user-orientated but under total organisation-wide control.

Documentation: collection of written information describing the internal systems and external (user) operations of a program.

Domotics: the field of domestic automation, including but not limited to the use of domestic robots.

DOS: *see* Disc Operating System.

Downtime: the elapsed time when a computer is not operating correctly due to machine failure.

DP: *see* Data Processing.

DPA: *see* Data Protection Agency.

Driver: part of operating system software responsible for controlling the basic operations of an individual device.

DTP: *see* Desktop Publishing.

EBCDIC: Extended Binary Coded Decimal Interchange Code. IBM standard coding system now used widely by other manufacturers for exchanging data between different computers.

EDI: *see* Electronic Data Exchange.

EDP: Electronic Data Processing: *see* Data Processing.

EFT: *see* Electronic Funds Transfer and Electronic Financial Transactions.

Electronic Data Exchange (EDI): transfer of structured information between computer systems in different organisations.

Electronic Financial Transactions: initiation of a financial transaction by electronic means; does not necessarily include electronic funds transfer.

Electronic Funds Transfer: transfer of funds by electronic message switching systems; *see also* SWIFT.

Electronic Mail: facility to send documents in electronic form ranging from the ability to interconnect word processors (*see* Teletex) to networks where documents/messages may be stored and subsequently forwarded or retrieved.

Electrostatic Printer: a non-impact printer in which electromagnetic impulses and heat are used to affix characters to paper.

Emulator: a program that instructs a computer to act as if it were another model of computer thus enabling object programs to operate on a different computer.

Encryption: coding or scrambling of information to prevent unauthorised use.

EPROM: Erasable Programmable Read Only Memory; *see* PROM and ROM.

Etching: stage in manufacturing process of integrated circuits where acid is used to remove unwanted layers.

Ethernet: local area network developed by Xerox using a baseband approach.

Executive: *see* Operating System.

Expert System: system for encoding knowledge in certain specialised domains capable of making inferences deduced from information and of having an English-like dialogue with the user.

Expert System Builder: a program designed to enable users to create expert systems.

Facsimile (Fax): technique of sending a pictorial copy of a document over a telecommunications link.

FET: Field Effect Transistor; one type of microelectronic device.

Fibre Optics: *see* Optical Fibres.

Field: a meaningful item of data, such as a social security number.

Fifth Generation: futuristic computers which will display intelligent features, not yet fully developed, though research continues in Japan and elsewhere.

File: a grouping of related records, sometimes referred to as a data set.

Flexible Manufacturing System (FMS): an integrated manufacturing system (usually computer controlled and including robots) capable of producing small batches of goods.

Floating Point: method of storing numbers which contain decimal parts and have a wide range. The number is stored as a mantissa (fixed point part) and exponent (the number of decimal places).

Floppy Disc: also called a diskette or flexible disc, a low-cost random access form of data storage made of vinyl and at present having a storage capacity of up to 2 MBytes.

Flowchart: the program flowchart which is a graphic representation of the types and sequences of operations in a program, and the system flowchart which shows the flow of data through an entire system.

FMS: *see* Flexible Manufacturing System.

Fortran: a programming language whose name is the abbreviation of FORmulation TRANslation, particularly suitable for the processing of scientific applications.

4GL: Fourth Generation Language, a modern type of systems software tool.

Frame: a screenful of information for storage and display in a videotext or teletext system.

Front End: a computer program which integrates various application programs, making it easy for the user to select them and swap from one to another, often employing graphics and other user-friendly devices.

Gate Array: a type of general purpose digital logic which is customised only at the final stage of manufacture; a specific form of uncommitted logic array.

Gateway: access point in some network to other networks or systems.

Gbs: Gigabits per second (*see* Bits per second).

Generation: term describing stages in the development of computer systems. State-of-the-art computers are considered to be fourth generation. Current research projects are aimed at developing a fifth generation.

Gigabit: One thousand million bits.

Hard-copy: printed output.

Hard Disc: a magnetic disc which is fixed in its drive, normally with a high data storage capacity (10 MBytes and upwards).

Hardware: the electrical circuitry and physical devices that make up a computer system.

Hashing Algorithm: the process whereby a record key is turned into a disc address in direct access file processing.

Head Crash: when the read/write head on a magnetic disc touches the platter surface data are irretrievably lost and considerable damage can be caused to the disc drive.

Hex: hexadecimal is a number system to the base 16. It is used by programmers to look at the contents of computer memory in a more convenient form than binary.

High-level Languages: English-like coding schemes which are procedure problem and user oriented. Must be translated to machine code instructions before computer can obey them.

Icon: a pictorial device used in front ends to guide users towards programs and files.

Impact Printer: a printer that forms characters by physically striking a ribbon against paper.

Index: an ordered reference list of contents of a file, or the keys for identification or location of the contents.

Index-sequential Processing: a file processing technique in which records are placed on a file in sequence and multiple level index is maintained, thus allowing both sequential and direct access processing (ISAM).

Information Resource Management (IRM): theory of management that identifies information as a key resource and treats it like other managed resources (i.e. finance, marketing, personnel etc.).

Information System: an integrated network of personal equipment and procedures designed to satisfy the information requirements of management.

Information System Manager: the manager responsible for planning, organising, staffing and controlling all data processing activity.

Ink-Jet Printer: a non-impact printer that uses a stream of charged ink to 'paint' characters.

Input: data that are submitted to the computer for processing.

Input/Output (I/O): a general term for the equipment used to communicate with a computer and the data involved in the communication.

Input/Output (I/O) Devices: devices capable of both transmitting input to a computer, and of receiving output back from it.

Instruction: a statement that specifies an operation to be performed and the associated values or locations.

Instruction Register: a register where each instruction is decoded by the control unit.

Instruction Set: the fundamental logical and arithmetic procedures that the computer can perform, such as addition, subtraction and comparison. Specific to a given computer.

Integer: method of representing a whole number. Positive numbers are simply their binary value while negative numbers are stored in '2s complement form'.

Integrated Circuit: a small chip, usually of silicon, which contains a large number of interconnected electronic components.

Integrated Program: a program which provides a number of different application modules, e.g. word processing, spreadsheet, graphics capabilities.

Intelligent Terminal: a terminal with an internal processor that can be programmed to perform specified functions, such as data conversion, and control of other terminals.

Interactive Computing: conversation (interaction) between a user and a central computer via an on-line terminal.

Interface: a shared boundary, e.g. the boundary between two systems, or between a computer and one of its peripheral devices.

Interpreter: a system program that interprets a high-level language instruction one at a time. Slower than a compiler in computing terms but potentially much faster for system development.

Interrupt: the ability of a processor to suspend operation on one process in order to service the requirements of some higher priority requests.

I/O: *see* Input/Output.

IRM: *see* Information Resource Management.

ISDN: Integrated Services Digital Network, the name for the set of standards being developed to integrate voice/data/image/text telecommunications in digital form.

ISO/OSI: International Standards Organisation/Open Systems Interconnection, acronym for a set of standards for network communications and management.

Job Control Language (JCL): a high-level language used by programmers to instruct the operating system.

Just in Time (JIT): a system in which the computer is used for precision scheduling of a supply situation.

K: a symbol used to denote 1,000 (strictly 1,024) where referring to specific capabilities of a computer system.

Kbs: Thousands of bits per second (*see* Bits per second).

Key: a unique identifier for a record; used to sort records for processing or to locate a particular record within a file.

Key to Disc: hardware designed to transfer data entered via keyboard to magnetic disc or diskette.

Keyboard: input device like a typewriter usually part of visual display unit or terminal.

Keyword: a word or phrase in a document that has been designated as a key for retrieval. A more sophisticated approach is using keywords in context (KWIC).

LAN: *see* Local Area Network.

Laptop: a battery-powered portable computer small enough to be held on a lap while working.

Laser Printer: a type of non-impact printer that uses a laser to produce images on the drum of an electrostatic printer/copier, and thus on to paper.

Laser Storage System: a secondary storage device using laser technology to encode data on to an optical disc; *see also* Optical Disc.

LCD: *see* Liquid Crystal Display.

Leased Line: a service offered by the common carriers in which a customer may lease, for his exclusive use, a circuit between two or more geographic points.

LED: Light-Emitting Diode.

Light Pen: a pen-shaped object with a photoelectric cell at its end; used to draw lines on a visual display screen.

Liquid Crystal Display (LCD): uses the property of certain materials to polarise light by applying an electric potential.

LISP: LISt Processing language, a high-level computer language much used for artificial intelligence applications.

Local Area Network (LAN): a technique for providing an internal communications ring main.

Local Loop: connection between a local exchange and subscribed on the switched telephone network.

Location: generally, any place in which data may be stored.

Log: a record of the operations of data processing equipment, listing each job or run, the time it required, operator actions, and other pertinent data.

Logging: keeping a copy of transactions on a separate file for audits and security purposes.

Login: introductory procedure when accessing an on-line computer system.

Loop: a sequence of instructions that can be executed repetitively with modified sets of data. Also describes the situation when a program goes into an 'infinite loop' and must be interrupted by the user.

Low-level Language: programming languages where each instruction maps on to a single machine code instruction.

LPM: lines per minute.

LSI: Large Scale Integration. A measure of the packing density on a chip.

Luggable: a personal computer that is portable but not of laptop dimensions; normally mains powered.

M: a symbol used to denote 1 million (strictly 1,048,576) when referring to specific capabilities of a computer system (often abbreviated as Mega).

Machine Code: the only set of instructions that a computer can execute directly; a cycle that designates the proper electrical states in the computer as combinations of 0s and 1s.

Machine Readable: information stored in such a manner that it can be automatically interpreted by a computer e.g. magnetic tape, punched cards.

Macro: a facility for defining a procedure that may subsequently be invoked as a simple command.

Magnetic Core: an iron-alloy doughnut-shaped ring about the size of a pin head of which memory can be composed; an individual core can store one binary digit; a technology used in second-generation computers, now overtaken by semi-conductor RAM memories.

Magnetic Disc: a storage medium consisting of a metal platter coated on both sides with a magnetic recording material upon which data are stored in the form of magnetised spots (a DASD).

Magnetic Tape: a storage medium consisting of a narrow strip upon which spots of iron oxide are magnetised to represent data; a sequential storage medium.

Mainframe: type of large scale computer built on a large frame or chassis. Used by large centralised dp department.

Management Information System (MIS): a formal network that extends computer use beyond routine transaction processing and reporting, and into the integration of applications and the area of management decision making; its goal is to get the correct information to the appropriate manager at the right time.

Manual: documentation provided by the originators of a particular system or piece of software to explain methods of operation.

Mass Storage Devices: a class of secondary storage devices capable of storing very large volumes of data; offers cost advantages over disc storage, but its much slower retrieval time is measured in seconds.

Master File: a file that contains relatively permanent data; updated by records in a transaction file.

Matching: comparing master records with transaction records to see if certain fields are identical.

Mbs: Megabits per second (*see* Bits per second).

Mechanisation: the application of computer related equipment to improve the productivity of specific tasks.

Megabits: one million bits.

Memory: part of the computer that stores binary-coded information; primary is working storage; secondary is permanent storage.

Merge: to form a single sequenced file by combining two or more similarly sequenced files.

Message Switching: a technique consisting of receiving a message at a connecting point in a network, storing it until the appropriate output circuit is clear, and then retransmitting it.

Microcomputer: a computer taking up a small amount of space and relatively inexpensive. Usually suited to running only single applications.

Microelectronics: the technique of manufacturing many different interconnected electronic components in a small physical space.

Microprocessor: the arithmetic/logic unit and control unit, some limited memory, and limited I/O capability of a processor, all manufactured on a single chip.

Microsecond: one millionth of a second; term used in specifying the speed of electronic devices.

Millisecond: one thousandth of a second; a term used in specifying the speed of electronic devices.

Minicomputer: a medium scale computer suited to supporting interactive applications for a large number of users.

Mips: millions of instructions per second; a measure of processing power. A modern large computer would be rated at over 10 mips.

Modem (data set): a device that modulates and demodulates digital signals transmitted over analogue communications facilities.

Modular Programming: a programming approach that emphasises the organisation and coding of logical program units, usually on the basis of function.

Modulation: a technique used in modems (data set) to transform digital signals to analogue form.

Module: a part of a whole; a program segment; a sub-system.

Monitor: *see* Operating System.

MOS: metal oxide semiconductor. Technique for building microelectronic circuits.

Mouse: a small wheeled device used to move a pointer on the computer screen.

MSDOS: Microsoft Corp.'s operating system, used on computers compatible with the IBM PC.

MSI: Medium Scale Integration. Referring to the packing density of integrated circuits.

Multiplexor: a device that permits more than one terminal to transmit data over the same communication channel.

Multiplexor Channel: a controller that can handle more than one I/O device at a time; normally controls slow-speed devices such as card readers, printers or terminals.

Multiprocessor System: a multiple cpu configuration in which jobs are processed simultaneously.

Multiprogramming: a technique whereby several programs are placed in primary storage at the same time.

MUX: *see* Multiplexor.

Name-linked Files: data files, one of whose keys is a person's name.

Nanosecond: one billionth (thousand millionth) of a second; a measure of the speed of electronic devices.

NC: *see* Numerical Control.

Network: the interconnection of a number of locations or devices by communications facilities; *see also* Public-Switched Network.

Non-impact Printer: a hard-copy output device that forms the images on paper by non-impact methods (e.g. electrostatic or ink-jet printers).

Non-procedural Software: software designed to cope with a general class of user processing requests in terms of 'what' the user wants, rather than 'how' a specific request is to be handled (e.g. Query Language; Report Generator).

Numerical Control: control of a piece of equipment (usually a machine-tool) by means of binary-coded data, usually prepared on paper-tape.

Object Program/Code: a sequence of machine-code instructions arising as the output from a compiler program with a source program/code as input.

OCR: *see* Optical Character Recognition.

Octal: a number system to the base 8; it is sometimes used as a more convenient way of representing binary numbers; *see also* Hex.

OEM: *see* Original Equipment Manufacturer.

Off-line: equipment or devices not under the direct control of the central processor.

On-line: equipment or devices in direct communication with the central processor.

Operating System (OS): a collection of programs designed to enable a computer system to manage itself, with minimum human intervention.

Optical Character Recognition (OCR): devices capable of 'reading' characters on paper and converting the optical images into binary-coded data.

Optical Disc: a system for storing binary-coded information optically rather than magnetically, with improvements in speed and reading density. *See* CDROM, WORMS.

Optical Fibres: fibres of finely-drawn, flexible, highly-reflective glass, down which pulses of light may be transmitted representing binary-coded data.

Oracle: the Independent Broadcasting Authority's (IBA's) Teletext system.

Original Equipment Manufacturer (OEM): a firm producing computing or telecommunications hardware, typically sold through third parties (dealers, system houses) to the final customer.

OS: *see* Operating System.

OS/2: the operating system developed for IBM's second-generation personal computers.

Output: information that arises as a result of some processing.

Output Device: a device capable of transforming binary-coded information either into human-interpretable form (e.g. hard-copy, display or voice), or into a form to control some mechanical device; *see* Actuator.

PABX: *see* Private Automatic Branch Exchange.

Package: an off-the-shelf computer program.

Packet: a standard-sized unit (in terms of numbers of bits) into which a message is broken down for transmission using a packet switching protocol.

Packet Assembler/Dis-assembler (PAD): a device capable of breaking a message into standard 'packets' for transmission using a packing switching protocol; and of re-assembling 'packets' into a message.

Packet-Switched Network (PSN): a telecommunications network operated using packet-switching protocols; may be a separate physical network, or a virtual network on an existing real network; may be public or private system.

Packet Switching: a transmission method in which the messages containing the data are broken down into fixed-length 'packets'; each packet contains routing information and shares the network with other packets, improving the overall utilisation of the network.

Packing Density: a measure of the closeness with which circuits may be placed to each other on the surface of a chip.

PAD: *see* Packet Assembler/Dis-assembler.

Pages: (1) in a virtual-storage environment, portions of programs or data which are kept in secondary memory and are loaded into primary memory when needed for processing; (2) in a viewdata environment, a screen-full of information to be displayed as such (*see* Frame).

Paging: a method of implementing a virtual-storage system; programs and data are broken down into fixed-size pages (or segments) in secondary memory, and are loaded into primary memory when needed for processing.

Parallel: processing or transmission of instructions or data simultaneously (as opposed to serial).

Parity: error detection technique using one bit of a byte or word.

Partition: in a multiprogramming environment, the primary memory area reserved for one program; may be fixed or variable.

Pascal: a high-level programming language, particularly designed to aid the implementation of structured design.

PC: personal computer, and in particular the IBM PC.

PCDOS: the operating system, based on MSDOS, used on the IBM PC.

PCM: *see* Plug-Compatible Manufacturer.

Peripherals: auxiliary computer equipment connected to the central processing unit (e.g. I/O devices, secondary memory devices).

Photolithography: a method of achieving a two-dimensional image on a surface by using an optical mask; in particular, defining the pattern for electronic circuits on the surface of a chip.

Picosecond: one thousand thousand millionth of a second; a measure of the speed of electronic devices.

Platter: the flat recording surface of a magnetic disc; the disc itself.

PL1: Programming Language One; a high-level programming language, designed by IBM for both business and scientific applications.

Plotter: an output device that produces hard-copy graphical images.

Plug-compatible: devices (usually peripherals) which are available from another company and are interchangeable with the devices from the original manufacturer.

Plug-Compatible Manufacturer (PCM): a manufacturer of hardware which is plug-compatible with equipment from the original manufacturer.

Pointer: a link used to indicate the location of another record (usually the next or previous in logical sequence) in an index-sequential file.

Point-of-Sale (POS) Terminal: a device incorporating a cash-register which can also capture the transaction details electronically, and store (and/or forward) them.

Portability: an attribute of a program which can be transferred to another computer system and run without modification to the program or its data.

POS: *see* Point-of-Sale Terminal.

Prestel: British Telecom's public videotext service.

Primary Memory: the part of the central processing unit which holds instructions for execution, data being processed; also known as primary storage, main memory or storage; typically made up from RAM chips.

Printer: an output device producing hard-copy.

Privacy: an individual's right to knowledge and control of personal information recorded on (computerised) files.

Private Automatic Branch Exchange (PABX): the internal telephone exchange for an organisation.

Private Leased Line: *see* Leased Line.

Procedure: a set of rules for achieving some defined goal.

Processor: an electronic device capable of interpreting and executing binary-coded instructions.

Program: a set of instructions which tell a processor how to perform a specific task. Of two types: application, concerned with end-user orientated tasks; and system, concerned with internal control and scheduling tasks.

Programmable: a procedure capable of being set out as a series of logical steps, in an unambiguous, deterministic manner; capable of being programmed.

Programmable Read-Only Memory (PROM): a read-only memory (ROM), capable of being re-programmed once by the user.

Prolog: PROgramming in LOGic, a computer language used for artificial intelligence applications.

PROM: *see* Programmable Read-Only Memory.

Protocol: a set of agreed rules by which communications may be established between devices, providing certain defined facilities.

Prototyping: a process for system development aimed at implementing a useable first-stage system at minimum cost and time; implies feedback, learning and an interactive process.

PSN: *see* Packet-Switched Network.

PTT: Post, Telephone and Telegraph; a generic name, typically used in Europe to refer to the telecommunications authority.

Public-Switched Network: the standard public telephone network provided in the UK by British Telecom.

Punched Card: a data recording medium in which characters are represented by vertical patterns of holes punched in the card; the basis for unit-record equipment.

Punched Card Reader: a device capable of sensing the pattern of holes punched in a card, and of converting them to binary-coded signals.

Query Language: software capable of handling enquiries expressed in English-language form on a database; an example of non-procedural software.

RAM: *see* Random Access Memory.

Random Access Memory (RAM): (1) memories giving a constant access time to any location independent of the last location addressed (as opposed to sequential memories). (2) a generic name for read/write memory (as contrasted to read-only memory), typically forming the primary memory of a computer system; presently implemented using RAM chips.

Random File: a method of file organisation to give known access time to any record in the file, when processing sequence is unknown.

Random Processing: a method of record processing in which retrieval of records is independent of sequence; transactions can be processed directly; average access time is fast and consistent, but processing is relatively expensive for high activity and volatility; *see also* Sequential Processing, and Index-sequential Processing.

Read: to copy the contents of some storage media containing binary-coded information; the storage contents are not destroyed by the reading process; *see also* Write.

Read-Only Memory (ROM): memory device from which the data can only be read and which cannot be written to; memory whose contents are fixed at time of manufacture; presently implemented using ROM chips.

Read/Write: an attribute of a device by which data (or instructions) may be both copied, i.e. 'read', and to which data (or instructions) may be stored, i.e. 'written', overwriting the previous contents.

Read/Write Head: an electromagnet used as a component in magnetic recording devices (e.g. tape or disc), either to sense a magnetised area (i.e. read) or to magnetise an area (i.e. write).

Real: a physical device or entity (as opposed to virtual).

Real Time: a term signifying that the results of some processing step will be available in a short enough time to influence or control the procedure or task which is the subject of the processing.

Record: a set of logically-related items pertaining to a single entity, which are retrieved from or updated in a file in a single operation; the logical unit within a file.

Recording Density: the number of binary digits stored within some unit length or area; typically measured as bits-per-inch on magnetic tape or disc.

Register: a dedicated memory location within the central processing unit used as immediate storage by the arithmetic and control units.

Remote Access: access to a computer system via some telecommunications link.

Remote-Job-Entry (RJE): a method for entering jobs for processing into the normal batch-processing queue of a central facility from some remote location.

Report Generator: software capable of producing reports from a database in response to instructions from the user; an example of non-procedural software.

Reprographics: equipment concerned with the reproduction of images on hard-copy; e.g. electrostatic copiers.

Response Time: the time that elapses between entering the last item of input into a processing task and the start of the output.

Retrieval: location of a specific item of information fulfilling some given criteria in a file, and copying it into primary memory.

Ring: a form or organisation of a communications network, especially applicable to local area networks; involves devices connected to a single transmission line in a ring arrangement; organised on some token-passing protocol.

RISC: Reduced Instruction Set Computer, a powerful form of computer architecture.

Robot: general purpose programmable device of human scale and facility, with some capability for sensing its environment.

ROM: *see* Read-Only Memory.

RPG: Report Program Generator; a business-oriented high-level programming language.

RS 232: a standard communications interface for connecting low-speed serial devices; especially used in connecting terminals to computer systems.

Run: to initiate the execution of a specific program (or the one presently resident in primary memory).

SAA: Systems Application Architecture, IBM's set of software interfaces, conventions and protocols designed to improve the portability of data and software across its range of computers.

Secondary Memory: memory used for long-term, large-scale storage of files; typically comprising magnetic tape or disc; also known as secondary storage or auxiliary storage.

Second Sourcing: an agreement whereby the original manufacturer of a chip design licences other manufacturers to produce the same design and provides production masks.

Security: precautions in a computer system to guard against unauthorised access, crime, natural disasters and accidental damage.

Segment: *see* Paging.

Segmentation: *see* Paging.

Self-documenting: a facility within a piece of software for providing several levels of explanation.

Semiconductor: any material which acts as an electrical conductor when the voltage is above a certain level, and as a resistor when it is below it (i.e. it can act as an electronic switch).

Semiconductor Memory: device capable of storing binary-coded information electronically; e.g. RAM or ROM.

Sensors: devices capable of sensing and/or measuring a change in status, and of transmitting that information to some controller.

Sequential Access: a method of retrieving data in which records have to be searched from the beginning of the file for those required.

Sequential File: a method of file organisation in which records are stored in a known sequence which will be used for retrieval.

Sequential Processing: a method of record processing in which records are retrieved in a known sequence; transactions to be processed have to be sorted in the same sequence prior to processing; average access times are slow, but processing is economical for high activity rates; *see also* Random Processing, and Index-sequential Processing.

Serial: processing or transmission of instructions or data in strict sequence, i.e. one at a time; not parallel.

Service Bureau: an organisation supplying computing services to other organisations; a computer utility.

Shared-Logic: an application implemented as a part of a general multi-programming system; sharing resources between several applications (i.e. not stand-alone).

Silicon Chip: *see* Chip.

Slave: a device whose capabilities are totally determined by some master control unit.

Small Scale Integration (SSI): a measure of the packing density of circuits of a chip; the lowest such measure.

SNA: *see* System Network Architecture.

Software: a collection of programs and routines providing instruction to a computer system; primary classification into application and system.

Software Package: a collection of programs and routines designed to provide a solution to problems in a specific area.

Sort: to arrange items of information into specific sequence (e.g. ascending alphabetic).

Sorter: a piece of unit-record equipment designed to sort records into a specific sequence.

Source Language: the language in which the problem statement is encoded (e.g. Cobol, Fortran, Basic, etc.).

Source Program: a program written in a specific source language; the input to the compiler program; *see also* Object Program, and Compiler.

SPC: *see* Stored Program Control.

Spooling: a technique for removing the direct connection between I/O devices and the central processor, in order to improve system throughput.

Spreadsheet: program package which provides spreadsheet-type financial analysis facilities.

SSI: *see* Small Scale Integration.

Stand-Alone: a processing unit not connected to any other system, typically dedicated to a single application; *see also* Shared-Logic.

Statement: a single instruction in a high-level language program.

Storage; a device capable of retaining information in binary-coded form for subsequent retrieval; synonymous with memory.

Store and Forward: an attribute of a message-handling system, such that it can accept and store messages to be forwarded when the addressee is active.

Stored Program Control (SPC): a processing unit operating under the control of instructions stored in its own memory, which may be modified as a result of processing by the host processor, or any other to which it can communicate.

Structured Design: a top-down modular approach to system design.

Structured Programming: a top-down design method applied to programming; imposes a formal structure on the design of programs which enables the correct functioning of the program to be established more quickly.

Supercomputer: a very large and powerful computer, used for especially demanding applications (e.g. scientific applications).

Supervisor Program: the major component of an operating system, co-ordinating the other parts of the system and scheduling tasks; also referred to as an executive or monitor.

Swapping: in a virtual storage environment, the process of transferring a block of program or data (*see* Pages) from secondary memory (virtual memory) to primary memory (real memory), and *vice versa*.

SWIFT: Society for Worldwide Interchange of Financial Transactions, an interbank organisation set up to manage and operate a worldwide electronic network for funds transfer between the participants.

Switch: a device capable of making or breaking a connection; a part of processing logic, or a telecommunications network.

Systems Analysis: the process of analysing a problem into its basic operations and specifying these in a programmable form.

Systems Analyst: one who carried out the systems analysis function.

System Architecture: a term designating the structure of a computer system or communications network.

System Design: the process of designing a processing system, with associated data capture, storage and output, to meet the need identified in the systems analysis phase within systems development.

System Development: the process of identifying a problem; evaluating alternative approaches to its solution; designing the chosen system; implementing and evaluating it.

System Network Architecture (SNA): a protocol for handling computer-to-computer communications; originated by IBM.

System Software: a collection of programs designed to control the computer system; major components are: controllers for the major hardware components, compilers and other utility programs, and a supervisor to manage the system and schedule tasks.

Tabulator: a piece of unit-record equipment capable of cumulating the number of occurrences of a particular set of characters in a group of records.

Tape Drive: a device which moves magnetic tape past a read/write head enabling binary-coded information to be written to or read from the tape.

Telecom Gold: British Telecom's public electronic mail service.

Telecommunications: a system incorporating the combined use of computer and telecommunications facilities.

Télétel: French PTT videotext system.

Teletex: an internationally agreed standard for message handling between simple terminal devices and word processors over the public-switched network.

Teletext: broadcast information system utilising spare bandwidth on the television broadcast frequencies; *see also* Ceefax and Oracle.

Teletype: a trademark of the Teletype Corporation; a low-speed hard-copy terminal device.

Terminal: an input/output device connected to a computer system via a communications link; originally low-speed and hard-copy.

Text: information stored and processed as characters, rather than numbers.

Text Processing: a system designed to facilitate the processing of large volume of textual material (e.g. articles, reports, books etc).

Thrashing: the situation occurring when a virtual system is exclusively swapping programs.

Throughput: a measure of the work done by a computer system over some specified time interval.

Time-sharing: a form of operating system which allows two or more users to share central resources, yet apparently receive simultaneous service.

Top down: methodology for approaching system and program design by breaking the problem down into levels, increasing detail.

Touch-tone: a device (usually a telephone with a key-pad rather than dial) capable of sending a coded sequence of tones over the public-switched network.

Track: the logical areas in which information is recorded on magnetic media; bands stretching the length of the tape, or concentric bands on disc.

Transaction: an event which generates one or more items of information which are captured and stored for processing.

Transaction File: a file containing transactions captured over a specific period to be processed against some master file(s).

Trans-border Dataflow: transmission of information in electronic form over national boundaries.

Transistor: a technological stage in the development of electronic devices; superior to valve technology, but inferior to integrated circuits (chips); the technology of second-generation computer systems.

Transmission Media: the media used to form the transmission link between two points (e.g. copper cable, fibre optics, microwave).

Transpac: the implementation of a public packet-switched network by the French PTT.

Transputer: INMOS's revolutionary form of microprocessor chip.

TTL: Transistor-Transistor Logic; a method of forming electronic circuits on chips.

ULA: *see* Uncommitted Logic Array.

ULSI: Ultra Large Scale Integration, a measure of the packing density on a chip.

Unbundling: the practice of charging a separate price for each individual component of a computer system, whether hardware or software; resulted from US Justice Department action against IBM, and created the opportunity for plug-compatible manufacturers.

Uncommitted Logic Array (ULA): a form of logic circuit on a chip where the final purpose of the logic can be determined at the final stage of manufacture, thus giving economies of scale in earlier stages.

Unit Record Equipment: equipment designed to process one physical record at a time; typically stored on punched cards.

UNIX: an operating system that is a current standard on minicomputers and more powerful microcomputers.

Update: to incorporate into a master file the transaction data that have arisen since the last update.

Upgrade: replacing an existing computer system by a more powerful (hopefully compatible) model in the manufacturer's range.

Upward-Compatible: the ability to move to a larger, more powerful computer system without having to amend or modify software.

Utility Programs: a set of programs performing commonly required tasks (e.g. sorting, merging, editing etc.); usually part of the operating system.

Valve: the original technology for manufacturing electronic components; inferior to transistor technology; characteristic technology of first-generation computer systems.

Validate: to check on the accuracy and authenticity of data capture or processing.

Value-added Network (VAN): a logical, virtual network created on a real network (typically the public-switched network), in order to market a specific service.

VAN: *see* Value-added Network.

VDU: *see* Visual Display Unit.

Verify: to check the accuracy of a transcribing operation, usually by a comparison procedure.

Very Large Scale Integration (VLSI): a measure of the packing density of circuits on a chip; presently the highest measure of density.

Videodisc: a storage of video images on an optical storage device.

Videotext: a system specifying standards for the storage of data in content-independent form, and for accessing such systems over telecommunications networks; *see* Prestel, Télétel.

Viewdata: *see* Videotext.

Virtual: implementation by software of physical resources (e.g. storage or processor); as opposed to real.

Visual Display Unit: an input/output device on which output is displayed on a cathode-ray tube; input is by means of keyboard.

VLSI: *see* Very Large Scale Integration.

Voice Message System (VMS): a system for the capture, storage and subsequent onward transmission of voice messages in binary-coded form.

Volatility: a measure of the rate of addition/deletion of records in a file.

Wafer: a slice of the semiconductor material (usually silicon) on which the chips are manufactured; wafers are the basic production unit for much of the chip-production process; there are multiple chips per wafer.

WIMP: windows/icons/mouse/pull-down menus: a philosophy guiding the development of user-friendly front ends to operating systems.

Winchester: a disc-drive technology in which the platters and read/write heads are enclosed in a hermetically sealed unit at time of manufacture; originally developed by IBM.

Window: a framing device that is used to enable two or more computer applications to coexist on the same screen display.

Wired Society: concept of a society organised around tele-processing networks for communications and transaction processing.

Word: a group of bits treated as a whole by the processor; a measure of the power of a processor.

Word Length: the number of bits in a word.

Word Processing: a system specifically designed for the manipulation of text, both as individual characters and as logically related groups of characters (i.e. words and phrases).

Work-station: a device designed as a user interface to a computer system.

Working Storage: an area (in primary memory) set aside by the programmer for local use within the program to hold non-permanent data.

WORMS: Write Once, Read Many times memory, a form of optical memory.

Write: the process of recording information in a memory location, or on a secondary memory media (i.e. tape or disc); writing destroys the previous contents of the memory location or memory area.

Xerographic Printer: a printer using methods similar to those of a xerographic copier to produce images on paper.

X.25: an international standard (from the CCITT) for packet-switched network protocol; adopted by PTTs and the majority of computer manufacturers.

X.too: an international standard (from CCITT) for public message handling services (MHS), including electronic mail; adopted by PTTs and the majority of computer manufacturers.

Yield: a measure of the proportion of good chips produced on a wafer.

Index

Access, 186
accounting, 3–4, 7–9, 16, 142, 201
Acorn, 144
actuators, 106, 119
Ada, 49
ADABAS, 88
address, 38–9
Adobe, 194
airline applications, 18, 60, 83, 158
Aldus, 194
Algol, 48
Alvey, John, 295
Alvey Programme, 295–6
American Express, 187
Amiga, 139, 254
Amstrad PC–1512, 259
analogue, 93, 159, 161–4, 195
ANSI, 37
Anthony, R., 205
Apple, 107, 138, 194, 225, 236
application:
    languages, 20, 47–57, 230
    software, 42, 44–5, 135, 229, 230–5
    see also package
APS Development Centre, 59
arithmetic:
    capabilities of chip, 106
    computer, used for, 30–31
    unit, 29
Arpanet, 174
artificial intelligence,
    see intelligence, artificial
ASCII, 34
Ashton-Tate, 89
Asimov, Isaac, 131
Assembler, 46–7, 57, 64, 227

Atari, 37–8, 139
Atlas, 71
AT&T, 66, 74, 118, 148, 176, 179, 180
automatic teller machines, 69, 158, 185–6
automation, 200, 204–5, 220–2, 228–9,
    269–70, 286–8
    office, 200–244

Baader-Meinhoff, 249
Babbage, Charles, 8, 10
badge engineering, 277
Baker, Kenneth, 295
bandwidth, 161, 178–9
banking, 158, 185–7, 242, 247
    home, 129, 187
Barclaycard, 186
bar code (reader), 29, 157–8, 222
baseband, 178
BASIC, 48, 52–3, 55, 59
batch processing, 17, 66–7, 79, 153–4
BBC, 144
    computer 145
Bell Laboratories 66, 159
binary, 30–1, 46, 103, 162, 195
bit, 33, 76
    processor size, 40–1, 107, 135
Bletchley Park, 12
block, 39
bootstrapping, 62, 64
British Telecom, 160, 165, 166, 171, 174,
    181, 196, 198, 295
broadband, 178, 180
broadcasting, 2–3, 5–7, 9
bubble memory, 124
buffer, 64
bugs, 234–5, 254–5

bureaux, computer, 18, 254
Bureau Fax, 196
Burroughs, 185, 291
byte, 33, 39, 76

C, 49, 53–4
cables, 163–4, 166–70
    transatlantic, 170
    see also fibre optics
Cable & Wireless, 166
CAD/CAM, 133–4
CAFS, 225
calculator, electronic, 13, 30, 95, 107, 117,
        125–6, 139, 204, 232, 270, 275
Cambridge,
    Distributed Computing System, 66
    Ring, 66, 176, 179
    University, 13, 176
Campbell, Duncan, 248
Čapek, Karel, 131
Cardbox, 231
CASE, 58–9
cassette tape, 34, 36, 130
CCITT, 180, 195–6
CDROM, 37, 39
Cellnet, 171
Centrex, 180
CFN, 166
China Express, 183
chip, silicon, 95, 96
    manufacture of, 96–9, 114–5, 116–24
    packing density, 99–100, 112–14, 121
    production control, 100
    see also microelectronics, microprocessor,
        RAM, ROM
CIM, 134
Cincom, 88
circuits, 173–4
CISC, 110–11
Citibank/Citicorp, 155, 187
City Fibre Network, 166
clerical work, 205–7
    see also skills
clock, 32, 107
clubs, computer, 265
CMOS, 98, 99, 104, 107
COBOL, 48, 51–2, 54, 58, 59, 227
code:
    breaking, 12
    encryption, 162–3, 256
Comal, 264
Commodore, 139, 144, 254
communications, 232
    see also telecommunications
compact discs, 37–8, 129, 259
Compaq, 137, 140–1
compiler, 49, 53, 59–61
computer:
    aided design, 133–4

electronic, 11–22, 135–45, 149, 230
    hardware of, 26–41
    industry, 275, 292
    integrated manufacturing, 134
    laptop, 139–40
    luggable, 137, 139–40
    pocket, 139
    uses of, 12
    see also home computer, microcomputer,
        minicomputer, mainframe, personal
        computer
Computer Programme, The, 144
Contel/Contelnet, 179
Control Data Corp., 291
controller, 63, 106, 127, 131
copier, 6, 13, 196–7
cost:
    of calculators, 126
    of chips, 105, 114–6, 117, 123, 288
    of computers, 15, 16–21, 135, 137, 144,
        200–1, 259
    of distributed systems, 152–3
    of electronic products, 119
    of printers, 191
    of program packages, 232
    of robots, 132
    of storage, 38–40
    of systems, 122, 200–1
    of workstations, 157
    office, general, 208–9
Council of Europe, 249
cpu, 26–30, 66, 113, 275
credit cards, 186, 247
    fraud using, 253
credit checking, 247
crime, computer, 253–6
critical success factors, 240–1
Crossbar, 165, 166
Crystal, 56, 238
CSMA, 178–9
Cullinane, 88
custom logic, 108–9, 118, 292

daisywheel, 189, 191, 197
data:
    entry, 152, 154
    havens, 251
    processing, 12–24, 43–5, 148–57, 200–1,
        218, 226–30
    see also distributed data processing
    processing department, 17, 20, 152–7,
        227–9
    protection legislation, 249–52
    storage, 224–5
    see also memory
Data Encryption Standard, 256
Data General, 18
Data Protection Act, 182, 247, 250–1

database, 53, 57, 75–7, 85–9, 218, 230–2, 238, 252, 259
  management systems: *see* DBMS
  public 143, 181–5, 210, 254
dBase II/III, 89
DBMS, 58–9, 77, 86–9, 240
DDL, 194
defence applications, 11, 14, 48, 73, 94, 116
  R&D relating to, 289–91, 297
Defence, Ministry of (UK), 295, 296
Defense, Department of (US), 48, 49
Department of Education and Science (UK), 295, 296
Department of Employment (UK), 248
Department of Health and Social Security (UK), 247, 248
Department of Trade and Industry (UK), 295, 296
DEC,
  see Digital Equipment Corp
design:
  computer aided, 20,133–4
  of chips, 296
  of systems, 226–30, 238–44, 287
desktop publishing, 137, 193–5, 213
diagnostics, 238, 260–1
Dialcom, 181
Dialog Information Services, 183
digital:
  tape, 130
telecommunications, 159, 161–80, 219
Digital Equipment Corp, 18, 66, 74, 219, 238
Digital Research, 236
disc:
  compact, 37–8, 129, 259
  drive, 33, 63, 71, 120, 139, 189
  magnetic, 34–6, 63, 64, 79, 82, 137–9, 215
  video, 8, 37, 129, 130
Displaywrite(r), 190, 193
distributed data processing, 12, 18, 24, 148–57, 217–8, 243
DL1, 88
document input, 223
  see also ocr
domestic products, 127–9, 141–3
domotics, 128–9, 143
Doslos, 360, 62
dot matrix, 191, 193
Draw, 194
driver, 63
  see also disc drive
DVLC, 247

Easylink, 181
EBCDIC, 34
Eckert, Presper, 13
economic impact of IT, 267–98
Edinburgh University, 237

EDSAC, 13
education:
  computers used in, 48–9, 144–5
  continuing, 265–6
  for an IT society, 263–6, 285
  further, 264
Education and Science, Department of (UK), 295, 296
EEC, 129, 295
EFT, 186
Electoral Roll, 247, 248
electronic:
  beam technology, 100
  data interchange, 220
  financial transactions, 186
  funds transfer, 186
  industry, 275–6
  see also semiconductor
  mail, 8, 143, 181–2, 190, 191, 204, 210, 211, 214–5, 218
  see also message sending
  office (systems), 216–225
  publishing, 194
employment, 257–8
  general pattern of, 268–9, 271–2
  impact of IT on, 269–71, 275–80
Employment, Department of (UK) 248
English Electric, 14
ENIAC, 13
environmental control, 128, 152–3
EPROM, 105
Equity Funding Scandal, 253
ERATO, 110
Ericsson, 180
error:
  checking, 37–8, 162–3, 214
  handling by programs, 234
ESPRIT, 129, 295, 296
Ethernet, 176, 178, 179
exchange, telephone, 160–1, 164–6, 180, 219
  see also PABX
Executive, 231–2
Eureka, 129
Eurofacts, 183
Eurofile, 183
Euromonitor On-line, 183
Euronet Diane, 183
European Silicon Structures, 118
European Space Research Agency, 169
expert systems, 22, 55–7, 213, 237–8, 240
  builders, 56, 137, 238
Expertech, 56, 238

Fairchild, 116
fault diagnosis, 238, 260–1
fax, 4, 195–6
Ferranti, 14, 71
FET, 96, 98
fibre optics, 166, 168, 169–70

fifth generation, 21–2, 292, 295–6
file, 211, 218, 224–5
  direct access, 82–5
  organisation of, 75–89
  random, 82–3
  sequential, 77–81
  storage equipment, 33–40, 224–5
Flagship, 296
flexible manufacturing system, 134
floppy disc, 35–6, 122, 136, 138–9, 140, 215, 259
  see also disc drive, magnetic disc
FMS, 134
Focus, 88
Ford, 220, 287
Fortran, 48, 50–1, 52, 54, 58
fourth generation languages, 49, 55, 58–9
friendly:
  operating environments, 235–7
  see also front end
  user, 21–2, 137, 232–7
front end, 137, 212–3, 235–7
Fujitsu, 118, 123, 291

gallium arsenide, 109–10
games, electronic, 62, 107, 126–7, 135, 141
gas plasma, 140
gate array, 109
Gateway, 184
Gem, 236–7
General Electric, 13, 14, 129, 165
General Motors, 124, 134, 149
generation, computer, 14–22
golfball, 189
graphics, 49, 58, 135–9, 142, 157, 158, 184, 194, 195, 213, 231, 237, 265
  tablet, 29
Grosch, Herb, 152
gross national product, 281
Groupe Bull, 291

hard disc, 34–6, 64, 71, 136
  see also magnetic disc
hardware, 26–41
  see also computer
hashing algorithm, 83
Health and Social Security, Department of (UK), 247, 248
Heathrow Airport, 255
Hewlett-Packard, 18, 74, 89, 111, 116, 181, 191, 193, 212–3
Hitachi, 117, 123, 291
Hollerith, Herman, 11, 14
holography, 224
home:
  computer, 21, 141–3, 265
  working at, 258–60
Honeywell, 14, 291

IBCN, 180
IBM, 10, 14, 34, 62, 65, 74, 88, 107, 108, 118, 121–4, 136–9, 148, 156, 176, 179, 180, 189, 190, 193, 206, 219, 236, 256, 291, 292
  PC, 65, 108, 121–2, 136, 153, 194, 259
ICL, 219, 225, 296
icon, 65, 73, 138, 236
ICT, 14
IDMS, 88
IKBS, 295
Image, 89
IMF database, 210
index-sequential access method, 83–5
indexing, 83–5
industrial products, 131–5
industry,
  see electronic, semiconductor
Info Builders, 88
information:
  exchange, 2–9
  flow of, 203–4
  in organisation, 175
  overload, 211–12
  technology, 8
Information Resource Management, 241
Information System Network, 179
Information Technology, Minister of, 295
infra-red, 168, 171–2
ink jet, 191
Inland Revenue (UK), 247, 248
INMOS, 111, 118, 275, 295
innovation:
  general, 280–86, 288–98
  UK performance at, 273
  see also research and development
input, 26–9, 42–5, 66–7, 106, 157–8
instruction set, 45–6, 59, 60, 106
instrumentation, 12, 73, 131
integrated:
  communications systems, 173–4, 180
  computer systems, 217
  home systems, 128–9
  programs, 212–3, 231–2
Integrated Business Network, 180
Integrated Services Digital Network, 174, 180
integration circuit, 21, 95–111
  see also microelectronics
Intel, 107, 108, 116, 117, 121, 136, 138, 149, 291
intelligence, artificial, 21–2, 49, 55–7
Intelligent Environments, 56, 238
interactive computing, 18, 67–9
InterCompany Comparisons, 183
International Standards Organisation, 219
interpreter, 49, 59–61
interrupts, 63, 67
IPSE, 59

ISAM, 83–5
ISDN, 174, 180
ISO, 219
  ISO/OSI model, 74, 219
ITT, 118

Jacquard, 11
Japan, 21, 110, 117, 124, 133, 195, 279,
  290–4
JIT, 134–5
Josephson junction, 124

Kelvin, Lord, 3
key:
  fields, 79, 80
  words, 211, 224–5
keyboard, 28–9, 120, 139, 189, 190
keyboarding, 206–7, 210, 213–4, 262
Knight Ridder, 184
knowledge:
  engineering, 238
  see also expert systems
  workers, 205, 208, 262

LAN
  see local area network
languages, computer, 20, 45–57, 230, 264
  fourth generation, 49, 55, 58–9
  high level, 47–57
  low level, 45–7
  procedural/declarative, 55, 296
  query, 20, 58, 86, 88
  standards and dialects, 49–50, 60–1
laptop computers, 139–40
laser:
  disc, 29, 37–8, 129–30, 259
  printer/copier, 6, 37, 149, 191, 193, 194,
    196–7
Laserjet, 193
LCD, 139–40, 189
leisure, 129–30, 270
  products, 129–30, 141–3
LEO, 14, 200
Lexis, 183
light pen, 29
LINK, 186
LISP, 49, 56–7
Lisa, 138, 236
local area network, 149, 173, 175–80, 217–9
logic:
  bomb, 254–5
  circuitry, 101
  see also microprocessor, custom logic
LOGO, 49
London Business School, 225
Los Angeles Water and Power Department,
  255
Lotus 1–2–3, 212–3, 230–1, 259
Lovelace, Lady Ada, 8, 10

luggable computers, 137, 139–40
Lyons, J., 13–14, 200

machine code, 45–7, 60, 64
Macintosh, 107, 138–9, 194, 236
mainframe computer, 16–18, 20–1, 65, 69,
  73, 149, 230
magnetic:
  card, 188–9
  core memory, 38
  disc, 34–6, 63, 215, 224
  tape, 36, 63, 79, 188–9
maintenance, 238, 260–1
  see also reliability
man–machine interface, 232–7
  see also user friendliness
Manchester University, 13
Mantis, 58
MAP, 134
Marconi, 118
Mark I, 13
Market Direction, 183
Marketing Week, 183
Martin, James, 259
Mastercard, 186
Matsushita, 118, 291
Mauchly, John, 13
MBA programmes, 263
MCC, 295
McFadden Act, 186
Mead Data Central, 183
measurement, 3
memory, 26–41, 119
  chips, 101, 103–5, 115–6
  manager, 71
  primary, 26–7, 29, 38, 64, 67, 71
  secondary, 27, 33, 34–8, 64, 67, 71, 120
  typewriter, 189
Mercury, 166
Merrill Lynch, 187
message:
  passing protocols, 178
  sending, 4, 210
  switching, 173, 185, 219
  see also electronic mail
Michie, Donald, 237
microcomputer, 19–21, 73, 135–45, 259
  see also computer, personal computer
microelectronics, 93–124
  applications of, 125–45
  development of, 93–6
  scale of, 99–100, 112–116
  see also semiconductor, chip
microprocessor, 62, 105–9, 119, 120–1, 135
  general-purpose, 102–3, 105–8
  special purpose, 62, 102–3
Microsoft Corporation, 65, 236
  Draw, 194
  Word, 193, 195

microwave, 166, 168, 169
Mietec, 118
minicomputer, 18–19, 26, 69, 73, 88–9, 149, 156, 218
Minitel, 184
MITI, 290–2, 296
Mitsubishi, 291
modelling, 69
modem, 162
Monodata, 181
Morgan Stanley, 208
MOS, 96
Mostek, 116
Motorola, 107, 116–18, 123, 138, 148, 291
mouse, 65, 136, 138, 236
MSDOS, 65, 66, 74, 136–7
Multimate, 193
Multiplan, 230, 259
multiprogramming/multitasking, 63, 67, 68, 71, 137, 138

NASA, 11, 169
National Semiconductor, 118, 126
NCR Corp., 14, 291
NEC, 117, 118, 180, 291
Net/One, 179
network, 73, 89, 135, 149, 204, 217, 232, 243, 249
  control of, 64
  informal office, 206–7
  telecommunications, 160–1
  word processing, 190–2
  see also local area network
Neumann, John von, 13
New Wave, 212
NEXOS, 275
Nippon T&T, 104
Nolan, Richard, 204
Northern Telecom, 180
numbers, 40–1
numerical control, 134

ocr, 29, 223
office, 201–2, 228
  automation, 200–244, 270
  electronic, 216–225, 228
  home, 258–60
  types of, 201–2
  work, nature of, 205–7
on-line systems, 67–9, 153–4
One Per Desk, 219
open systems, 65, 73–4, 219
operating systems, 42, 53, 62–74, 136–7, 153, 218, 235–7
optical media, 224
  see also ocr, fibre optics, laser
OS/2, 65, 66, 74, 136–7, 236
OSI, 74, 219
output, 26–9, 42–5

PA, 111
PABX, 160, 164, 172, 217, 219, 243
package, program, 19–20, 122, 230–5, 259
packet switching, 173–5, 176, 179
page, 182, 183
page description language, 194
Pagemaker, 194
paging, 71
Paintjet, 191
parallel processing, 107, 111
PARC, 244
Parker, Donn, 255
Pascal, 10, 48, 264
pattern recognition, 56, 132–3
PC, IBM, 65, 121–2, 136–7, 194, 213
  see also personal computer
PCDOS, 65, 74, 137
Pennsylvania University, 13
peripherals, 27, 66, 106, 119, 120, 122, 144
personal computer, 74, 121–2, 135–45, 149, 230–2
personnel, 122, 209
  see also skills
Philips, 118, 129, 291
photolithography, 97–8, 99–100
PICK, 66
Planning and Control Systems, 205
Plessey, 118, 165, 296
PL1, 48
plotter, 29, 158
point–of–sale, 157–8, 186
police, 247
Police National Computer (UK), 247, 248
portability:
  of computers, 139–40
  of programs, 65
POSIX, 74
power requirements, 113
Powerhouse, 58
Precision Architecture, 111
Presentation Manager, 236
Prestel, 184
printing/printers, 6, 28–9, 37, 66, 176, 189, 193–7, 218
  types of printer, 191
privacy, 246–51
process control, 12, 69, 73
processor, 26–7
productivity, 273, 280, 292–4
  office, 208–9
  programming, 57–8
program, computer
  see package, software, application
programmability, 102–3, 287–8
programmed array logic, 109
programmers, demand for, 262
programming, 11, 42–59, 121, 227–30, 234–5
  home computers, 141–2
  languages, see languages

non-procedural, 58–9, 229–31
productivity in, 57–8
robots, 132
structured, 54
Prolog, 49, 57
PROM, 105
Prospector, 238
prototyping, 238–40
PRO–IV, 58
PS/2, 107, 136–7
PSS, 174
PTTs, 164, 173, 174, 180, 195, 197
  see also British Telecom
publishing, electronic, 193–5
punched card, 11, 28–9

Racal, 171, 296
RACF, 256
RAM, 38–40, 64–5, 101, 103–4, 121, 189
  dynamic, 104, 106, 118
  static, 104
random access memory,
  see RAM
RCA, 14
read only memory,
  see ROM
real time, 18, 67–9
  pseudo real time, 156
register, 46–7
reliability:
  computer, 13, 17, 94, 113, 114, 152, 225
  telecommunications, 159
remote job entry, 69
reprographics, 6, 13, 196–7
  see also laser
research & development, 11, 116, 117,
  123–4, 283–4, 288–98
  see also innovation
Research Machines, 144
Retail Consortium, 222
retrieval systems, 211–12
  see also file
RISC, 110–11
Roach, Stephen, 208
robots, 131–3
Rockwell, 126
ROM, 37–40, 64, 101, 103–5, 140
  programmable, 105
RPG, 48

satellites, 159, 168–9
schools, computers in, 20, 48–9, 144–5,
  263–4
second sourcing, 123
Secret Society, 248
Securicor, 171
security:
  home, 128–9, 143
  of information, 252–3

system, 184, 254–6
semiconductor, 120–2, 125–45
  development of industry, 116–24
  industry, 112–124, 268
  products, 101–9, 117, 125–45
sensor, 106, 119, 120, 128, 131
SERC, 295
Servis, 127
shared logic, 190–2
Siemens, 129
SIGMA, 292
silicon chip
  see chip, silicon
silicon compiler, 109
skills:
  at risk, 260–2
  changing balance of, 260
  general level of, 285
  in demand, 262–3
Sinclair Spectrum, 141, 144
Sloan Management Review, 204
SNA, 74
software, 42, 74, 122, 200
  applications, 59, 119
  see also package
  development of, 19–20, 292
  engineering, 58–9
  system, 61–74, 119, 153
  see also operating system
  word processing, 190, 192–5
Software AG, 88
Software Generation, 59
Sony, 129
space, 159, 169
speed:
  chip, 103, 107, 112–13
  computer, 26, 63, 136, 138
  fax, 195–6
  memory, 39
  message–sending, 173, 181
  Teletex, 197
Sperry Corp., 291
spooling, 67
spreadsheet, 20, 53, 137, 205, 212–13,
  230–1, 265
standard:
  BBC micro as, 144
  data encryption, 256
  for languages, 49–50
  for operating systems, 65, 74
  for telecommunications, 175, 176, 180,
    195–6, 219
Stanford University, 66, 255
StarLan, 176
STC, 165
stock control, 134–5, 220–2
strategic planning, 205–6
Strasbourg Convention on Data Privacy,
  258

Strassman, P.A., 244
Strowger, 165, 166
swapping, 71
SWIFT, 173, 185
system:
    analysts, demand for, 262
    computer, *see* computer
    design and implementation, 226–30,
        238–44, 287
System X, 165, 166, 276
System Y, 165
Systems Network Architecture, 74
S/3X, 65
S/360, 62, 65
S/370, 65, 66, 74

tabulator, 8, 11, 30
tape:
    cassette, 34, 36, 130
    file, 66–7
    magnetic, 29, 36, 39, 130, 188–9
    paper, 28–9, 188
tariffs, 118
Telecom Gold, 181
telecommunications, 4–5, 118, 148, 159–87,
    195–6, 219, 232, 259
    trade in, 276
Telemail, 181
Telenet, 174
telephone, 142, 210, 219, 220
    portable, 5, 170–1
Télétel, 143, 184
Teletex, 197–8
teletext, 130, 185
television, 8, 9, 130, 185, 275, 292
telex, 4, 181, 198, 219
terminal, 21, 69–71, 135, 149, 152, 157–8,
    190, 219, 230, 232, 259
    intelligent, 157, 191, 218, 219
    multipurpose, 219
    point of sale, 157–8, 186–7
    testing, 227, 235
Texas Instruments, 116, 118, 123, 124, 126,
    127, 291
text processing,
    see word processing
text retrieval, 225
    see also file
Thorn EMI, 129
Thorn Ericsson, 165
time sharing, 20, 69–71
Times-Mirror LA, 184
token, 198–9
Token Ring, 179
Toshiba, 118, 291
TOTAL, 88
touch screen, 29, 49
trade, international:
    in chips, 117–18

in data, 251–2
Trade and Industry, Department of (UK),
    295, 296
training, 232–3, 244, 263–6
trans-border data flow, 251–2
transistor, 94, 99, 159
Transputer, 111, 295
Turing, Alan, 296
Turing Institute, 296
TVEI, 264
TXE, 165, 166
Tymnet, 174
typewriter, 4, 13, 214
    memory, 188–9
typing, 206–7, 210, 213–14, 262

unemployment, 269, 278
Ungermann-Bass, 179
unions, trade, 282
UNIPART, 220
Univac, 13, 14, 88, 227
universities, 14
UNIX, 66, 71, 74, 157
US Sprint, 181
user friendliness, 21–2, 137, 232–7
utility programs, 62, 63, 64

V, 66
value-added network, 172, 185
valve, 93–4, 283
VAX, 66
Ventura, 194
vertical integration, 118–20
video, 130
    camera, 194, 219, 270, 292
    cassette recorder, 130, 270, 292
    disc, 8, 37, 129, 130
    display unit, 28–9, 63, 106, 189
    tape, 130
Videotext, 130, 183–5
viewdata, 183–5, 187
Viewtron, 184
virtual system, 71–2
virus, computer, 254–5
Visa, 186
Visicalc, 212, 230
VLSI, 95, 295
Vodaphone, 171
voice:
    input, 29, 223–4
    output, 29

Wall Street Journal, 183
Wang, 178, 190
Wangnet, 178, 179
watch, digital, 13, 62, 106, 117, 120–1,
    125–6
Western Union, 181
Wilkes, Maurice, 13

WIMP, 65, 138, 236
Winchester disc, 34–6,
  see also hard disc
window, 65, 138, 213, 230, 236
Windows, 236
Wired Society, The, 259
word:
  length, 38, 107
  processing, 20, 137, 142, 188–95, 210,
    212–15, 218, 259, 261–2
  processor 189–92, 197–8, 204, 206, 230–2,
    235
Word, 193, 195

Word Perfect, 193, 231–2
WordStar, 193
work, nature of, 257–8
work-station, 34–5, 135, 157, 218
WORMS, 37

Xeros, 194
Xerox, 138, 148, 176, 189, 218, 236, 244
Xi, 56, 238
X/OPEN, 74

Zisman, Michael, 204